v9/v9

±20

Financial Calculations for Business

Christian de Lisle

KOGAN PAGE

By the same author

The Sinclair Book of Management Calculations
The Martin Book of Management Calculations
Programs for Financial Calculation
  (A Solutions Book for the Hewlett-Packard 17B and 19B
  Financial Calculators)
Business Interest Calculations

Available direct from the author:

UK Securities, Loans and Banking Calculations Book
  (and programs related to the HP67 & 97
  programmable calculators)
Solutions Handbook Fixed Interest Loans
  (related to the HP-12C programmable calculator)

First published in Great Britain in 1990 by Kogan Page Limited,
120 Pentonville Road, London N1 9JN.

British Library Cataloguing in Publication Data
A CIP catalogue record for this book is available from the British Library.

1-85091-978-X

Printed and bound in Great Britain by Biddles Ltd, Guildford

Contents

Chapter 9   Hire Purchase and Leasing   **134**

Chapter 14   Anomaly and Annuity Bonds   253

Chapter 15   Bills, Certificates of Deposit, Notes etc   272

INTRODUCTION

It is clear that the increasing use of the personal computer in recent years has meant that a growing number of users require to know how many of the financial calculations employed by banks and institutions are done – so that they can program these calculations for themselves, on their own PCs.

Over the years in which I have acted as a consultant to various computer manufacturers, software houses and financial institutions – as indeed I still do – I have received many queries on financial calculations from individual members of the public. As a result, some years ago, I wrote a book, *Business Interest Calculations*. This addressed many of the queries I had encountered and provided a variety of formulae and detailed explanations. It could, perhaps, be best described as a publication which was intended to be useful to anyone wishing to construct their own programs for their own personal computer or programmable calculator.

Markets evolve over the course of time and changes, such as the "big bang" on the UK Stock Exchange in 1987, have had a substantial effect on, *inter alia*, financial calculations. Furthermore, in the last two or three years computers have become far more widely used, the range of languages and off the shelf programs has increased, and calculators have become more powerful and thus able to undertake the solving of far more complex problems.

It thus became clear that *Business Interest Calculations* needed to be updated – and considerably amplified.

Moreover, in 1988 Hewlett-Packard updated their range of hand-held business/financial/statistical calculators, producing the new 17B, 19B and 27S Business and Stats calculators. These new calculators are extremely sophisticated, with greatly increased memories, and a new and refreshing method of programming. The requirement for a book related to these business calculators became obvious and I wrote *Programs for Financial Calculations (Applications for the Hewlett-Packard 17B & 19B Financial Calculators)* which went on sale early in 1989.

As a result the production of this book, *Financial Calculations for Business*, was delayed some months and it became not only an update of *Business Interest Calculations* but also a useful adjunct to *Programs for Financial Calculations.*

For whereas the latter book is designed to provide a number of programs with explanations in a form quite adequate for the user to understand the program usage, *Financial Calculations for Business* delves in far greater depth into each financial discipline, giving formulae and explicit explanations, with related examples fully worked through.

Many will want to employ the formulae and explanations, in this book, in order to program their own personal computers but some, I suspect, while wishing that they had this or that discipline on their desk have neither the time nor, perhaps, the expertise to undertake the programming themselves.

The good news is that professionally produced disks are now available with all the required calculations – and answers!

More information on the disk(s) in question will be found in Appendix D.

On some occasions readers, I hope not too much to their annoyance, may see some formulae and explanations repeated in different chapters. The reason for the duplication is simple: some readers, as I know to my cost, do not always "start at the beginning" but instead go straight to the chapter in which they are primarily interested. If they then meet an unfamiliar abbreviation or perhaps an actuarial term and find they have to go back to an earlier chapter, they may become lost and frustrated!

In view of the recent growth of interest in desk top publishing it was thought that a comment on the typesetting of this manual would not be amiss.

The font employed is Times Roman (11 point) which reverts to mono spacing for the formulae, tables, etc. The lay out and general format was entirely the author's responsibility. The text was word processed, using "PC-Write", the pages then being used as camera-ready copy for the printer.

My thanks to two friends, Tony Collinson, for undertaking the unenviable task of checking the calculations and to Tony Vann for proof reading. Their respective expertise, help and encouragement leaves me greatly in their debt.

Immense pains have been take by all concerned to combat those gremlins who always seem determined, in books such as this, to misplace signs and transpose formulae. Should any reader discover any residual errors information as to the target area would be much appreciated.

C.de L. 1990

An abridged version of this book, "Programs for Financial Calculations", related entirely to the Hewlett-Packard Business Calculators (the HP-17B, HP-19B and the HP-27S), is available from the publishers, Kogan Page Ltd.

CHAPTER 1

Percentages and Conversions

Calculations

Readers who will be following the calculations on their own calculators or PCs will appreciate that different calculators or computers have different "full precision" facilities, which will affect the number of accurate significant figures displayed. Also the answers can vary, fractionally, if the calculations are worked through in a different order to that shown.

For instance, 1.50^{50} (or 1.50^50 or again 1.50**50), namely 1.50 raised to the power of 50 should be precisely the same as $1/1.50^{-50}$. But two types of calculators might display fractionally different answers. The precision used in the calculations in this book is 13 places rounded to 12, the *display* being curtailed to taste; for instance actual payments are usually rounded to 2 decimal places, £/p or $/c. Thus if an example is started in the middle there may be a minor difference between the book answer and the display.

The examples usually refer to either dollars or sterling but can, of course, be applied to any decimal currency, providing that, occasionally, some mental adjustments are made. For instance, the cost of a home loan, considered reasonable in the States or in the UK, might scarcely, perhaps, purchase an elegant dog kennel in those countries whose currencies have suffered from a high rate of inflation!

The difficulty of writing a book such as this is to know where to start. One can only guess at the mathematical knowledge of the reader; if one presumes a high level of numeracy one can lose those who seek general knowledge rather than the more detailed information available later. Alternatively, starting with the simpler problems the experienced statistician, losing interest early, may well turn to those sections which interest him most, thus perhaps missing important notes and comments.

I have tried to steer a course between these two alternatives and have devoted this chapter to general information for beginners and some reminders for the more experienced.

To start with then, percentages and interest rates: these are used as generic terms covering the many – far too many – different ways of referring to such values as interest, interest rates, interest percentage, the return, the yield, internal rate of interest (IRR), inflation rates, currency rates, sterling rates, key rates, forward rates and so on.

Whether we like it or not, we had better fully understand the calculation of percentages for, in the guise of bank lending rates, which affect mortgages, inflation rates, which affect pensions, VAT which affects shopping, or tax, which affects everyone, they play a vital part in our lives. But sadly, not everyone does understand percentages

Even in the best regulated circles mistakes are often made. Some years ago, during the run up to a General Election, *two* political parties, believe it or not, "got it wrong". At the time the annual inflation index was running at around 20% and both parties stated, in their respective manifestos. that if inflation continued unchecked the pound would be worth only 80 pence the following year. In fact, of course, the correct figure was 83 pence.

The mistake was to calculate:

$$100 - (100 \times 20/100) = 80.00$$

whereas the correct calculation would have been:

$$100 \div (1 + 20/100) = 83.\overset{..}{3}3 \text{ (recurring)}$$

An elegant bank in Canada some years ago, in an endeavour to explain to its shareholders the dangers of inflation, outlined an example in the Chairman's report – and got it wrong. I treasure the Chairman's most courteous reply to my innocent inquiry! So do think twice about exactly which method is appropriate when dividing or reducing the percentage rate.

The UK Consumer Credit Act (1974)

Two friends were walking home from work, when one asked the other for a loan of £25 until next pay day – in two days' time. When the lender hesitated his friend suggested that on repaying the loan he would stand the lender a couple of drinks, worth at least £1.50.

The lender had no intention of charging interest and would no doubt have been surprised to learn that the arrangements he had agreed to meant that interest was, in fact, charged at over 4 million per cent. And before you consign the book to the wastepaper basket, pray follow the explanations below!

Most countries have some methods of protecting the consumer from fraudulent promotion, in the UK this is covered by the Consumer Credit Act of 1974.

In the days before the Act the consumer had no way of telling the true rate of a loan, unless he or she was particularily numerate – and few were. A quotation of 10% could in those days mean practically anything! It could represent a 10% flat rate or a 10% nominal rate, with various periodic repayments resulting in different effective rates.

In those days the simple interest was the normal high street method of quotation and yet, over a two year term, the true cost of borrowing, the effective rate, is almost exactly double the flat rate quote.

So something had to be done to protect the ignorant and innumerate borrower from apparently innocuous loans. A loan of £240 over 24 months with £24 monthly payments may sound quite reasonable but the effective is 170%!

As the Act conditions many of UK lending calculations, and in some cases the actual rates offered, it may be useful to consider the regulations straight away. The Act itself and the disclosure regulations are somewhat complex; for not every loan or lease requires disclosure.

Nevertheless many firms now disclose in all circumstances, either from social conscience or to be on the safe side. The (UK) Office of Fair Trading (OFT) provides various pamphlets, etc related to the regulations.

In brief, any "loan" (which includes leasing to a private individual) from May 1985 if below £15,000 (and all loans where the collateral is based on land or "property") requires the disclosure of the term of the loan, the Annual Percentage Rate of charge (usually shortened to APR), and the Total Amount Payable (TAP). The TAP is the total amount of payments made *plus* any extra fees, balloon payments etc, relating to the loan in question. The Total Charge for Credit (the TCC), if required, is the TAP *less* the original capital (loan) amount.

The British and American APR
In Britain the APR is the effective rate of interest, as opposed to the nominal rate, *truncated* (*not* rounded) to one place of decimals. Unhappily, in the United States APR refers to the nominal rate, not the effective, consequently confusion has been known. In the pages below the APR refers to the UK APR – where there is any room for doubt (US)APR or (UK)APR will be used.

Flat rates to APR%
Whereas simple interest, or flat rate, quotations are quite normal in the USA they are used less in the UK than they used to be. For if a UK lender is legally bound to reveal the APR it means that he will have previously needed to calculate the true nominal and effective rates of interest – and if you know the true nominal rate, why not quote it? In the States, incidentally, the simple interest rate is called the "add-on" rate, implying, very sensibly, that something has to be added to find the true rate – as indeed it has.

The effective rate
Returning to the example on page 3 of the rate of "over 4 million percent", we will see how this comes about once we understand what an effective rate is, how it is calculated and why many advertisements for loans in the UK have to carry an Annual Percentage Rate, shortened in the UK to "APR".

A lender of £100 receiving interest at 10% will, at the end of one year, get $100 + (100 \times 10/100) = £110$. An equally good way of calculating would be $100 \times (1 + 10/100)$ and in a formula this is usually shown as $(1 + i)$.

If the loan is for 10 years the lender will then receive $(1 + i)$ ten times over, namely 1.10 to the power of 10 or $(1 + i)^n$, where "n" stands for the number of years.

Most readers will know all this, but remember you still gasped in disbelief over the 4 million percent effective interest rate quoted above.

If the payments were monthly, instead of annual, the formula and calculation would be $(1 + i/p)^{np}$, with p being the number of compounding periods in any one year, sometimes referred to as "rests". The value of a £100 loan, with monthly payments, would be $£100 \times (1 + 10/1200)^{10 \times 12} = £270.70$, whereas if the calculation was annual instead of monthly, $(1.10)^{10} = 2.5937$ which when multiplied by £100 = £259.37

Clearly, if interest is compounded each month, instead of at the end of each year, the amount received by the lender will be greater.

If our lender had merely told us that he was charging us 10%, we might have reasonably thought that he meant payments at the end of each year; and then been most annoyed to find that he wanted paying monthly. How are we to know?

Others might try and attract our custom by offering 10%, saying that payments would be at the end of each half year, or at the end of each quarter. How can we tell which is best?

If we bring all these loans onto a common base, namely the *effective* rate, our problems will be solved. For the moment a simple conversion will suffice:

$$((((1 + (NOM\%)/(px100))^P) - 1) \times 100 = \text{Effective rate}$$

$$(1 + 10/1200)^{12} - 1 \times 100 = 10.47\%$$

And to prove that it makes sense – if this is correct then a loan of £100, at the rate of 10.47%, should (must) provide the same end result as the monthly rate, namely £270.70, and £100 x 1.1047^{10} = 270.67. the decimal discrepancy being due to the rounding of the rate. If the correct value to the "full precision" of the computer or calculator was employed the values would be precise.

Having verified the above method of calculating effective rates, let us return to the 4 million per cent rate of interest!

The loan of £25 was for 2 days only, so let us put that on to an annual basis. For a loan of £25 the lender received (theoretically) £1.50 (for his drink), consequently his return was (25 + 1.50)/25 = 1.06, namely a rate of interest of 6% – *for two days*.

For a year therefore the *nominal* rate interest must be 6 x 365/2 = 1095% and converting the nominal to the effective rate, as we did above:

$$[(1 + \frac{1095\%}{182.5 \times 100})^{182.5}] - 1 \times 100 = \underline{4,152,502\%}$$

Another, somewhat similar, type of loan caused some amusement, a few years ago, to the committee charged with producing the Crowther Report (on which the Credit Act was largely based). Apparently, in the North of England, it used to be a common practice to borrow "x" shillings for a week and repay "x" shillings and "x" pence. The committee found that this works out as an effective rate of about 6,400%!

For those too young to remember there were 20 shillings to the pound and 12 (old) pence (d) to the shilling; consequently, if a man borrowed 10 shillings he would repay, after 7 days. 10 shillings and ten pence or 10.833333 shillings. If we divide this by the original 10/- we will get an *annual* percentage rate of 8.33%

Converting to a weekly profile, 8.333 x 365/7 = 434.523636

$$((1 + 434.523636/5200)^{52} - 1) \times 100 = \underline{6,392.33\%}$$

Nominal/Effective conversions formulae
To find the effective rate which, when truncated, provides the APR, first calculate the periodic rate, and thence the nominal rate, from which the effective rate can be determined.

To convert a given nominal rate to the effective one:

$$100 \times [\,(\,1 + \frac{NOM}{100 \times p}\,)^{p} - 1\,] = \text{Effective rate \%}$$

Where p = the number of compounding periods in any one year
(e.g., 12 monthly, 4 quarterly or 2 semi-annual)

Thus 10% nominal with monthly "rests" converts to:

$$100 \times [\,(\,1 + \frac{10}{100 \times 12}\,)^{12} - 1\,] = 10.471307\%$$
$$\text{(effective)}$$

To (re)convert an effective rate to its nominal merely reverse the above formula:

$$(100 \times p) \times [\,(\,1 + \frac{EFF}{100}\,)^{1/p} - 1\,] = \text{Nominal \%}$$

$$(((1 + (10.471307 \div 100))^{\wedge}1/12) - 1) \times 1200 = 10.00$$

When the compounding periods differ from the payment periods
The tip is to calculate the effective rate of the interest, based on the *interest* compound period, and then, using that value, to find its nominal rate from the *payment* structure.

For example, Canadian mortgages are usually calculated by assuming that interest is charged semi-annually but repayments are required monthly. If the quoted rate is 11% nominal what is the "working" rate? Convert the interest of 11% nominal to its effective rate, employing the *interest* rests namely semi-annually (2), and then reconvert this effective to its nominal using the *payment* rests, namely monthly (12).

$$100((1 + 11.000000/200)^{2} - 1) = 11.302500 \text{ effective}$$
$$1200((1 + 11.302500/100)^{1/12} - 1) = 10.756073 \text{ nominal}$$

As can be seen, the effective rate is, correctly, the same for both the semi-annual conversion and the monthly conversion, namely 11.30%.

Nominal rate converted to continuous effective rate
What is the effective rate for 10% with daily rests?

$$100((1 + 10/36500)^{365} - 1) = 10.515578\%$$

But there is one more rate which is just fractionally greater than the days rate, and that is if the compounding was continuous, from minute to minute, so to speak.

This is found by using the exponential factor (symbol e) namely 2.718281828. If the reader has a calculator with logs natural the input of 1 to the anti–log key or the key marked (e^x) will display the above 2.718281 factor.

$$2.718281828^{.10} = 1.105170918 - 1 \times 100 = 10.5170918\%$$
$$\text{continuous}$$

This continuous rate must surely be the ultimate interest rate. Or is it?

There is another calculation, somewhat suspect to my mind, which is apparently acceptable to those using the 30/360 calendar:

$$£100 \times \quad 1.105170918 \quad = £110.52$$
$$\$100 \times (1 + 10/36000)^{365} = \$110.67$$

"Discrete" and "exact" interest
Considering American practices, anent APR and the above spurious calculation, I am reminded that technically all compound interest is considered to be discrete interest unless it is "continuously compounded" – a term rarely employed in the UK, but is sometimes met in financial and computer journals in the States. In other words for 10% nominal rate the "force of interest" is considered to be 10.52%

Actuaries, incidentally, call the *force of interest* "the nominal rate of interest per unit time converted momently".

In the USA the term "exact" interest is used for interest based on the "actual" calendar (365), whereas that based on the financial calendar (30/360) is often referred to as "ordinary interest".

Some percentage reminders

It is easy to make mistakes when percentages have to be added or subtracted.

For example, the result of adding 15% + 20% + 10% – 4% is *not* 41% but is:

$$[(1.15 \times 1.20 \times 1.10 \div 1.04)] - 1 \times 100 = 45.96\%$$

Another common misconception is to suppose that if inflation is running at, say, 20% p.a. and if the current lending rate is 10% the return is a negative 10%. In fact, the true return is:

$$[(1.10/1.20)] - 1 \times 100 = -8.33\%$$

And, incidentally, with a simple interest profile, 10% – 10% is *not* zero! In fact, it is – 1% and the keystrokes below will prove the point, which some continue to disbelieve!

$$((100 \times 1.10) - (110 \times .10)) - 100 = -1\%$$

We have already seen that even in the best circles percentages are sometimes wrongly calculated, that banks and political parties have been known to make mistakes.

It is true that £100 less 15 percent is 100 x (1 – .15) = £85.00 if you employ simple interest but if, for example, you are discounting, deducting, VAT (at 15%) from a purchase to find the gross value you would be wrong to calculate by that method.

The gross value of a purchase costing £86.96 plus VAT is:

$$£86.96 \times 1.15 = £100.00$$

consequently the true gross value of £100 less VAT at 15% must be:

```
            £100 ÷    1.15    =   £86.96
    NOT     £100 x (1 - .15) =   £85.00
```

Thus, we should always be absolutely clear , for any particular problem, exactly which type of percentage is required; and politicians could, perhaps, do well to remember this when discussing inflation!

Sometimes it is necessary to find the VAT amount from a given [value + VAT]: in that case the simplest method is to divide by the "useful factor" of $1.15/.15 = 7.66667$:

```
£100 ÷ 7.66666 = 13.043478
Check               13.043478/.15 = 86.956522 and x 1.15 = 100.00
```

When considering annual percentages against periodic rates, another error is, unhappily, very prevalent – many people seem to think that 12% per annum is 1% monthly. The *effective* rate of 1% monthly is 12.68% and *not* 12%.

$$(((1 + 12/1200)^{12}) - 1) \times 100 = 12.68\%$$

The UK "Composite Rate"

Years ago, when the British Government first instructed building societies to pay interest to their depositors net of tax and, at each year end, to remit to the Revenue the tax value of all the interest due to their depositors, the building societies argued that such a demand was grossly unfair and unrealistic.

For, they pointed out, many of their investors were non-tax payers.

In the event, it was agreed that only a "composite rate of tax" (CRT) need be remitted. The CRT stood for many years at 25.25% against a basic income tax rate of 30%.

At the beginning of 1989 the CRT was adjusted to 23.25%, which related to the then basic rate of 25%.

For many years, after the advent of the CRT, building societies paid their investors net, whereas banks paid gross; and a bewildering plethora of rates, provided by various competing building societies and institutions, appeared in advertisements aimed at inducing the public to invest.

In 1985 the Government produced legislation whereby interest on all loans, with a few minor technical exceptions, would be paid to investors net of the basic rate of tax. One of the results was that a major problem arose, namely how should the institutions advise their clients of the true effective rate of their loans.

For example, in the old days, if the interest on a loan was paid monthly at 10% gross the effective rate was well known to be 10.47%. But if the tax rate was, say, 25% the advertised net rate is 10 x .75 = 7.50% What then is the effective rate?

Some banks, happily, advertised the effective rate, as 10.47% (UK APR 10.4%), grossing up the net rate to its gross nominal *before* converting to the effective. Others, more correctly, advertised as 10.35% (UK APR 10.3%) converting the net rate to its effective and *then* grossing up.

The subsequent confusion was so great that the Bank of England had to step in; the rule being to convert the net rate to its effective, *before* converting to the gross profile.

$$10\% \text{ at } 25\% \text{ basic tax rate is } 10 \times .75 = 7.50\% \text{ net nominal}$$
$$(100 \times ((1 + 7.50/1200)^{12}) - 1)/.75 = 10.35\% \text{ gross effective}$$

The gross equivalent
A loan of £100 at a 10% interest rate will provide annual interest of £10. If this amount was taxed at, say, 25% the spendable amount, the net amount after tax, would be 10 x (100 – 25)/100, namely 10 x .75 = £7.50 and this net annual interest value could also be determined by £100 x 7.50%. Consequently, the *gross equivalent* of the 7.50% above is, obviously, 10%

But some years ago, to the surprise of many, this conventional and well known concept was challenged in a well-orchestrated campaign. In the past, the argument ran, we had all been wrong in grossing up the net *rate* (as outlined above) for this related to a *one* year profile; but over a ten year loan the capital and interest is rolled up to become £100 x 1.075^10 to equal £206.10

Given this return and assuming a basic tax rate of 25%:

$$(206.10/100)^{1/10} = 1.075 = 7.50\%$$

But what we should apparently have been doing was to net the *amount*:

$$(206.10 - 100)/.75 = 141.47 \text{ and } \left\{\frac{100 + 141.47}{100}\right\}^{1/10} = 1.092160 = 9.22\%$$

In which case the grossed up net would not be 10%, as we all thought, but 9.22%.

Not surprisingly the institutions, presumably advised by their in-house actuaries, ignored the whole thing but advertising for the National Savings Certificates, at that time the direct responsibility of the Treasury, suddenly ceased to quote the grossed up net as has previously been the practice. And some wondered if perhaps the campaign had some substance.

In fact, of course, it had not, and to my personal knowledge a year or two later an incoming Treasury official inquiring as to the caveat on the advertising of the grossed up net for any of the money instruments, for which they were responsible, sent for the file.

After a few moments perusal he succinctly pronounced it a nonsense – or words to that effect! For he said, (that which we all knew!) in law all tax must be paid annually and cannot be accumulated and held over for years to come.

Questionable calculations...
We started off by saying we had better understand interest rate; for although if it does not exactly rule our lives it certainly plays a large part.

But even if we understand it, it does not necessarily follow that all the answers must be accepted without question – as the next two examples will show!

The examples are not tricks, however strange you may think the structure of the loans, nor were they designed to prove a point – they actually happened.

A loan of $490 was made to be repaid by $200 six months in advance and $300 to be paid six months after the loan was made. At a semi-annual rate of $490 – (200 x 1.20) = $250 and $250 x 1.20 equals the last required payment of $300. Nothing wrong with that – except that a rate of 25% will find precisely the same parameters!

A family decided to go on holiday and estimated the total cost would be in the area of £2,270. This cost was funded as follows; £200 to be paid *six* months in advance of the start of the holiday, £480 some *three* months in advance of the start, and then, three months after the end of the holiday, a final payment of £1,650 was to be made.

What is the interest rate on which these payments are calculated? The simple answer is *either* 10% or 50% per quarter!

```
2,270 – (((200 x 1.10) + 480) x 1.10) =  1,500
1,500 X 1.10                           =  1,650 (final repayment)
2,270 – (((200 x 1.50) + 480) x 1.50) =  1,100
1,100 X 1.50                           =  1,650 (final repayment)
```

This anomaly became a matter of litigation and the Actuary's Department, a low profile but invaluable branch of Government, subsequently ruled that the lesser rate should stand correct.

Agents' (percentage) commissions
Agents' commissions inevitably vary according to the work which they do. Active assistance, with the agent having

considerable expenses, is probably worth a higher fee than a mere introduction at an "old-boy" luncheon. The following formula may be useful to finance directors:

$$\frac{\text{Category} \times 20}{2 \times ((\text{LOG Capital Value}) - 1)} = \text{commission percentage}$$

The logs must be logs(10), *not* logs natural, Logs(LN).

The "categories" are the prerogative of the finance director and can range from 1 (the lowest) up to any value he wishes.

If the capital value of the contract was worth, say, £250,000 and the agent was category 2, the equation would be:

$$\frac{2 \times 20}{2 \times ((\text{LOG } 250,000) - 1)} = 4.55$$

In the case of a transaction of (say) £100,000 where the finance director decided that the agent was category 3, the interest rate would be 7.50% and the amount (cash) due is £7,500. Another agent, working on a £125,000 project, launched at considerable cost to himself, might be considered to be category 6, and his percentage would thus be 14.645184 which, if curtailed to 14%, would provide him with £17,500.

Above it was necessary to employ Logs_{10}, but as some modern calculators only have Logs natural(LN) it may be necessary to convert as follows: $\text{LN}value/\text{LN}10 = \text{logs}_{10}$

For example, find 1.12345 based on logs_{10} when the only logs available are logs natural.

logs(LN)1.12345 = 0.116404 and logs(LN)10 = 2.30258509299
and 0.116404/2.30258509299 = 0.050554 = logs_{10} for 1.12345

To reconvert, that is having logs_{10} only and wishing to convert to LN:

$$\frac{1}{(\text{logs}_{10}2.1828182846)} = \text{factor } 2.30258509299$$

and having found the factor it is simple to multiply the factor, i.e., to "unscramble" the original conversion calculation.

The profitability index

This index, widely used in the States, is the present value of the anticipated cash flows discounted at the investor's required yield, all divided by the initial investment.

$$\frac{\text{Present Value Cash Flows}}{\text{Initial Investment}} = PI$$

If the PI is greater than 1 the investor's required yield has been exceeded, conversely if less than 1 the yield is not met.

For example: assume that a purchase with an original cost of $10,000, and with an annual income of $1,580, was sold after 7 years for $7,500. If the investor requires a rate of return of 13% what is the profitability index?

First find the future value:

$$10,000 \times 1.13^7 - (1,580 \times (1.13^7 - 1)/.13) = 7,086.70$$

But given that the sale amount after 7 years was £7,500, the difference must be discounted and added to the present value, namely:

$$10,000 + ((7,500 - 7,086.70) \times 1.13^{-7} = 10,175.68$$
and $\quad 10,175.68/10,000 \quad = 1.02$ PI

The true yield of the investment and subsequent cash flows is 13.429% and in that case the PI will, of course, be 1.

Some of the calculations above will become clearer after the chapter on savings has been digested.

Vulgar fractions

It is simple to convert a vulgar fraction to a decimal, 10 and 5/8th becomes 10.625, but less easy to reverse the process.

There is no simple way of finding the "nearest to the true" and it becomes a matter of trial and error. The method below may be of use to those who deal constantly with such conversions as a matter of routine.

The method is to multiply the decimal fraction by different base values, say, 8, 16, 32, or even 64 until the resulting *rounded* integer is an *un*even number. Divide this uneven number by the base and the answer is a vulgar fraction. If the result does not appear sufficiently close to the given requirement, double the base value and try again.

For example, a decimal found as .1875 converts as follows:

```
                    .1875 x  8 = 1.5 = integer 2
        try again   .1875 x 16 = 3   = 3/16th vulgar fraction
```

A digression
The "PI" factor above, naturally, must not be confused with the mathematical sign π. And while the following has nothing to do with financial calculations it may be if some interest!

In most modern scientific calculators a key to obtain π is usually provided, but not so on the cheaper conventional vest-pocket credit-card type calculator that many carry in their wallet or filofax. And sometimes this value may be required.

To obtain the π value, somewhat more accurately that the schoolboy method of 22/7, take the first three uneven numbers (113), then the next three uneven number (355). Now divide the first factor by the second factor and the *reciprocal* will be an extremely accurate value for π !

$$\frac{1}{113/355} = 3.14159292035$$

– against statistical value taken from a high grade scientific calculator of 3.14159265359 – a difference of less than 0.0000003

CHAPTER 2

Repayment Loans
(and Calendar Calculations)

Actuarial shorthand

The presentation of formulae, mathematical legends and languages naturally differs from country to country. Actuaries, however, have devised a standard form of shorthand which can be extremely useful in reducing the length of well-known formulae – saving space and often assisting clarity of thought. This shorthand will be used on many occasions in the following pages.

Compounding and discounting

If £100 is invested for 10 years at 10% at simple interest then each year the lender is due to receive $100 \times .10 = £10$

Readers will appreciate that if a lender does not wish to receive the interest every year but "leaves it with the borrower", what the lender is, in fact, doing is to re-lend to the borrower the interest engendered the previous year. The problem is to calculate the future value of the loan at the end of the term.

An interest rate is normally referred to as a percentage, say 10%; but when set out in a formula it is divided by 100, shown as a decimal and referred to as "i". For example 10% is shown as $.10 = i$.

If compounding occurs, then the number of "rests", or compounding periods, in any *one* year is referred to as the "p" factor.

Consequently 10% interest, compounded monthly, converted to a decimal fraction becomes $10/1200 = 0.008333$ and in formulae this figure is referred to as "i/p".

The value "n" refers to the number of years in the term. If an interest rate is compounded over a term of n years the value of the loan at the end of the period is calculated by dividing the percentage value by both 100 and the number of periodic (p) rests in any one year, adding 1 and raising the result to the power of n.

Thus if 10% is compounded *annually* over a term of 25 years the formula would be presented as:

$$(1 + i)^n \quad \text{or} \quad (1 + i)\text{^}n \quad \text{or} \quad \text{sometimes} \quad (1 + i)\text{**}n$$
$$1.10^{25} \quad \text{or} \quad 1.10\text{^}25 \quad \text{or} \quad 1.10\text{**}25$$

If the interest is compounded *monthly* the equation becomes:

$$(1 + i/p)^{np} \quad \text{or} \quad (1 + i/p)\text{^}np$$
$$(1 + 10/1200)^{300} \quad \text{or} \quad 1.008333\text{^}25x12$$

So the value of £100 at the end of 25 years compounded annually or monthly at a rate of 10% nominal is:

$$£100(1 + i\ )\text{^}n = 100(1 + 10/100\ )^{25} = 1,083.47$$
$$£100(1 + i/p)\text{^}np = 100(1 + 10/1200)^{25x12} = 1,205.69$$

In many cases statisticians assume that if a borrower makes payments to a lender he is "out of pocket" for that amount, and therefore these payments should be given a negative value. Conversely, a lender, treating payment(s) received as positive, may need to make an "out of pocket" payment at the end of the term, if so the future value (FV) must be negative.

If this method is used, then it does not matter which perspective is employed, but it is vital to be consistent; especially so far as deposits, withdrawals and balloon payments are concerned.

Discounting is merely compounding in reverse. Your great aunt leaves you £5,000 in ten years' time and instead of waiting for your inheritance you want to "cash in" now. Providing you can get someone to give you the cash now you can spend the money – now.

As a "banker" will not receive the £5,000 until the end of 10 years, he will only give you what he considers that amount is worth *now*. If the current lending rate, the "going rate", is 10% then all you will get is just under £2,000 to spend *now*:

$$5,000/(1 + i)^n \quad = \quad \text{Present Value}$$
$$\text{or} \quad 5,000/(1 + i)^\wedge n \quad = \quad \text{PV}$$
$$\text{or} \quad 5,000/1.10**10 \quad = \quad 1,927.72$$

An alternative method of calculating discounting, much favoured in formulae, is by the use of the negative power, with the value multiplied rather than divided, for example:

$$5,000 \times 1.10^{-10} = 1,927.72$$

The actuarial sign for this negative factor $(1 + i/p)^\wedge -n$ is "v", in other words the *discount* sign. Consequently -v represents the compounding factor of $(1 + i)^\wedge n$. As this can be confusing to those not dealing with such matters on a day-to-day basis, in the following pages the full $(1 + i/p)$ will always be used even where the rate concerned is annual with no periodic rests, in which case p = 1.

Repayment loans

The formula for repayment, or mortgage type, loans is:

$$\text{Repayments} \times \frac{[1 - (1 + i/p)^\wedge -np]}{i/p} = \text{Loan}$$

$$\text{Loan} \div \frac{[1 - (1 + i/p)^\wedge -np]}{i/p} = \text{Pmts}$$

and the acturarial sign for the above factor is a___
$$_{np|}$$

$$\frac{\text{loan}}{a\underline{\quad} } \quad \text{at } x\% = \text{pmts} \quad \text{or} \quad \text{pmts a}\underline{\quad} \quad \text{at } x\% = \text{loan}$$
$$_{np\,|} \qquad\qquad\qquad _{np\,|}$$

Now what exactly are repayment loans, and why are they so important? Their importance is the result of the fact that this type of calculation is used not only in relation to mortgages and the like, but is used for many requirements quite unrelated to "loans" as such.

But the general structure and usage is frequently not fully understood; and many years ago in an endeavour to assist the Court I submitted, *inter alia*, the following small parable.

Assume that you lend a friend £1,000, and you tell him that you require 10% interest, *simple interest*, each year. You would expect to receive £100 each year until such time as either you or he wished to conclude the arrangement, at which point the £1,000 loan would be finally returned to you.

But you rightly consider that these *open-ended* types of loan, those without a term, are unsatisfactory. For example, it may not be convenient for you to receive the loan back when the lender wants to return it, for the current leanding rate may have fallen in the meanwhile and you may not be able to relend again at 10% elsewhere; or, which might be even more worrying, when you ask the borrower for your loan back he may not be able to accomodate you for some time.

So you suggest, and your friend readily agrees, that he should pay you £100 each year (at simple interest) and that, *at the end of 10 years*, he should automatically return the loan. But now you have another worry; whereas he can no longer embarrass you by returning the £1,000 before the 10 years is up, what happens if at the end of 10 years he has not made suitable arrangements to repay you exactly what the contract says?

Taking him to court or waiting until he pays up will be expensive and tiresome, so you suggest to your friend that he repays part of the capital each year so that at the end of the term the whole loan will be repaid. As £1,000 neatly divides into £100 each year for 10 years and as the 10% simple interest is also £100 a year the total repayment each year will be £200. Your friend agrees, in fact he thinks it is an excellent idea – until one day, a few months later, he has second thoughts.

For, he tells you, he has just realised that in the 10th year he will be paying you 10% (simple) interest on £1,000, namely £100, *when in fact he has already repaid some £900.* "And", he continues, sounding slightly aggrieved, "It looks to me as if, in the last year, you are charging me 100% interest, and the year before 50% and so on".

And he would be perfectly correct – as I told the Court!

Correct, that is, if the perspective is *simple interest.* But in fact in repayment loans the payments are even throughout the term of the loan, with each periodic payment being made up of both interest and capital in differenet portions. Consequently the interest calculations can no longer be regarded as simple interest, but must be considered as compound based because, obviously, in this example, whatever it is, the *true* rate is considerably in excess of 10%. In fact it is 15.098414%

Repayment loan calculations
At the beginning of Chapter 4 is a schedule relating to a sum of the digits calculation. Just look at the schedule, ignoring the particular calculations, and notice how the interest and capital repayments change each month.

The loan under consideration is for £3,000 to be repaid over a term of 24 months at a *simple* interest rate of 6%. Consequently the monthly payments are:

    ((3,000 x .06 x 2) + 3,000)/24 = £140 per month.

In the schedule it will be seen that each month the "interest paid" and "capital repaid" add up to a total of £140.00. It will also be seen that in the early months the interest is large and the capital small (in relation to later months), but as the capital is repaid, and the balance falls, so the interest naturally reduces – and the capital portions of the payments rise to compensate. The actual calculations and values are not precisely those of a conventional repayment loan, but the differences are small.

The concept to which the readers attention is being directed, is that the repayments are a mixture of capital and interest, the same as *annuities ordinary*; and juxtaposition of the values should also be illuminating.

Taking the *true rate of interest*, namely 11.126664% nominal, (monthly 0.927222%) the correct interest and capital repayments, for comparison purposes, can be seen from a similar schedule, having the first two payments as follows:

```
3,000.00 x .009272 = 27.82 (interest) − 140 = 112.18 capital repaid
3,027.82 · 140     = 2,887.82 and
2,887.82 x .009272 = 26.78 (interest) − 140 = 113.22 capital repaid
2,914.59 · 140     = 2,774.59 and so on
```

As will be seen from the above, the payments are made (subtracted) *after* the interest has been engendered, in other words the payments are made *in arrears*, as opposed to *in advance*.

If you save £100 each year and the bank agrees to pay you interest on it each year, it is obvious that you will get the most interest if you bank at the beginning of the year rather than waiting until the year is half over, or indeed paying it in on the last day of the year.

Thus the conventional, and sensible (!), method of saving is by instalments at the *beginning* of the interest period, be it year, quarter or month – and this generally known as payments *in advance*.

With repayment loans, however, the conventional method is to make payments at the end of each periodic payment period, *payments in arrears*, "annuities ordinary". In other words the building society advances you the money to buy your house and you start repaying them a month later.

In the case of the £3,000 loan with £140 payments for 2 months the true rate was 0.927222%, and to verify that this is the correct the formula/equation, outlined at the beginning of the section, should be employed:

$$\text{Loan} \div \frac{[1 - (1 + i/p)^{\wedge} - np]}{i/p} = \text{Pmts}$$

$$3,000 \div \frac{(1 - 1.00927222^{-24})}{.00927222} = 140.00$$

If, therefore, we had a simple repayment loan of, say, £10,000.00 over a term of 25 years at a nominal rate of 11%, with monthly payments, the formula/equation would be:

$$\frac{10,000.00}{a \underline{\quad} \atop 300 \mid} \quad \text{at 11% nominal (monthly)} \atop \text{or at (11/12)%}$$

£10,000 ÷ [(1 − 1.009167^−300)/.009167]   =
£10,000 ÷ [(1 − 0.064734)   /.009167]   =
£10,000 ÷   (.935266/.009167)   =
£10,000 ÷ 102.029044 (loan ÷ factor)   = £98.011308 pmts monthly
                                        (in arrears)

Alternatively:

a___   factor multiplied by payments = 98.01 x 102.03 = 10,000 loan
 n |

When we come to consider leasing it will be seen that the repayments are in advance, one payment being made as soon as the contract commences. This is called *annuities due*.

The actuarial sign for annuities due has two dots above the letter "a" thus:

a____ (ord)   ä____ (due)
 np | p |
a____ (ord) ÷ (1 + i/p) =   annuities due
 np |

£98.011308 ÷ (1 + 11/1200) = 97.12 (payments in advance)

Algebraic transposition

Looking back we can see that the above payments of 98.01 stemmed from the *factor* of 102.029044 being divided into the loan amount; the factor not being "money" but purely a mathematical quantity employed to determine financial values.

It might, therefore, be both useful and of interest to discover how this factor is derived.

Using the geometrical progression general formula below:

$$\Sigma = \frac{rl - f}{r - 1}$$

with r = ratio of the progression
    f = first term
    l = last term where $l = fr^{n-1}$
    n = number of terms

and taking the rate of 11.126664/12, namely 0.92722197288 and treating the constant multipier, the ratio of the progression, as $1/1.0092722197288 = .990813$ the factor becomes:

$$\frac{rl - f}{r - 1} = sum = \frac{(.990813 \times .990813^{24}) - .990813}{.990813 - 1} = factor$$

$$= \frac{(.990813 \times .801310) - .990813}{-.009187} =$$

$$= \frac{-.196865}{-.009187} = 21.428571$$

and now applying this factor to the actuarial formula we can see how the progression becomes the conventional format employed above for annuities ordinary, namely:

$$Loan \div \frac{[1 - (1 + i/p)^{-np}]}{i/p} = Pmts$$

$$\frac{3,000}{a\underline{\quad}}_{24|} = \frac{3,000.00}{21.428571} = 140.00 \text{ monthly payments}$$

This formula is used throughout the following pages, but there are other ways and other formats for expressing the same structures.

To save confusion, in case the reader should come across these elsewhere, the various alternative formulae, all meaning precisely the same thing, are set out below:

$$\frac{1}{i} - (\frac{1}{i} \times (1 + i^{-n})) \quad = \quad a_{\overline{n}|}$$

$$\cfrac{1}{i/p + \cfrac{i/p}{(1 + i/p)^n - 1}} \quad = \quad a_{\overline{n}|}$$

$$\frac{(1 + i/p)^{np} - 1}{(1 + i/p)^{np} \times i/p} \quad = \quad a_{\overline{n}|}$$

"Mission Impossible"

Occasionally when after the relevant data for finding the term of a loan on a computer or calculator has been input an *error* message (or some such wording to denote that the calculation is found wanting) will display, much to your surprise.

The obvious conclusion that there has been an input error need not necessarily be the right one; the problem could be the result of a combination of impossible data values.

To illustrate this consider the case where rates suddenly rise sharply and some borrowers have difficulty in meeting the higher payments. When this happens the building societies may be able to assist by lengthening the term.

But beyond a certain point in the future the repayments will merely be covering the *interest* engendered, the capital portion of the loan itself not being conventionally reduced – consequently the loan can never be redeemed.

For this reason assistance is usually limited to extending the term to no more than than 35 to 40 years.

Assume that a building society loan had been running for several years, with monthly payments of £70 (derived from £840 annually, the societies always dividing by 12), and an existing balance of £6,950. The rates suddenly rise to 13% which requires the monthly payments to rise to £81 (annual £972).

The borrower, finding the new payments beyond his means, wishes to continue with his previous loan of £70 monthly and asked his society if they would lengthen his term accordingly.

When the society worked out the new term the computer came up with a "no solution" response.

Fortunately the statistician knew how to calculate without the aid of a computer and identified the problem:

$$\frac{\text{LOG (pmts/(i/p))} \div \text{(pmts/(i/p))} - \text{loan}}{\text{LOG} \quad 1 + i/p} = np$$

$$\frac{\text{LOG (850/.13)} \div \text{(850/.13} - 6,950}{\text{LOG} \quad 1.13} = \frac{\text{LOG} \quad - 15.89}{\text{LOG} \quad 1.13}$$

Since logs can never be negative, and this example produced a negative log it follows that the calculation could not be done – mission impossible!

The lender then needed to find a point at which the calculation ceased to be impossible, namely some value fractionally greater than LOG zero. Multiplying the outstanding balance by the interest rate gives £6,950 x .13 = £903.50. This value worked through the formula will find that the value 6,950 must be divided by 0, an impossible requirement. So to find the longest possible term for this particular loan, add .1 to 903.50, making an annual payments of £903.51.

In the event, monthly payments of £75.80 (annual £909.60) were agreed, and this provided a term of just under 41 years.

Should the reader wish to find the term for the £903.51 annual payments above he will find it a matter of some 93 years plus, a term which failed to appeal to either lender or borrower!

To find the interest rate, namely "solve for i"
Above we have discussed methods of obtaining the payments values by formula, or the loan amounts, and touched on finding the term. In the next chapter the methods of finding balloon payments and/or the current balances will be fully outlined, but for now the reader doubtless is wondering how to find the investment rate.

Now for the bad news!

By transposition of the repayment loan formula we have found what we required, but unhappily no one has yet discovered how to transpose the formula to isolate all the "i" values on one side or the other of the equation – one tiresome "i" value always seems to remain un-transposable!

So, in the old days before computers, one had to guess and guess again, until a rate was eventually found that did fit the parameters required. Nowadays of course the user is relieved of all such tedium; for computers can "loop" continually interpolating and trying new rates, until the correct one is found in micro-seconds – to 12 places of decimals!

In Appendix B a method, based on the Newton-Raphson discipline, is outlined showing how to "find i" by interpolation; useful perhaps to those who wish to program their own computer to perform the "looping" operation.

Pro rata values
All annuity calculations are pro rata, in that the size of the payments will be directly proportional to the size of the loan – if all other factors remain constant. Thus the methods employed by building societies (see below) involves basing all their calculations on a £1,000 loan, with the annual payments divided by 12; this enables them to find the value of any loan payments pro rata.

If, for example, the annual payments for a £1,000 loan over a term of 25 years require building society payments of £9.90 monthly a loan of, say, £65,300   would require to meet monthly payments of 9.90/1000 x 65,300 = £646.47

The next chapter delves somewhat more deeply into annuities, ordinary and due, and various other types of loans based on the same principles.

The Calendars
In financial matters, time is inevitably an important consideration and must be clearly understood. For many interest calculations depend entirely on the number of days between the beginning and the end of an interest period, usually referred to as the settlement date and the maturity or redemption date.

The difficulties arising from trying to divide 365 exactly into two, or to have months with even days throughout, resulted in the evolvement of the "financial" calendar (referred to as 30/360) as opposed to the "actual" (365 day year) calendar to which we are normally accustomed.

The 30/360 calendar has 360 days, divided into 12 months of 30 days each – hence the nomenclature. In Appendix C there is some historical data about calendars in general and the necessary calculations, for programming purposes, are given in detail.

Sometimes interest bearing obligations, especially in the States, require the employment of both calendars, and this is denoted by *actual/360*.

The modern calculator with a date program becomes quite invaluable in most calculations related to finance/time problems. But if momentarily mislaid there are two charts at the end of the book; a "month/days" chart in Appendix C, and a days chart on the final pages, which may be of some asistance.

Leap days

By convention, some obligations require that leap days are ignored and should the calculator employed not have the extra facility of determining how many leap days there are between two dates, or which years are leap years, the following short formula may perhaps be found useful.

$$(INT\frac{year\ 1}{4}) \quad - \quad (INT\frac{year\ 2}{4}) = - \ leap\ days$$

When the actual date falls between January 1 and February 29 (both inclusive) subtract 1 from "year".

What are the number of leap days between January 1, 1980 and June 1, 2000

$$(INT\frac{1980 - 1}{4}) \quad - \quad (INT\frac{2000}{4}) = - \ leap\ days$$

$$INT\ 494.75 \quad - \quad INT\ 500.00 = - \quad " \quad "$$
$$494 \quad - \quad 500 \quad = - 6$$
$$(1980 \cdot 1984 \cdot 1988 \cdot 1992 \cdot 1996 \cdot 2000)$$

To find the day of the week

In many financial interest calculations it is assumed that the interest engendered is immediately reinvested and if the day on which the interest is due falls on a non-banking day then the "return", the relevant yield, is thus fractionally reduced.

One day's interest on a redemption amount of £1M, at 18%, is around £500, so on occasions it is obviously of considerable interest to know which day is, or is not, a non-banking day.

For long term loans a calculator/computer date program is usually essential to find the day of the week of the redemption; but for a short term 90 day loan the payment date is just as important and a "back of the envelope" calculation can be useful.

Providing the number of days between is known, and the day of the week of one of the dates is known, the other date can be found as follows:

Let 1 = Monday, 6 = Saturday and 7 or 0 = SUNDAY

$$\text{known/day/week} + ((\text{FRAC}\frac{\text{days between}}{7}) \times 7) = \text{Day of Week}$$

If today is January 30, 1989 (a Monday) what is day of the week, 90 days hence, on April 30, 1989?

1 + ((FRAC   90/7) x 7) = day of week

1 + ((FRAC 12.857143) x 7) =

1 + (.857143 x 7) =

1 +   6.00   = 7 = SUNDAY

(if the sum is greater than 7 subtract 7)

CHAPTER 3

Annuities Ordinary and Due

General

In the last chapter we saw how annuities ordinary and due (payments in arrears or in advance) were represented by the actuarial symbols below:

$$a\underline{}_{np\,|} \quad \text{or} \quad \ddot{a}\underline{}_{np\,|} \quad \text{respectively}$$

What happens when the payments are sensibly rounded to 2 decimal places to represent the correct values, namely £/pence or $/cents?

Naturally, if there is a change in any particular value other data is automatically affected. But most changes become obvious; for example, if payments rise from 400.1567 to 400.16 the TAP will be, say, 24 x 400.16 = 9,603.84 instead of 9,603.76. Obvious and not very worrying.

But if payments are rounded, though not lifted substantially, is it necessary to recalculate the interest rate in order to find the correct effective rate, and hence the APR?

Fortunately, no. It was this problem which led to the decision to *truncate* the effective rate to one place of decimals and call it the APR. Mind you, this does not absolve the statistician from re-calculating if a major change occurs in the structure of the loan, such as the addition of a front-end fee.

Balances for annuities ordinary payments

A balance, or the "loan outstanding" (LOS), can be found for any loan by finding the future value (FV).

Let us remind ourselves what happens to a repayment loan, period by period; taking, first, a simple case of a 25 year loan of £1000 with payments of £100, in arrears, at a rate of 11%.

```
1,000.00 x 1.11) −100  = 1,010.00  (balance at end of year 1)
(1,010.00 x 1.11) −100  = 1,021.10  (   "      "  "   " year 2)
(1,021.10 x 1.11) −100  = 1,033.42  (   "      "  "   " year 3)
```

Now take a slightly more complicated loan, a monthly loan of £10,000 at 11% nominal, over 25 years (300 months); the payments will be found as:

$$\frac{10,000.00}{a_{\overline{300}|}} \text{ at } (11/12)\% = \text{payments}$$

$$10,000 \div (1 - (1 + 11/1200)^{-300})/0.009167 = 98.011308$$

If one wished to find the balance of the loan at the end of the 22nd year (264 month) the calculation will be as follows:

$$(loan \times (1 + i/p)^{np}) - (pmts \times ((1 + i/p)^{np} - 1)/(i/p)) = balance_{np}$$

$$10,000 \times 1.009167^{264} - (98.01 \times (1.009167^{264} - 1)/0.009167) =$$

```
   111,225.62        −       108,230.43            = 2,995.19
```

The values underlined above, of $((1 + i/p)^{np} - 1)/(i/p)$, will be explained more fully in the chapter on "Savings"; it is a calculation employed to find *savings ordinary*, where payments are in arrears. and is represented by the actuarial term of:

$$s_{\overline{np}|}$$

To find the term

$$\frac{LOG \frac{pmts}{i/p} \div (\frac{pmts}{i/p} - loan)}{LOG \quad 1 + i/p} = term$$

$$\frac{LOG \frac{98.01}{0.009167} \div (\frac{98.01}{0.009167} - 10,000)}{LOG \quad 1.009167} = 300.02$$

(decimal descrepancy due to rounded pmts)

If the structure of the loan included a balloon payment the formula would change to:

$$\frac{LOG \; (\dfrac{pmts}{i/p} - balloon) \div (\dfrac{pmts}{i/p} - loan)}{LOG \qquad\qquad 1 + i/p} = term$$

To find the interest rate
This requirement is not easy and cannot be met by a simple formula/equation as above; for unhappily no one, as yet, has been able to isolate all the "i" values to one side, or the other, of an equation, there is always just one too many!

Consequently, all that one can do is to guess a rate, work through the formula and see if the answer is correct, and if not guess and guess again! In other words "interpolate".

Nowadays, of course, this presents no problem, for computers or programmed calculators can interpolate so rapidly that, in the above equation, the nominal rate of 11% would be found in micro-seconds.

Throughout this book, in order to explain a formula by working through an equation, it will often be necessary to present the rate; and in that case the comment will always be that is has been, or must be, found by computer/calculator interpolation,

And whatever the presentation is, in terms of significant figures, the calculation will always be to the full precision of the computer or calculator employed (in this book some 12 significant figures).

Balances annuities due, payments in advance
With payments in advance the balances are assumed to be those at the beginning of each period under review, ready to accept the interest for the following period.

Having found the balance, as outlined above, for annuities ordinary, payments in arrears, divide by $1 + i/p$ to find the balance for annuities due.

With £1,000 at 11% with £100 advance payments:

```
1000.00              -100    = 900      (balance at  commencement)
( 900.00 x 1.11) -100        = 899     (    "       beginning year 2)
( 899.00 x 1.11) -100        = 897.89 (    "            "       "  3)
```

A number of advance payments

Some years ago a client company, for reasons best known to themselves, decided to ask certain borrowers to make 3 payments in advance. To find the required payments the statistician was apparently guessing a possible payment structure and, when this was found to be incorrect, interpolating and essaying further attempts, often taking, I gathered, 20 to 30 minutes to find a correct answer to 3 places of decimals. Hence his urgent request to me to write a suitable program for his calculator.

Apart from the fact that he obviously knew little about interpolation, the whole exercise was totally unnecessary.

But first, interpolation: assuming a loan of £20,000 at 12% nominal over a term of 5 years with three payments in advance, with intelligent interpolation *any* guess (within reason) can be made *ab initio*.

If we guessed the payments were £400 we must check against the loan amount, less three payments:

$$\frac{400}{a_{\overline{60-3|}}} \quad \text{at 1\% monthly} \ = a \ \ \text{PV of } 17,314.85$$

and 17,314.85 + (400 x 3) is not the required £20,000.

A quick interpolation provides the payments *but for 57 months only*, namely 400 x 20,000/17,314.85 = 462.03 (adjusted for 3 advance payments).

$$\frac{462.03}{a\underline{}_{60-3|}} \quad \text{at 1\% monthly} = 19{,}999.998 \text{ decimal}$$

discrepancy due to rounding

But for the correct payments for the full 60 months, I invited my client to consider a simple junior school equation:

$$\frac{100-3X}{7} = X \quad \text{Find X}$$

$$
\begin{aligned}
100 - 3X &= 7X \\
100 &= 7X + 3X \\
100 &= X(7 + 3) \\
100 \\
\overline{} &= X \ = 10 \\
7 + 3
\end{aligned}
$$

I chose 7 as it closely resembles the actuarial sign and we merely find the factor and subtract 3 (for 3 advance payments).

$$\frac{20{,}000.00}{a\underline{}_{60-3|} + 3} \quad \text{at 1\% monthly}$$

$$\frac{20{,}000.00}{((1 - 1.01^{-57})/.01)) + 3} =$$

$$\frac{20{,}000.00}{43{,}28712 + 3} = 432.085633$$

(see above)

How to find the interest between ... ?

The capital balance for any period less the balance for the next period must equal the capital repaid for the intervening period, and so if that amount is deducted from the payments made during that period the result must be the total interest paid.

For a £1,000 loan at 11% over 25 years the payments (*in arrears*) are £118.74

To find the interest for period 3 the formulae are below:

```
Payments in arrears - balances:
(1,000 x 1.11²) - (118.74 x (1.11² - 1)/.11)) = 981.56 balance(2)
(1,000 x 1.11³) - (118.74 x (1.11³ - 1)/.11)) = 970.79 balance(3)

  Payments  - (balance₂ - balance₃) = interest(per 3)

  118.74    - ( 981.56 - 970.79 ) = 107.97
```

Remember the precise order of the formula above is important because, if for some reason, the payments are *less* than, conventionally, they should be, the interest will be greater than it otherwise would be.

```
Taking the payments above for £100 (instead of £118.74):
(1,000 x 1.11²) - (100 x (1.11² - 1)/.11)) = 1,021.10 balance(2)
(1,000 x 1.11³) - (100 x (1.11³ - 1)/.11)) = 1,033.42 balance(3)

  Payments  - (balance₂ - balance₃) = interest(per 3)

  100.00    - (1,021.10 - 1,033.42  = 112.32
```

The reason for the higher interest above, when the payments are less than they should be, is because the loan outstanding is being reduced by lesser amounts, and consequently the interest engendered for each period must be higher.

For a £1,000 loan at 11% over 25 years the payments (*in advance*) are £106.97, and the schedule below is somewhat different:

```
Payments in advance - balances:
```

$$(1{,}000 \times 1.11^2) - \frac{(106.97 \times (1.11^2 - 1) \times 1.11)}{.11} = 981.57 \text{ balance(2)}$$

$$(1{,}000 \times 1.11^3) - \frac{(106.97 \times (1.11^3 - 1) \times 1.11)}{.11} = 970.80 \text{ balance(3)}$$

```
  Payments  - (balance₂/1+i/p - balance₃/1+i/p) = interest(per 3)

  106.97    - ( 981.57/1.11  -  970.80/1.11  ) = 97.27
```

Home loans - low start mortgage repayments
High interest lending rates, with consequent high periodic repayments, naturally cause considerable concern to home owners, especially the first-time borrower, and many institutions have become adept at creating a variety of alternative methods to ease the burden. Below are examples of some of them.

The guiding concept is to have lower repayments at the start of the home loan on the assumption that, as the owner's pay and prospects increase over the years, he will become better able to afford the higher payments in the later years of the loan period.

Annual percentage uplifts
One of the most obvious ways of organising a low start loan with gradually rising payments is by having an annual percentage lift each year.

Payments are usually monthly, but the percentage increment is almost always annual: in other words the payments remain constant for 12 months before rising.

There are many useful variations on this type of calculation. Usually the percentage increment does not obtain throughout the full term of the loan, although it can of course do so if required. The conventional low start loan has rising levels of payments over (say) the first five years (in the formula below #yr, here, would equal 5) and from then on the payments remain at that level, or (more usually) one level higher. The complex and regrettably long formula is below:

$$\frac{loan}{((1 - (1 + i/p)^{-p})/(i/p)) \times \frac{(((1 + incr/100)/(1 + i/p)^{p})^{\#yr}) - 1}{((1 + incr/100)/(1 + i/p)^{p}) - 1} + (1 + incr/100)^{\#yr} \times \frac{(1 - (1 + i/p)^{-(px\#yr)})/(i/p)}{(1 + i/p)^{px\#yr}}}$$

A loan of £50,000 over a term of 25 years at a nominal rate of 15.00% requires monthly payments to be increased, each year by 5% per annum for the first five years; and for the remaining years to run one level higher. What is the monthly payment in the first year and in each subsequent year?

$$\frac{50,000.00}{(1-1.0125^\wedge-12)/.0125 \times [((1.05/1.0125^\wedge12)^\wedge5)-1] \div [(1.05/1.0125^\wedge12)-1] \\ + 1.05^\wedge5 \times (1-1.0125^\wedge-240)/.0125 \div 1.0125^\wedge60}$$

$$\frac{50,000.00}{11.079312 \times [((1.05/1.160755)^\wedge5) - 1)] \div [(1.05/1.160755) - 1] \\ + (1.05^\wedge5 \times 75.942278 \div 2.107181)}$$

$$\frac{50,000.00}{[11.079312x-0.394318 \div -0.095416] + [1.276282x75.942278 \div 2.107181]}$$

$$\frac{50,000.00}{45.786606 + 45.996862} = 544.76 \text{ payment}$$

For the 12 months		= £544.76	year 1
	x 1.05	= £572.00	year 2
	x 1.05	= £600.60	year 3
	x 1.05	= £630.63	year 4
	x 1.05	= £622.16	year 5
	x 1.05	= £695.27	year 6 – year 25

If, the above graduated–payment mortgage called for annual increments of 5% each year for the full 25 years, the first payment would be £468.82 and the payment in the last year:

(year 1)   £468.82   x   1.05^24   =   £1,511.99   (year 25)

Two tier loans
Another method is to have a high and low rate. Assume a £1,000 loan at a nominal 11% over 25 years (300 months). If the first 3 years' payments were £7.00 per month (36 months) what are the remaining 22 years' (264 months) payments?

Traditionally, the monthly payments would be:

$$\frac{1000.00}{a_{\overline{300}|}} \quad \text{at } (11/12)\% = £9.80$$

For a two tier payment structure, with the first payment of £7.00 for the first three years (36 months), what are the payments for the remaining final 22 years (264 months)?

$$\frac{\text{loan} \times (1 + i/p)^{np'} - \text{pmts's}_{\overline{np'}|}}{a_{\overline{np'' - np'}|}} = \text{pmts''}$$

Where: np = the total number of payments   (300)
         np' =   "   "   "   "   "   1st tier period (36)
         np" =   "   "   "   "   "   2nd   "   "   (264)
         pmts' = 1st tier payments   (£7.00)
         pmts" = 2nd tier payments   (?)

$$s_{\overline{np}|} = ((1 + i/p)^{np} - 1) \div i/p$$

$$\frac{1000.00 \times 1.009167^{36} - 7(1.009167^{36} - 1)/0.009167}{(1 - 1.009167^{-264})/0.009167} = \text{pmts''}$$

$$\frac{1,091.916767}{99.2828351} = 10.99804$$
$$= 11.00$$

Employing a nominal rate of 11.001728% (because of the rounded payments) a DCF calculation will display as follows:

Loan   = −1,000.00
(3 yrs pmts) $7a_{\overline{36}|}$ =   213.81
(22 yrs pmts) $11a_{\overline{264}|} \times 1.009168^{-36}$ =   786.19
                                   NPV =   0.00

Alternatively,

$$\frac{1,000.00 - (11 \times (1 - 1.009167^{-264})/.009167 \times 1.009167^{-36})0}{(1 - 1.009167^{-36})/0.009167} = \text{pmts'}$$

$$\frac{213.67}{30.54} \qquad = 6.995$$
$$\qquad = 7.00$$

To find the balances

This presents no difficulty if the balance to be found is for a period *before* the cross over point (36 months), for example the balance at the end of the 12th month is:

$$(1,000 \times 1.009167^{12}) - (7 \times (1.009167^{12} - 1)/0.009167) = \text{£}1,027.35$$

But for a balance, in month 120, after the cross over point, the value of the loan at the 36th month, the cross over point, must first be found, namely:

$$(1,000 \times 1.00916736^{36}) - (7 \times (1.009167^{36} - 1)/0.009167) = \text{£}1,091.92$$

And employing this value as the loan amount, for payments of £11 find the balance for the $120 - 36 = 84$th month:

$$(1,091.92 \times 1.00916736^{84}) - (11 \times (1.009167^{84} - 1)/0.009167)$$
$$= \text{£}967.38$$

This method is probably easier to understand than the long and rather complex formula!

Multi-tier loans

In this case, as the name implies, there are a number of differing monthly payments, with constant lifts between certain years in the life of the loan.

In other words the borrower knows exactly what his monthly payments are for each year of the loan.

There is of course no mathematical reason why the "tiers" should not be less than a year, say quarters; but I know of no case where this is so.

For such an arrangement would, I suspect, tend to confuse the borrower and complicate his tax affairs – and it would certainly not be cheaper, because the lender would decide on the return required and calculate accordingly.

Assume a £7,000 loan at 11% nominal over a term of 25 years, and that the payments for the last (20 x 12) = 240 months are £80.

If the monthly payments for each of the first five years have constant increments what are the borrower's monthly payments for each of the first 5 years?

Taking the monthly working rate as (11/12)% the i/p becomes 0.009167

$$\frac{80a_{\overline{300|}} - 7{,}000}{a_{\overline{60|}} + a_{\overline{48|}} + a_{\overline{36|}} + a_{\overline{24|}} + a_{\overline{12|}}} = \text{the difference factor}$$

$$\frac{8{,}162.32 - 7{,}000}{45.99 + 38.69 + 30.54 + 21.46 + 11.31} = \frac{1{,}162.32}{148.00} = 7.8753514$$

Therefore:

Months		Payments
300 – 60		£80.88
60 – 48	80.00 – 7.86 =	£72.15
48 – 36	72.15 – " =	£64.30
36 – 24	64.30 – " =	£56.45
24 – 12	56.45 – " =	£48.60
12 – 0	48.60 – " =	£40.75

The difference in the nominal rate due to the rounding of the payments is too small to affect the APR (11.5%); nevertheless a DCF calculation (see Chapters 6 and 7) is always of value to verify one's equations. Employing an i/p of 0.00916742115:

```
Loan                                      = -7,000.00
40.75 ä___   x  1.0091674^-1
        12|                               =    461.07
48.60 ä___   x  1.0091674^-13
        12|                               =    492.85
56.45 ä___   x  1.0091674^-25
        12|                               =    513.08
64.30 ä___   x  1.0091674^-37
        12|                               =    523.81
72.15 ä___   x  1.0091674^-49
        12|                               =    526.79
80.00 ä___   x  1.0091674^-61
       240|                               =  4,482.41
                                   NPV =      0.00
```

Instead of this somewhat unwieldy difference method suppose that the constant lift (CL) for these five years was exactly £5 per year.

$$\frac{\text{loan} + [\ (a_{\underline{60|}} + a_{\underline{48|}} + a_{\underline{36|}} + a_{\underline{24|}} + a_{\underline{12|}}\ )\ \times\ CL\ ]}{a_{\underline{300|}}} = \text{last pmt}$$

$$\frac{7,000 + (148 \times 5)}{102.03} = £75.86$$

The schedule of the month's payments will be:

Months		Payments
300 – 60		£80.88
60 – 48	75.86 – 5.00 =	£70.86
48 – 36	70.86 – " =	£65.86
36 – 24	65.86 – " =	£60.86
24 – 12	60.86 – " =	£55.86
12 – 0	55.86 – " =	£50.86

Finding the intermediate balances *before* the end of the 5th year will involve working through each years' balances. For instance, find the balance at the end of the 22nd month:

$$7,000.00 \times (1 + j/p)^{12} - 50.86s_{\overline{12|}} = 7,167.98$$

$$7,167.98 \times (1 + i/p)^{10} - 55.86s_{\overline{10|}} = 7,270.61$$

Specific payments (non-constant)

Sometimes, there are specific payments in certain years, instead of constant lifts, and the only way of obtaining the correct periodic interest rate is by a DCF calculation.

Assume you wish to quote the APR of a 25 year £10,000 loan with the payments as shown:

```
Year 1   payments £ 50.00 (remember a year has 12 months!)
     2       "     £ 80.00
     3       "     £100.00
     4    onward   £108.00 (namely 300-36 months = 264 "times")
```

Employing a DCF calculation the monthly interest rate will come to 0.917313%, providing a nominal rate of 11.007758% and thus an APR of 11.5%.

Employing these values find the balance at the end of the 16th month:

$$10,000.00 \times (1 + i/p)^{12} - 50.00s_{\overline{12|}} = 10,526.83$$

$$7,167.98 \times (1 + i/p)^{4} - 80.86s_{\overline{4|}} = 10,594.00$$

Short-term bridging loans

Let us assume that a lender provides a short-term bridging loan to cover the period between the purchasing of one house and the selling of another. Since this is a property transaction, disclosure will be required. Assuming the loan is for £10,000 at 15% simple interest for 18 days, what is the the UK APR and the TAP?

£10,000 at 15% = £1,500.00 and 1,500/365 x 18 = 74.00 interest. The total amount paid, the TAP, is therefore £10,074.00

The UK APR, the truncated effective rate, cannot be found from the above 15% rate for that rate is a simple interest rate, and the effective must be deduced from a true rate for the APR disclosure. As a rough test, the effective is usually approximately double the simple rate.

The first thing is to find the payments over the 18 days:
10,074 [÷] 18 [=] 559.666667 and so using the interpolation of a computer/calculator program the nominal rate will be found as 28.3920081%

```
        10,000.00
        559.67a____                         0.077787% days periods
               18 |    = 0.077787 x 365 = 28.392081% nominal
                                         = 32.818114% effective

                                      365
        (deduced from ((1 + 28.392081/36500)    ) – 1 x 100)
```

Simple interest additional periods
When interest is added each period, month by month or year by year, it is almost always calculated by compound interest. When, then, would the additional period interest be at simple interest?

A good example is the UK 1988 National Savings "Yearly Plan" in which, according to the prospectus, monthly deposits are made only during year 1 and, providing the certificate is held for a further 4 years, the full 5-year tax-free return is stated to be precisely 7%. To effect these parameters the accruing interest over the first 12 months had to be at *simple* interest at a rate of 5.25%. The remaining four years being at 7.25% at annual compound interest.

Employing a schedule for a £100 monthly deposit, each month being at 5.25% simple interest, will find a value at the end of the year of £1,234.68, and 1,234.68 x (1 + 7.25/100)^4 = 1,633.59

The schedule would look like this:

```
£100                  x (1 + (5.25/1200)) = 100.4375
(100.4375 + 100)  x       1.004375      = 201.3144
(201.3144 + 100)  x          "          = 302.6327  and so on...
```

Is there not an easier method of finding the end value without making a schedule?

A useful tip is to "average the term", in this case $1+2+3+4\ldots+12 = 78$ and $78/12 = 6.5$. The rate multiplied by this factor will be *almost* correct. The "average" can be achieved by $(12 + 1)/2 = 6.5$ Using this method the value of the investor's savings at the end of the first year is:

```
(((Term + 1) ÷ 2 x Rate ÷ 100 ÷  P)+1) x Deposit x Term =  Value
((( 12  + 1) ÷ 2 x 5.25 ÷ 100 ÷ 12)+1) x  100   x  12   = £1,234.13
                        against the schedule value (above) of    £1,234.68
```

The above tip can be checked by calculating a schedule of the same parameters over a term of 6 months which will provide a value of £609.25, near enough to the result obtained when calculated by algorithm:

```
(1 + (((6 + 1)/2 x 5.25)/1200)) x 600 = £609.1875
```

Taking a further example, assume $50 is being deposited each month for 3 months at 10% simple interest. A schedule produces:

```
 50.00 x (1 + 10/1200) =
 50.00 x    1.00833    =  50.42 + 50
100.42 x       "       = 101.25 + 50
151.25 x       "       = 152.51        = $152.51
```

Whereas the algorithm yields:
```
(1 + (((3 + 1)/2 x 10.0)/1200))  x 150 = $152.50
```

and over a whole year:

```
(1 + (((12 + 1)/2 x 10.0)/1200)) x 600 = $632.50
as against a schedule value of         $633.51
```

It will be seen, therefore, that although the algorithm method is not precise it is sufficiently accurate for most requirements – and is an extremely useful check on a schedule if such a method has, in the end, to be employed.

The sum of percentages
In January 1989, in the UK, a Government National Savings bond, known as the Lawson Bond – after the then Chancellor of the Exchequer – was issued. The terms were that if the bond was held for five years the gross return would be 12% and the net return, for those paying tax at the basic rate of 25%, would be 9.012%.

These rates were achieved by rating the bond at 5.50% for the first year, 8.50% in the second year, 11.50% in the third year, 14.50% in the fourth year, and 20.60% in the fifth and final year – the rolled up income being subject to tax *each year*, which slightly took the gilt off the ginger bread!

$$((1.0550 \times 1.0850 \times 1.1150 \times 1.1450 \times 1.2060)^{1/5}) -1 \times 100 = 12.00\%$$

And as tax had to be paid each year on notional income (!), each of the above the percentages have to be brought to net, as exampled by 5.50% x .75 = 4.125% which divided by 100 plus 1 = 1.041250:

$$((1.041250 \times 1.063750 \times 1.086250 \times 1.108750 \times 1.15450)^{1/5})$$
$$-1 \times 100 = 9.021\%$$
$$(net)$$

From the above it will be seen that the gross return is *not* the five annual rates merely added, and then divided by 5, which would show an erroneous 12.12% but, as mentioned elsewhere, is correctly calculated above by *multiplying* the factor $(1 + i)$.

CHAPTER 4

Less Conventional Loan Methods

Rule of 78 or "sum of the digits" calculation
The correct name for this type of calculation is "sum of the digits" (or, nowadays, more politely the sum of the *years'* digits – SOYD), for "Rule of 78" only really applies to *one* year, namely 12 months. Since $1+2+3+4+\ldots\ldots10+11+12 = 78$ (or more simply $12 \times 13/2 = 78$). A two-year loan, as will be seen from the loan example below, is not literally Rule 78 but $24 \times 25/2 = 300$ (SOYD).

This method of calculating repayment loans was used almost exclusively before the advent of computers, for it is based on simple interest calculations and can find the value of the monthly payments and balances without the necessity of finding the true rate of interest. Mind you, these values, as we shall see below, are not as precise as the actuarial calculations which now obtain almost universally.

But while this method is still used extensively in the USA, the UK Credit Consumer Act requires the disclosure of the APR(UK), and as this entails the calculation of the loan by actuarial means, there seems less and less point in employing the so-called simpler methods of calculation. Except for a few Rule of 78 calculations required by the regulations of the Consumer Credit Act when, to give one instance, early redemption penalties are being considered.

Assume a loan of £3,000, over a term of 24 months, at a simple interest quoted rate of 6%. The charge is £3,000 x 6(%) x 2(yrs) ÷ 100 = £360.00, consequently the monthly repayments must be $(3000 + 360) \div 24$ (months) = £140.

From an examination of the table below it will be seen that interest paid is also reduced month by month by a factor of the charge (total interest) ÷ SOYD, namely $360/300 = 1.20$

Sum of the Digits Schedule

Loan £3000.00   Term 24 Months   Payments £140 monthly
Flat rate 6%   True rate 11.126664%

Mth	Int: paid	Capital repaid	Rebate	Balance loan	Actuarial equivalent	Balance note
1	28.80	111.20	331.20	2888.80	2,887.82**	3220.00
2	27.60	112.40	303.60	2776.40	2,774.60	3080.00
3	26.40	113.60	277.20	2662.80	2,660.33	2940.00
4	25.20	114.80	252.00	2548.00	2,545.00	2800.00
5	24.00	116.00	228.00	2432.00	2,428.60	2660.00
6	22.80	117.20	205.20	2314.80	2,311.12	2520.00
7	21.60	118.40	183.60	2196.40	2,192.55	2380.00
8	20.40	119.60	163.20	2076.80	2,072.88	2240.00
9	19.20	120.80	144.00	1956.00	1,952.10	2100.00
10	18.00	122.00	126.00	1834.00	1,830.20	1960.00
11	16.80	123.20	109.20	1710.80	1,707.17	1820.00
12	15.60	126.40	93.60	1586.40	1,583.00	1680.00
13	14.40	125.60	79.20	1460.80	1,457.68	1540.00
14	13.20	126.80	66.00	1334.00	1,331.20	1400.00
15	12.00	128.00	54.00	1206.00	1,203.54	1260.00
16	10.80	129.20	43.20	1076.80	1,074.70	1120.00
17	9.60	130.40	33.60	946.40	944.66	980.00
18	8.40	131.60	25.20	814.80	813.42	840.00
19	7.20	132.80	18.00	682.00	680.96	700.00
20	6.00	134.00	12.00	548.00	547.27	560.00
21	4.80	135.20	7.20	412.80	412.34	420.00
22	3.60	136.40	3.60	276.40	276.16	280.00
23	2.40	137.60	1.20	138.80	138.72	140.00
24	1.20	138.80	0.00	0.00	** 0.00	0.01
	360.00	3000.00				

** Assumes that all payments are rounded to 2 places of decimals.

The rebate and balances

The "capital repaid" is the payments less the "interest paid"
e.g. in the 14th month, 140 – 13.20 = 126.80 The "rebate", the
unearned interest, is the interest *not* paid to date and for the
14th month is the interest due for months 15 to 24 = £66.

Legend   This example

```
I   = The Charge                                    360
P   = The Payments per month                        140
N   = The total number of months                     24
T   = The total number of months of UNpaid interest
```

$$T \times \frac{I(T + 1)}{N(N + 1)} = \text{rebate}_n$$

$$(24 - 14) \times \frac{360(24-14+1)}{24 \times 25} = \underset{(66.83)}{£66.00} \quad \text{rebate}_{14}$$

$$PT - (I \times \frac{T(T+1)}{N(N+1)}) = \text{balance}_n$$

$$140(24-5) - 360(\frac{19 \times 20}{24 \times 25}) = \underset{(2,428.58)}{£2,432.00} \text{ balance}_5$$

$$\text{Int.factor} \times (T + 1) = \text{interest month}_?$$

$$1.2 \times (24 - 5 + 1) = \underset{(23.60)}{£24.00} \text{ interest month}_5$$

Penalties for early settlement
(according to the UK Consumer Credit Act regulations)

Early redemption is irritating to a lender in that it upsets his cash flow arrangements and often entails considerable paper work. Consequently he is entitled to demand a *penalty* to recover some of his cost. In the old days, the conventional penalty was "three months payments". Nowadays, the CCA rules that for early redemption of a loan under five years the rebate can be calculated as if it was *two* months ahead, namely *two periods of interest* can be added; if over five years then only one additional period is permissible.

Assume that in the above schedule calculation it was required to redeem the loan after the 14th month. As this is under five years the statutory penalty is two months' interest, namely £12 and £10.80, which added to the normal balance at the end of month 14 = £1,334.00 + 22.80 = £1,356.80, namely, in this case, the balance due at redemption.

Assume that a loan is for £5,000, over a term of 144 months, at a *flat* rate of 20% and that the borrower wishes to redeem the loan after only 11 months. If the lender imposes the maximum permissible penalty what is the final balance? As the CCA regulations assume that the Rule 78 method will apply, the calculations will be as a follows:

```
The "charge" is (144 x 118.06) - 5,000 = £12,000.64
The rounded payments per month will be:
(5,000 x 20/100 x 12 + 5000) ÷ 144 = £118.06
```

As the redemption period is under five years, two periods of added interest are permissible as a penalty, so the "rebate" must be found for the $(144 - 11 - 2) = 131$ periods

```
(131 x 132)/(144 x 145) x the "charge" = 9,938.46 rebate
Rebate - ((144 - 11) x pmts)          = 5,763.52 balance
```

In this particular loan some payments were missed and made up, in the first eleven months of the loan, and as both the lender and borrower agreed to cancel the loan the requirement is to discover the correct final balance due.

The schedule of the first eleven months' payments are:

End of month			End of month	
1.	118.06		7.	200.00
2.	118.06		8.	0.00
3.	30.00		9.	50.00
4.	0.00		10.	0.00
5.	75.00		11.	30.00
6.	118.06			

The *true* rate of interest by computer/interpolation will be found as a nominal rate of 27.212463:

$$\frac{5000}{118.06a_{\overline{144}|}} = 2.267705\% \text{ monthly}$$

$$5,000 \div ((1 - 1.02267705^{-144})/.02267705) = 118.06$$

Having established the correct true nominal rate the payments can be inserted where relevant:

MONTHS	PV	x (1 + i/p)	PMT	FV
1	5,000.00	x 1.022677	118.06	= 4,995.33
1	4.995.33		118.06	= 4,990.54
1	4,990.54		30.00	= 5,073.72
1	5,073.72		0.00	= 5,188.77
1	5,188.77		75.00	= 5,231.44
1	5,231.44		118.06	= 5,232.01
1	5,232.01		200.00	= 5,150.66
1	5,150.66		0.00	= 5,267.46
1	5,267.46		50.00	= 5,336.91
1	5,336.91		0.00	= 5,457.94
1	5,457.94		30.00	= 5,551.71

To find the value at the end of 11 months, if all the payments had been made in due time:

$$5000 \times (1 + 27.212463/1200)^{11} - 118.06 \times ((1.022677^{11} - 1)/.022677)$$
$$= 4,942.33$$

The interest due, (the result of missed payments £5,551.71 – 4,942.33 = £609.38) must be added to any calculation regarding the conventional balance. Consequently, the balance due, with no penalty added, therefore must be 4,942.33 + 609.38 = £5.551.71

Now what about penalties? In law the lender, if he wishes, may charge two month's *interest*, that is the interest for months 12 and 13.

These two month's interest will be found by:

$$5000 \times (1 + 27.212463/1200)^{11} - 118.06 \times ((1.022677^{11} - 1)/.022677)$$
$$= 4,942.33$$
$$5000 \times (1 + 27.212463/1200)^{13} - 118.06 \times ((1.022677^{13} - 1)/.022677)$$
$$= 4,930.23$$

Two months' interest 118.06 x 2 – (4,942.33 – 4,930.23) = 224.02

The presumption is that £224.02 added to £5,551.71 = £5,775.73, but unhappily the Regulations require that the penalty calculations are determined by the Rule of 78.

Thus, if the Rule of 78 interest for months 12 and 13 are *less* that the £224.02 above the lesser amount must be adopted.

With two penalty payments the month required is 11 + 2 = 13 so 144 - 13 = 131 months for the rebate.

Hence the balance, *with* the two penalty months, is as below:

```
(131 x 132)/(144 x 145) x the "charge"      = 9,938.46 rebate
Rebate - ((144 - 11) x pmts)                = 5,763.52 balance
```
and *without:*
```
(133 x 134)/(144 x 145) x the "charge"      =10,243.08 rebate
Rebate - ((144 - 11) x pmts)                = 5,458.90 balance
Two months' interest 5,763.52 - 5,458.90    = 304.62   interest
```

As the two months' interest found by Rule of 78 (£304.62) is *more* than that found by actuarial means (£224.02) the balance of £5,775.73 above therefore stands; indeed, it will be observed that all Rule 78 balances are always greater than their actuarial equivalent – and this can be costly to the consumer.

When the regulations were drafted, over 15 years ago, PCs and sophisticated calculators simply did not exist, consequently there was no sensible alternative to Rule of 78. But now surely the Office of Fair Trading should give some thought to amending these somewhat ancient regulations.

Constant payments to principal (CPP)
This method of repaying both interest and capital for a repayment loan is structured by the principal being repaid in equal instalments, the outstanding interest being paid at the same time, the periodic payments will thus be *uneven.*

With a loan of £1,000 over 10 years at 10% nominal the capital is repaid in even slices, namely 1,000/10 = £100, the interest being due on each periodic balance.

The schedule below shows how the interest is added at each period to the basic periodic capital repayment to principal (CPP), to find each periodic payment, each instalment reducing by the interest payable.

Year	Int due	CPP	Total pmts	Balance
1	100	100	200	900
2	90	100	190	800
3	80	100	180	700
4	70	100	170	600
5	60	100	160	500
6	50	100	150	400
7	40	100	140	300
8	30	100	130	200
9	20	100	120	100
10	10	100	110	0
	550	1000	1550	

Find the data according to the 5th and 7th periods:

```
loan ÷ (years x number of pmts per year)        =  CPP
1000 ÷ (  10   x   1  )                          = £100
```

$$\frac{(loan \times i/p) + (CPP \times i/p)}{2} \times term = total\ interest$$

$$\frac{(1000 \times .10) + (100 \times .10)}{2} \times 10 = £550$$

```
loan x   i/p x ((CPP x   1/p – (# per – 1))) – CPP = balance
((1000 x .10) x ((100 x .10) – (  5   – 1))) – CPP =
     (100     x   ( 10    –      4  )) – 100 = £500
     (100     x   ( 10    – (  7   – 1))) – 100 = £300
```

```
CPP + (i/p x  (loan – (CPP x (# per – 1))))      = total pmts
                                                   for # period
100 + (.10 x  (1000 – (100 x (  5   – 1))))      =
100 + (.10 x  (1000 –      400))                 =
100 + (.10 x        600)                         =
100 +   60                                       = £160 pmts
100 + (.10 x  (1000 – (100 x (  7   – 1))))      = £140 pmts
```

```
Total payments for # period – CPP               = interest due
                                                   for # period
        160              – 100                   = £ 60 per (5)
        140              – 100                   = £ 40 per (7)
```

Alternatively, find the interest due by:

```
(loan x i/p) - (CPP x i/p x (# per - 1))      = interest due
(1000 x .10) - (100 x .10 x ( 5   - 1))       = £ 60 per (5)
(1000 x .10) - (100 x .10 x ( 7   - 1))       = £ 40 per (7)


         The interest due + CPP               = payments
              60.00       + 100               = £160 pmts(5)


         loan - (CPP x # per)                 = balance(7)
         1000 - (CPP x  7  )                  = £300
```

To find the interest due between two period:

```
int(j) - int(k)                               = interest
───────────────  x ((k - j) + 1)                between
       2                                        j and k

      70 + 30                                 = £250
      ───────    x 5                            interest
         2
```

Banker's Loans - Constant Payments to Principal

In practice such loans are not always quite as simple as those shown above. For when contracting a CPP loan from a bank the usual practice is for the interest to be calculated daily and for the payments to be monthly with quarterly compounding.

For precise accuracy a computer program is usually essential for if the interest due falls on a Sunday, or a non-banking day, *some* banks, but by no means all treat the next interest day to be the following Monday and the adjust the month following by reducing the days accordingly.

Ignoring the somewhat esoteric calculations of some banks a commonplace type of CPP loan might well be £4,000 over a term of 3 years with monthly payments and quarterly compounding, the nominal rate being 16.50%

First find the CPP: £4,000/(3 x 12) = £111.1111111 rounded, of course, to £111.11. The total quarterly interest found by:

```
4000 + (111.11 x 3) + .04
─────────────────────────  x 16.50/400 x 4 x 3 =  £1,072.51
           2
```

The reason for the "loss" of 4 pence, and don't forget that lenders dislike losing even 4 pence (!), is that the CPP was rounded, and consequently the total interest calculated has become £111.11 x 36 = £3,999.96 – instead of £4,000.

Alternatively, if the payments were monthly and the interest charged was also monthly the total interest will be:

$$\frac{4000 + 111.11 + .04}{2} \times 16.50/1200 \times 36 = £1,017.51$$

In the event that it was required to find the interest due, payments and balances for the 30th month:

```
(loan   x    i/p ) – (CPP     x    i/p  x (# per – 1)) = interest due
( 4000 x .01375) – (111.11 x .01375 x      29    )  = £10.69        30
                       10.69 + 111.11               = £121.80 pmts
                       4000 – (111.11 x 30)          = £666.70 bal   30
                                                                    30
```

CPP loans with a balloon profile

Occasionally, perhaps more in the States that in the UK, a balloon method is applied whereby the interest due is withheld until the end of the term.

The schedule below will go some way to explaining why this type of loan is sometimes called the "upside down serial loan".

Year	CPP	Total pmts	Balance	Int due
1	100	100	100 x .10	10
2	100	100	200 x .10	20
3	100	100	300 x .10	30
4	100	100	400 x .10	40
5	100	100	500 x .10	50
6	100	100	600 x .10	60
7	100	100	700 x .10	70
8	100	100	800 x .10	80
9	100	100	900 x .10	90
10	100	100	1000 x .10	100
	1000	1000		550

The formula to find the charge remains the same as the conventional CPP method above. For instance in the previous loan the total interest would still be £1017.51 for nothing is altered, save that the interest is withheld until redemption, whenever that may be.

To find the interest due at the end of any particular period, do not, as previously, subtract 1 from the number of the period concerned, but instead add 1:

```
(CPP x (#per + 1)) - (loan x i/p)     = bal(#)
(100 x (  6  + 1)) - (1000 x .10)     = £600
          balance x i/p               = int(#)
            600   x .10               = £60
```

Days' Money

In the early days of computers I suspect that in some cases the programmers, instead of being asked their expert opinion of what could and could not be done, were told by some banks and institutions, succinctly, to "calculate the way we do" - and consequently some archaic methods, taken on board then, still remain enshrined to this day as their way of doing things. But this does not necessarily mean that they should be regarded as "market practice"!

For instance, it may not be generally known, that for short term "days money" on loan to institutions *some* banks, calculated the interest due by compound means for weekdays but by *simple interest methods* at weekends and bank holidays.

Assuming there are 4 weekends (of 2 days each) intervening in a 30 day month, the difference between 5 days of compounding and 2 days simple interest for a £1,000,000, for "days' money" is negligible – around some 70 pence!

Also assuming, a somewhat unlikely event, that the rate of 15% remains constant for the whole 30 days.

$$PVx(1 + (NOM\%/36500))^{30-(2x4)} \times (1 + (NOM\%/36500x\ 2))^{4} = FV$$

$$1,000,000 \times (1 + 15/36500)^{22}x (1 + (15/36500 \times 2))^{4} = £1,012,401.83$$

whereas:

$$1,000,000 \times 1.000411^{30} = £1,012,402.52$$

With the above nominal rate of 15%, a £1,000 days money over 14 days could be:

$$1,000.00 \times (1 + 15/36500)^{10} \times (1 + (15/36500 \times 2))^{2} = £1,005.7685$$

$$\text{whereas:} \qquad 1,000.00 \times 1.000411^{14} \qquad = £1,005.7688$$

I need hardly remind readers that the calculations above stem from "full precision", namely 1.0004109589.

Odd days

Inevitably the structure of real life loans often differs from book theory! Lending institutions, with computer accounting, usually prefer all their repayments to be made on a particular date, such as mid- or end-month. In that case there are often some "odd days" which have to be taken into account.

If the payments are monthly and the first payment is due on, say, July 1 and the advance is made 18 days before that date, there will be 18 odd days' interest to be accounted for. In effect, what is happening is that, irrespective of the main loan, the borrower is taking out a secondary loan just for the odd days – at the original rates.

Assume a loan of £3,500 over a term of 3 years, the quote being a *true* rate of 11.08%, as shown below, but which is treated as (11.0824532592/12)% monthly: the reason for employing the full precision of 10 decimal places is that the rate so shown is precisely equivalent to a flat rate of 6% over 3 years – and comparisons are made later.

The conventional payments for this loan would be:

$$\begin{array}{ll} \dfrac{3,500}{a\underline{}} & \text{at } (11.0824532592/12)\% = £114.7222222222 \\ \quad 36\mid & \qquad\qquad\qquad\qquad\quad = £114.72 \text{ monthly} \end{array}$$

But with the extra 18 odd days the loan is no longer £3,500 but becomes £3,500 plus the interest above and, given the rate, the new payments can be determined.

Simple versus compounding calculations for the odd days
There are four different ways of calculating, either by
compound or simple interest methods, depending on whether
the original interest on the loan is quoted simple or true.

A true rate quotation

$$3{,}500 \times (1 + (11.08/1200))^{18\times12/365} = £3{,}519.092715$$
$$3{,}500 \times (1 + (11.08/1200 \times 18 \times 12/365)) = £3{,}519.128618$$

It will be seen that, paradoxically, the simple interest
calculation produces a slightly larger future value. That being
the case, in a repayment loan, the larger the loan amount the
larger are the payments required to service the loan.

Employing the actual calendar and the normal UK methods
and if there were 18 odd days the payments would become:

$$3{,}500 \times 1.009235^{18\times12/365}$$
$$a_{\overline{36}|} \quad \text{at } (11.0824532592/12)\% \quad = £115.348039 \text{ monthly}$$
$$\text{(compounded)}$$
$$3{,}500 \times (1 + .009235\times18\times12/365)$$
$$a_{\overline{36}|} \quad \text{at } (11.0824532592/12)\% \quad = £115.349216 \text{ monthly}$$
$$\text{(simple)}$$

A simple interest quotation

In the United States a different system is employed in that, as
the loan interest is usually found from a quoted "flat rate", the
interest engendered is divided by the number of payments due
and added to the conventional non-odd-day payments.

In this example, the quoted rate in the States would be a flat
rate of 6%, the "add-on" rate in the States being 11.082453%
(the true rate used above), the period being a 3 years term.

With 18 odd days the US statistician, using the 30/360
calendar, would first find the monthly payments and then add
the value for the odd days, calculating as follows:

$$\frac{3,500 + (3,500 \times 6/100 \times 3)}{36} = \$114.722222$$

and working in a simple interest profile the payments become:

$$114.72 + \frac{3,500 \times 6/100 \times 18/360}{36} = \$115.0138888889$$
$$\$115.01$$

$$\frac{3,500 \times (1 + (i/p \times 18 \times 12/360))}{115.01a\underline{\quad\quad}} \quad \text{at} \quad 0.90671605859\% \text{ monthly}$$
$$36\ | \quad\quad\quad 10.88059270310\% \text{ nominal}$$

$$3,519.04 \div (1 - (1.009067^{-36})/0.009067)) = \$115.01 \ (SI)$$

$$\frac{3,500 \times (1 + i/p)^{18/30}}{115.01a\underline{\quad\quad}} \quad \text{at} \quad 0.90677044846\% \text{ monthly}$$
$$36\ | \quad\quad\quad 10.88124538150\% \text{ nominal}$$

$$3,519.00 \div (1 - (1.009068^{-36})/0.009068)) = \$115.01 \ (CI)$$

To find the number of odd days

$$\frac{(\text{odd days pmts} - \text{conventional pmts}) \times \text{ months}}{\text{capital} \times i/p \text{ (flat rate)}} \times \text{base} = \text{odd days}$$

$$\frac{(115.01 - 114.72) \times 36}{3,500 \times .06} \times 360 \quad = 17.90 \quad = 18 \text{ days}$$

The odd days/months

Whether the actual or the financial calendar is employed, with days times 12/365 or 12/360 respectively, the days must be less than one month, if they are not then there is one month in advance.

For example, assume a loan of $100,000 with monthly payments of $400, with a balloon payment of $3,000 at the end of 24 months.

Normally the first payment would occur one month after the date of the advance, and if the advance occurred, say, 15 days prior to the month end there would be 15 odd days interest to be calculated.

But suppose that the first payment made was to be 8 days after the advance what exactly does this mean?   Surely it would mean that the payments are in advance and that there is an 8 day gap, namely *annuities due* with 8 odd days to be calculated.   By the same token, 24 months and 38 odd days, and this sometimes happens, would mean there are 25 months and 8 odd days payments to be calculated.

If the above example did stipulate that payments of $400 monthly commenced 8 days after the advance, the nominal rate, would be 19.675959% and 1.639663% monthly for compound interest calculations and 19.673647% and 1.639471% monthly for simple interest calculations.

With a balloon payment, the tip is to increase the capital amount by the value of the odd days *before* discounting the residual:

Let us see if the equations fit, remembering that the calculations, in this instance, are annuities *due*:

Compound interest

$$\frac{(10,000 \times 1.016397^{(8\times12/360)}) \quad - \ (3,000 \times 1.016397^{-24})}{(1 - 1.016397^{-24})/0.016397 \quad \times \ 1.016397}$$

$$\frac{(10,000 \times 1.004346) - 2,030.50}{19.709233 \times 1.016397} \ = \ \frac{8,012.96}{20.032398} \ = \ \underline{\$400.00}$$

Simple Interest

$$\frac{10,000 \times (1+(0.016395 \times 8 \times 12/360)) - (3,000 \times 1.016395^{-24})}{(1 - 1.016395^{-24})/0.016395 \times 1.016395}$$

$$\frac{(10,000 \times 1.004372) - 2,030.60}{19.709671 \times \quad 1.016395} \ = \ \frac{8,013.12}{20.032805} \ = \ \underline{\$400.00}$$

Because of the balloon payments the calculation must employ compound interest discounting, and consequently the short formula above to find the odd-days cannot be used.

In fact, I have yet to find a method of "finding the odd-days" if a balloon, or a residual, intrudes in the structure of the loan.

Unhappily, the method of finding the term by using logs, as is done for conventional loans, is not valid.

Wrap around mortgages – with no balloon payment

The wrap around loan, a United States nomenclature, is, in effect, merely a secondary loan. In other words if the existing holder of a mortgage wants to raise other funds, for some reason such as home improvements, the borrower can refinance his existing loan by wrapping around his present mortgage with a secondary loan, receiving the difference between the present value of his existing loan and the capital value of the new loan.

The mortgagor covering the new loan need not be the same one as for the original loan. If a new mortgagor is involved, he now owns the whole loan and is responsible for paying the first lender the original repayments, taking from the borrower sufficient instalments to cover both the original repayments and the payments in respect of the new capital injected into the existing loan. Should the borrower fail, the second lender is still responsible for the original instalments.

The calculations below to find the various data, resulting from the joining, or possible joining, of the two loans, are reasonably easy to calculate providing there are no balloon payments in the structure of either of the loans in question, and providing the term of the secondary loan is the same as that of the original mortgage. Should either of these complications arise a method, different to that shown directly below, is needed.

Assume that the present value of an existing loan is exactly £120,000, at a nominal rate of 11.50%, and that there is a further 200 months to termination. The borrower wishes to refinance his original loan so as to receive an injection of £80,000 in order to build various additions to his property and thus substantially increase its value.

The secondary lender requires a final yield of 12% and works out by computer that his £200,000 loan, in that case, would need to be serviced by a nominal rate of 11.70%. Is he correct?

In general terms, the idea is to find the yield after the differences of loan amounts, and the payments per month, have been determined. Consequently, in this example, we must first find the payments of the original loan in order to find the value after the two payments have been subtracted – and from this data we can find the resulting yield.

(1) *Find the monthly payments of the original loan*

$$\frac{120,000.00}{a\underline{\qquad}_{200\,|}\ \text{at}\ (11.50/12)\%} = \text{payments}$$

$$120,000.00 \div ((1 - 1.009583^{-200})/.009583) = 1,350.47057$$
$$= 1,350.47$$

(2) *Find the monthly payments of the secondary loan*

$$\frac{120,000 + 80,000}{a\underline{\qquad}_{200\,|}\ \text{at}\ (11.70/12)\%} = \text{payments}$$

$$200,000.00 \div ((1 - 1.009750^{-200})/.0097500) = 2,277.037729$$
$$= 2,277.04$$

(3) *Then check final yield return*

$$\frac{200,000 - 120,000}{(2,277.04 - 1,350.47)\ a\underline{\qquad}_{200\,|}} = \text{yield}\%$$

$$= 11.998263$$
$$= 12\%$$

Wrap around mortgages – with a balloon payment
In this case the calculation method above will not be possible for there are two unknown variables, the final yield must be found before the original or secondary loan can be reduced by the discounted balloon amount, and the yield cannot be found unless the balloon amount is correctly discounted!

So what to do? The only way is either to employ a computer program which will have to iterate until the two sides of the equation are equal (see below) or employ a discounted cash flow program using, perhaps, a sophisticated programmed (or programmable) calculator (see below).

Or use the method outlined previously for calculating the cash flow values by formula/equation and not by scheduling.

If the borrower in the above example said that he would prefer to make a final down payment (balloon) of £50,000, at the end of the term, what would be his reduced payments?

The computer program method is to outline both the respective values of the two loans, with one value, (the required value) missing. Given the yield return required and all the other parameters, save the unknown – in this case the secondary payment which must be found before it can be subtracted from the original monthly payment – the program will then experiment with the unknown variable iterating until both sides of the equation are equal:

$$\frac{120,000}{1,350.47a_{\overline{200|}}} = \frac{200,000 - (50,000 \times 1.0100^{-200})}{?????a_{\overline{200|}}}$$

If both sides of the equation are serviced by 12% nominal it will be found that the payments come to £2,197.97 (rounded)

$$\frac{(200,000.00 - (50,000 \times 1.01^{-200})) - 120,000}{(2,197.97 - 1.350.47)a_{\overline{200|}}} \quad \text{at } x\%$$

If correct, taking 12% nominal the payments must 2,197.97 – 1,350.47 = 847.50.

$$\frac{193,165.68 - 120,000}{a_{\overline{200|}}} \quad \text{at } (12/12)\%$$

$$73,165.68 \div (1 - 1.01^{-200}/.01) = 847.50 \quad (\text{Q.E.D})$$

Cash flows

Discounted cash flow (DCF) calculations are extremely valuable as a check on any abnormal loan structure. Taking the wrap around example, with the balloon payment above, the cash flows would be as follows:

The investment would be £120,000 – 200,000 = –80,000 and *input* as a negative.

The payments would be £2,197.97 – 1,350.47 for 199 months, and £847.50 plus $50,000 (the balloon) for 1 month. This will provide an IRR of 1.000002 which when multiplied by 12 = 12.00%.

Cash flow by formula

Investment $= -80,000.000000$

$$847.50 \; a_{\overline{199}|} \quad \text{(at 0.01\%)} \quad =$$

$$847.50 \times (1 - 1.01^{-199})/.01 = 73,049.987543$$

$$(847.50 + 50,000) \times 1.01^{-200} = \underline{6,950.160734}$$

$$= 80,000.148277$$

The decimal discrepancy is due to payments being rounded.

If the terms are varied due allowance will have to be made. For instance if in the example above the secondary loan was required to continue for a further 40 months, then secondary payments would be £2,114.06 and consequently there would be 2,114.06 – 1,350.47 for 200 months, 2,114.06 for 39 months and 50,000 + 2,114.06 as the final payment.

Secondary mortgage deeds

When this type of mortgage loan relates to UK Local Authorities, the payments are usually made twice a year on 31 March and 30 September in accordance with their customary and immutable payment methods.

Assume therefore that the deed was purchased for £500,000 on December 12, 1990, having a nominal coupon of 14, 5/8th and that maturity falls on January 7, 1997. The yield is 11% the requirement is to find the cost (price).

As maturity falls on a date different to the conventional anniversary of the payment dates a specific calculation is required:

The formula which should be employed is:

$$\frac{(RV + (D \times t)) \times (1 + i/p)^{-n+t} + Da_{\overline{n}|} + D}{(1 + i/p)^{k}} = Price + a/i$$

where:

RV is the redemption value

D is the half coupon

n+k is the number of days between settlement and the LPD divided by 182.5 (here 2488/182.5 = 13.632877)

t is the odd days between last payment date (LPD) and maturity divided by 182.5 (here 99/182.5 = .542466)

RND is rounding the adjusted interest (here 3.97) to £/pence.

$$\frac{(100 + RND(7.3125 \times .542466)) \times (1 + 11/200)^{-13.542466} + 7.3125(1 - 1.055^{-13})/.055 + 7.3125}{1.055^{.632877}} = 120.190240$$

$$\frac{50.351499 + 66.668637 + 7.3125}{1.034465} = 120.190240$$

As the equation above is percentage-based the loan value must be multiplied by 500,000/100 to find the cost of the secondary mortgage deeds, namely £600,951.20.

The calculation of some odd one–off loans

Inevitably, sometimes individual loans will have structures that follow no conventional pattern. The tiresome one-off loan. Because of this there is often no precedent, there will be no standard method, which can be followed, and consequently the manner of dealing with each peculiar loan must be thought out from scratch.

And if the various financial requirements sometimes assume rather alarming proportions, and I stare at my desk and wonder how on earth to solve this or that complicated problem I remind myself of the following story and think, now, *what actually happens to the money.* In World War II, in one particular area of operations, certain objectives were limited by the arrival, or not, of various supplies, the most noticeable being gas and lubricants for the forward areas.

One day a fairly senior staff officer left his desk, drove smartly off towards the docks – and turned himself, metaphorically, into a "jerry can" of petrol. Wherever this can went, and however it was transported to the forward areas, so went this officer. He was loaded, unloaded, temporary stored, left standing in sun and rain, reloaded, again and again, in his journey by water, rail and road.

A week or so after he returned to his office it quickly became apparent that the previous delay in the arrival of supplies "at the sharp end" no longer obtained – and that there had been a considerable reallocation of certain key personnel!

Sometimes a formula can be worked out, and the result checked by a Discounted Cash Flow (DCF) calculation (see Chapter 6). Sometimes the converse is equally valid, the requirement can be found by interpolating on a DCF computer or calculator program, and, the precise answer required having been found, a suitable equation that allows other variables to be calculated can be worked out. With the three problems below, using the rule "what happens to the money", find the answers – before reading on!

The first is a loan which, initially, apparently caused no little concern in the department concerned with establishing the required payments. The structure was such that a capital amount of $288,000 at a rate of 14% nominal, was advanced on May 1, 1989. As one payment in advance was required, the borrower (or lessee?) received, at the time of the advance, the principal less one payment.

The remaining instalments were required on January 1, for the years 1990, 1991 and 1992. All the four payments, the advance and the three following, had to be the same; in other words the payments were to be even throughout the term.

What are the required payments?

The cash flows, after the advance payment, would be none for 7 months, then one payment on January 1, 1989.

The there would be no payments for 11 months, and then one payment on January 1, 1990. And this structure would be repeated once more with the last payment on January 1, 1991.

It was considered that the time spent on DCF interpolating, could be better employed in thinking out the correct equation.

The original concept, and indeed the correct method, was to discount each payment back from the end of the term to the advance. As the total number of payment (or missed) months between May 1989 to January 1991 is 32, the last payment must be discounted by $(1 + i/p)^{-32}$, and the previous one by 32–12 and so on.

The formula was then rearranged into a conventional format, the "1 + " in the denominator accounting for the one advance payment:

$$\$ \ \frac{288,000}{1 + (1 + i/p)^{-8} + (1 + i/p)^{-(8+12)} + (1 + i/p)^{-(8+24)}} = \text{payments}$$

As the rate is known, namely 14% nominal, there is no need for any interpolation, consequently the payments can easily be found as follows:

$$\$ \ \frac{288,000}{1 + 1.011667^{-8} + 1.011667^{-(8+12)} + 1.011667^{-(8+24)}} = 84,848.95$$

$$\$ \ \frac{288,000}{1 + \ 0.911382 \ + 0.792960 \ + 0.689925} = 84,848.95$$

$$\$ \ \frac{288,000}{3.394267} = 84,848.95$$

A discounted cash flow calculation on the lines suggested above will provide, not unnaturally, the same answer!

Another example of a one-off loan, being the type of problem that is unlikely to reoccur is that of a bridging loan of £30,000 for a nominal six months at 2% monthly interest. The interest is deducted from the capital amount at the time of the drawdown, a processing fee of £150 and a single endowment insurance premium of £750 are also deducted at drawdown. Find the UK APR.

If you think about it, as the interest has been paid front end, there are no payments, but the capital has to be repaid at the end of the 6 months. Is this not therefore a simple and uncomplicated compound interest sum?

The loan the borrower actually receives is £30,000 – (30,000 x .02 x 6) = £26,400, and less £150 and less £750, which equals £25,500 and therefore to find the rate:

$$((30{,}000/25{,}500)^{1/6} - 1) \times 1200 = 32.947994\% \text{ nominal}$$
$$((1 + (32.947994/1200))^{12} - 1) \times 100 = 38.408305\% \text{ effective}$$
$$= \underline{38.4\% \text{ APR}}$$

A problem from Australia this time. The "amount financed" is Aust\$13,991.15 and the term is 48 months. The true (nominal) rate of interest is 26.82% The client pays A\$100 monthly for the first 6 months, A\$467.33 monthly for the next 36 months, how much does he need to pay monthly for the last 6 months?

As we know the interest rate, 26.82% nominal, 2.235% monthly, the answer is merely a case of finding each balance and then using that value as the PV – a continuation annuities ordinary calculation:

$$A\$13{,}991.15 \times 1.022350^6 - (100.00 \times (1.022350^6 - 1)/0.022350)$$
$$= 15{,}340.83$$

$$15{,}340.83 \times 1.022350^{36} - (467.33 \times (1.022350^{36} - 1)/0.022350)$$
$$= 8{,}568.74$$

$$\frac{8{,}568.71}{a_{\overline{6}|}} \quad \text{at } (26.82/12)\% \quad = \text{payments}$$

$$8{,}568.71 \div (1 - 1.022350^{-6})/0.022350 = \underline{1{,}541.89}$$

Alternatively, assuming that the first and last payments were known, A$100 and A$1,541.89 respectively, how can the middle payment of A$467.33 be determined?

Working backwards from the end of the term we know, or it is reasonable to assume, that the final payments of A$1,541.89 completes the loan and that the end balance is 0.00.

In that case the present value. over 6 months, at the known monthly rate servicing a payment of A$1,541.89 can easily be found. In fact, of course it will be A$8,568.71; and this present value will become the end balance, after 36 months, from a present value of A$15,340.83 (which was originally found, above, from the data provided.

$$
\begin{array}{ll}
\overline{1{,}541.89 \ a \underline{}} \quad \text{at } (26.82/12)\% & = \text{PV} \\
\qquad\qquad 6 \ | \\
1{,}541.89 \times (1 - 1.022350^{-6})/0.022350 & = \underline{8{,}568.71} \\[2mm]
\dfrac{15{,}340.83 - (8{,}568.71 \times 1.022350^{-36}}{\ } \\
a \underline{} \qquad\qquad \text{at } (26.82/12)\% & = \text{payments} \\
\ 6 \ | \\[2mm]
(15{,}340.83 - 3{,}866.60) \div (1.022350^{36} - 1)/0.022350 = \underline{467.33}
\end{array}
$$

The reducing payment loan

Perhaps one of the most imaginative and interesting of the less conventional loans, is the *reducing payment loan* whereby the periodic payments, which comprise conventionally both capital and interest, *reduce* each month. instead of remaining constant throughout the term of the loan.

The table below will probably provide an easier perspective than pages of explanation. Assume a commercial loan of $500,000 and suppose that the lending institution's nominal rate was 14.75 and that they themselves required a "minimum" return of 10.25%

Loan Outstanding (beginning)	Monthly int (x 14.75/1200)	Capital repayments	Monthly ** repayments	LOS_t (ending)
1. 500,000.00	6,145.83 +	1,178.92 =	7,324.75	498,821.08
2. 498,821.08	6,131.34	1,188.99	7,320.33	497,632.09
3. 497,632.09	6,116.73	1,199.15	7,315.87	496,432.94
4. 496,432.94	6,101.99	1,209.39	7,311.38	495,223.55
5. 495,223.55	6,087.12	1,219.72	7,306.84	494,003.83
6. 494,003.83	6,072.13	1,230.14	7,302.27	492,773.69
7. 492,773.69	6,057.01	1,240.65	7,297.66	491,533.05
8. 491,533.05	6,041.76	1,251.24	7,293.00	490,281.80
9. 490,281.80	6,026.38	1,261.93	7,288.31	489,019.87
10. 489,019.87	6,010.87	1,272.71	7,283.58	487,747.16
11. 487,747.16	5,995.23	1,283.58	7,278.81	486,463.58
12. 486,463.58	5,979.45	1,294.54	7,273.99	485,169.04

~ ~

and so on – the last two months values being:

179. 10,761.43	132.28	5,357.83	5,490.11	5,404.11
180. 5,404.11	66.42	5,403.60	5,470.02 **	0.00

** Assumes that all payments are rounded to 2 places of decimals.

Whereas, while the table is clear, the method, how the structure is calculated, is set out below.

Equally important it is shown, how the loan outstanding, the interest and capital repayments each month, are determined.

Do not forget, that the same scheme **might** have to provide for a small non-commercial loan and, in that case, the APR and TAP may need to be disclosed.

The first capital repayment

$$a\frac{Loan}{180|} \quad at\ (10.25/12)\% - capital \times 10.25/1200 = 1st\ cap\ repayment$$

$$\frac{\$500,000}{(1 - 1.008542^{-180})/.008542} - (500,000 \times .00854167) =$$

$$5,449.7545902 \qquad\qquad - 4,270.83 = \underline{\$1,178.92}$$

The schedule calculations

```
Month 1.
500.000.00  x .012292           =   6,145.83
6,145.83    + 1,178.92          =   7,324.75
500,000     - 1,178.92          = 498,821.08
Month 2.
498,821.08  x .012292           =   6,131.34
6,131.34    + (1,178.92 x 1.008542) =  6,131.34 + 1,188.99
                                              = 7,320.33
498,821.08  -  1,188.99         = 497,632.09 and so on -
```

The APR is based on the actual lending rate, and so in this example of 14.75% the APR is 15.7%

The TAP/TCC are based on the minimum return rate and the *notional* payments are:

$$a\frac{500{,}000.00}{180 \mid} \text{ at } (10.25/12)\% = 5{,}449.75458902$$

These notional payments should NOT be rounded, for they are NOT cash payments.

```
((Notional pmts  x np ) - capital) x 14.75/10.25)  = TCC
((5,449.75458902 x 180) - 500,000) x 14.75/10.25   = $  692,107.16

TCC        + loan                           = TAP
692,107.16 + 500,000                        = $1,192,107.16
```

Conventionally, the TAP would be $1,244,254 based on the payments of $6,912.52, resulting from amortising the capital amount by the nominal rate of 14.75% – the reduction loan TCC being consequently cheaper by a little over $50,000.

Although a schedule is useful to see what happens to the various series of capital, interest and/or payments, it is essential to know how to find the intermediate factors by calculation.

For instance what was the balance and the interest paid in the 5th month?

To find the balance

$$\text{loan} \times (1 + 10.25/1200)^5 - \$5{,}449.75458902 \; s_{\overline{5}|} = \text{Balance}_5$$

$$500{,}000 \times 1.008542^5 - (5{,}449.75458902 \times (1.008542^5 - 1)/.008542)$$
$$= 494{,}003.83$$

To find the monthly interest
To find the balance of the 5th month calculate the LOS for the month *prior* to the month required, here $645,276.29, and then multiply this value by 14.75/1200 = $6,087.12

To find the capital repayments
Find the *first* capital repayment namely $1,178.92 (see above) and build on that: For the fifth month, the calculation will be: $1,178.92 x 1.008542^(5-1) = $1,219.72 (note the exponent is (t-1), here 4 and not 5).

For the 180th month, with exponent (180-1) the interest will be $5,403.59

To find the monthly repayments
Add the above two values, $6,087.12 + 1,219.72 = 7,306.84 Should rates change in the middle of the loan term merely find the balance just prior to the point of change-rate and, treating this balance as if it was a new loan, proceed accordingly with new the parameters.

The reader will be able to compare the above values with the table above, but he will have to accept my word that the TAP is correct; the addition of each correctly rounded payment, on any small calculator will, however, confirm the value shown!

Specialist mortgage loans
There is a never ending supply of ingenious mortgage loans, designed to attract the first time buyer or those looking for something different, coming onto the market. Two examples will illustrate the diversity of thinking.

The *Cushioned Carolina Mortgage*, so named after an American bank which owns an independent brokerage firm in the UK, and which is designed to assist borrowers faced with increasingly high interest rates.

Research into the mortgage rates in the UK, over the five years previous to 1989, revealed that the average rates, as quoted by four of the largest UK institutions providing home loans, fluctuated between 9½ per cent and 14 per cent.

Consequently the cushioned mortgage base rate is rounded to 12% (derived from 9.50 + 14)/2) and the borrower is then rate charged half the difference between this 12% and the current average rates of the above four institutions.

The cushion, for a 25 years home loan, lasts for some 5 years only, and thereafter the monthly payments will be based on the conventional variable rates, i.e., the rate then current.

To illustrate: if the average current mortgage rate charged by the four institutions above was 14%, then the payments required would be based on a rate of 12 + (14 - 12)/2, namely a cushioned rate of 13%, some 1% less than the going rates.

Should the rates suddenly fall, however, to say 11% then the cushioned borrower would pay a rate 11.50% (derived from 12 - (12 - 11)/2) - instead of the current 11%. So it is largely a matter of swings and roundabouts, and using the proverbial crystal ball, to decide whether the average rates over the following five years will beat the conventional market or not.

Should a borrower decide to redeem early in order to seek more competitive rates elsewhere, as opposed merely to selling his property, then, quite understandably, an early redemption penalty is required.

The penalty, therefore, is some 1.5% of the original sum borrowed.

At first glance this might seem a rather substantial fee. In fact, this is not so, rather the reverse; for, again to assist borrowers as far as possible, it is *less* than the statutory penalty at present permissible in the UK!

The Shared Appreciation Mortgage (SAM) is something different. Dreamed up in the States some years ago as a result of a substantial rise in rates, and the cost of mortgages, to which the Americans were then unaccustomed and which they resented.

In order to shift a backlog of condominiums, then priced around $60,000, the real estate developer offered purchasers a package deal whereby 1/3rd off the loan value was allowed providing they agreed to surrender a 1/3rd of the sale value, or the valuation price, at the end of ten years.

The then home loan rate in the States was a fixed rate of 15%, consequently the borrower was charged only 2/3 of 15%, namely a fixed 10%, over a term of ten years.

His monthly saving in cost is therefore:

$$\frac{60,000}{a_{\overline{120}|}} \text{ at } (15/12)\% \text{ less } \frac{60,000}{a_{\overline{120}|}} \text{ at } (10/12)\%$$

Payments $968 − $793 = $175 monthly saving

Assuming, at the end of 10 years, that the property had neither appreciated or depreciated, the rate cost to the purchaser would be:

$$\frac{60,000 − (20,000 \times (1 + i/p)^{120})}{793 a_{\overline{120}|}} \text{ at } (x/12)\%$$

= 1.039922% monthly
12.479061% nominal
13.218140% effective

The developer, while losing $173 a month for 10 years, hoped to recoup this shortfall by the capital inflow of the 1/3rd surrender value at the point of sale or at valuation. His break even figure can be calculated by taking the monthly rate as being $(15 − 10)/12$, namely $(5/12)\%$, and:

$$175 \times (1.004167^{120} − 1)/.004167 = 27,174.40$$

And so in round terms the property must be sold, or valued at the end of 10 years, for a capital value of not less than $27,000 x 3 = $81,000

The requisite benefit of the scheme, to both purchaser and developer, obviously rests on the hope that house prices will rise, an assumption perhaps not altogether without some justification!

However, *in case prices fail to rise* a shrewd owner could protect himself. For while the property cost $60,000 the "loss", owing to the surrender value, is roughly some $27,000, so an investment of $175 each month, probably at $(10/12)\%$ monthly, would provide a future value of $36,000 at the end of 120 months!

Home Annuity Schemes
Such schemes involve the purchase of an annuity to equate with the required future mortgage payments. There is nothing wrong with such schemes in general, in fact some are quite excellent; but others may not always be what they seem, nor may they always be suitably tailored to the existing financial fabric of the individual borrower, and indeed to his future circumstances and requirements.

Consequently it is a wise precaution to refer all such schemes of this nature to reputable financial consultants for their advice.

ECU mortgages
Mortgages for UK properties based on the European Currency Unit are not for those who are merely seeking to save money by borrowing at a cheap rate of interest, or what might appear to be a cheap rate.

These loans are for the wealthy and financially sophisticated borrower who understands currency fluctuations and who realise that to protect the capital value of a loan a sinking fund may have to, indeed should, be set up to lay off some of the interest saved.

A loan of £100,000 will, over a number of months, reduce in the familiar way and, for the sake of argument, let us assume that, with a 7.50% nominal rate, at the end of the first 12 months the balance of the loan is around £98,580. But if, during those 12 months, sterling fell substantially against the basket of Euro currencies then the balance of the loan might well stand in several thousands of pounds higher than the above figure. Admittedly, if the pound rose in the currency listings then the borrower would benefit – but for how long?

No! Even if you are wealthy and financially clued-up, if you decide to interest yourself in a Spanish or Swiss loan, ECU funded, for goodness sake seek professional advice first!

A word of warning
The reader cannot have escaped the realisation that one of the main themes running through this, and the previous, chapter is the desire of lenders to find ways of providing cheaper and easier mortgages.

Desirable as this may be for the first time borrower, with finance there is usually another side to the coin.

Money is like water, it will usually find its own level sooner or later, in one way or another. And if dammed for too long it may burst its banks with disastrous results.

Cheaper mortgages, in times when house prices are almost continually rising, means that building societies and other institutions providing home loans, are increasing their returns and, more important, their security.

For the higher prices rise, after the initial advance, the more secure the lender will be if there is a default and he has to sell the property at best. But conversely, if prices are falling, selling may be difficult and possibly the initial valuation, on which the loan was originally based, may not be met.

In awkward times when a high bank rate results, for the first time in years, in falling house prices, building societies, under great pressure to raise their mortgage rates, face a nasty dilemma.

If they raise their rates there is likely to be a considerable increase in the number of defaults, which in itself may start a vicious circle of falling house prices, leading to a loss of security – which is the last thing that the societies want.

My point is, that those who provide easy or cheap loans, in abundance when times are good, may rue the day when the Country's fiscal drive, the economy as a whole, is temporarily slowing down.

CHAPTER 5

Savings and Sinking Funds

General
The normal method, for repayment loans, is for payments to be made in arrears at the end of the year or month.

But where savings are concerned the opposite is true, for in order to obtain the most interest, deposits are usually made at the beginning of the compounding period, payments in advance – "savings due".

Sometimes, more rarely, deposits made at the end of the compounding period, and payments in arrears – "savings ordinary" – are sometimes called "sinking funds", as opposed to savings.

The actuarial formulae and signs

$$\frac{(1 + i/p)^{np} - 1}{i/p} \times (1 + i/p) = \text{Savings DUE factor} = S\underline{}$$
$$\text{(advance)} \qquad np\,|$$

$$\frac{(1 + i/p)^{np} - 1}{i/p} = \text{Savings ORD factor} = s\underline{}$$
$$\text{(arrears)} \qquad np\,|$$

The actuarial signs above. a capital "S" (*correctly* an "s" *with two spots over*) for savings due and a lower case "s" for savings ordinary, or sinking funds, will be used throughout this book.

Taking an example involving a deposit of £500 each year, with an annual interest rate of 10%, the difference between the balances of savings and sinking funds is shown over page:

With a term of 5 years the credit balance would be:

$$£500 \times (1.10^5 - 1)/.10 = \underline{£3,052.55}\ \text{ord}$$
$$£500 \times (1.10^5 - 1)/.10 \times 1.10 = \underline{£3,357.81}\ \text{due}$$

Savings due			year end	savings ord
500.00	x1.10 =	550.00	1	500.00
(550.00+500)x1.10 =		1,155.00	2	(500.00x1.10+500 = 1,050.00
(1,155.00+500)x1.10 =		1,820.50	3	(1,050.00x1.10+500 = 1,665.00
(1,820.50+500)x1.10 =		2,552.55	4	(1,665.00x1.10+500 = 2,320.50
(2,552.55+500)x1.10 =		3,357.81	5	(2,320.50x1.10+500 = 3,052.55

To find the balances

Divide the savings due factor found from the equation above into the total amount required at the end of the term and the result will be the necessary deposits to be made per period: alternatively multiply the factor by the periodic payments to provide the future value, namely the "balance at the bank".

To find the term for savings

$$\frac{LOG \quad 1 + \dfrac{FV \times i/p}{pmt \times (1 + i/p)}}{LOG \qquad 1 + i/p} = \text{term (due)}$$

$$\frac{LOG \quad 1 + \dfrac{3,357.81 \times .10}{500 \times 1.10}}{LOG \qquad 1.10} = 5.00 \text{ (due)}$$

$$\frac{LOG \quad 1 + \dfrac{3,052.55 \times .10}{500}}{LOG \qquad 1.10} = 5.00 \text{ (ord)}$$

To find the "i"

Unhappily, if this is a requirement it will need interpolation by a computer/calculator.

Even so, a small point to remember: given the (*ord*) balance of £3,052.55 and the knowledge that the periodic payments are £500, to find the "i" rate (by computer interpolation) for savings *due* will be difficult.

The only method is to take one less period and subtract one deposit from the (ord) balance and the rate will be correctly found:

$$\frac{3,052.55 - 500}{500s_{\overline{5-1}|}} = 10\% \text{ (due)} \qquad \frac{2,552.55}{(1.10^4 - 1)/.10 \times 1.10} = 500.00$$

Alternatively:

$$\frac{3,357.81 + 500}{500s_{\overline{5+1}|}} = 10\% \text{ (ord)} \qquad \frac{3,857.81}{(1.10^6 - 1)/.10} = 500.00$$

DCF calculations (see Chapter 6)
If a discounted cash flow discipline is employed and the deposits are made at the beginning of the compounding periods, savings due, the Net *Future* Value, (NFV) must be multiplied by $(1 + i/p)$ to find the correct final balance. For the convention in DCF calculations is to assume that all payments are made in arrears.

Readers will, of course, recall that the to convert the net present value to its future format the following calculation is necessary:

$$NPV \times (1 + i/p)^{np} = NFV$$

Employing the cash flow sign convention
Your account at the bank has a healthy credit balance of £10,000 and consequently you decide to withdraw £500 a month for 2 years. Assuming the bank gives interest, at 10% nominal, each month on credit balances held to your name what is your balance at the beginning of the third year?

$$(+10,000 \times 1.008333^{24}) + (-500 \times (1.008333^{24} - 1)/0.008333 = -1,129.74$$

£10,000 is positive because the account at your bank is in credit to that amount; the £500 negative because you are withdrawing this from your credit account. The £1,129.74 is negative because you are overdrawn!

Interest/payment periods

If the intervals at which the bank calculates interest do not coincide with the payments periods then some adjustment must be made. The tip is, first convert the nominal *interest* rate to its effective, and then reconvert that value to a nominal rate related to the *periodic* (p) payment periods.

Assume you deposit £100 at the beginning each month for two years and that the bank in question provides 16% nominal interest compounded quarterly, what is the balance due [FV] at the end of the term?

$$((((1 + 16/400)^4)^{1/12}) - 1) \times 1200 = 15.791285\% \text{ nominal}$$
$$\div\ 12 = 1.315940\% \text{ monthly}$$

$$\frac{(1 + 15.791285/1200)^{24} - 1}{15.791285/1200} \times 1.013159 \times 100 = 2,837.660463$$

Varying deposits

Sometimes deposits do not remain constant during the term. Assume that each payment is made at the beginning of each year and that the commencing deposit is $500 at an interest rate of 10%. But in the third year the rate rises to 12% and the deposits fall to $300. Finally, in the sixth and last, year the deposits are $25 *per month* and the monthly rate is $(15/12)\%$. What is the value of the fund at the end of the 6th year?

Actuarially the equation is:

$$500\ S_{\underline{2}|} \text{ at } 10\% \times 1.12^3$$
$$+\ 300\ S_{\underline{3}|} \text{ at } 12\% \times 1.0125^{12}$$
$$+\ 25\ S_{\underline{12}|} \text{ at } 15/12\%$$

$$(500 \times (1.10^2-1)/.1) \times 1.10 = 1,155.00$$
$$(1,155.00 \times 1.12^3) + (300 \times (1.12^3-1)/.12) \times 1.12 = 2,756.49$$
$$(2,756.49 \times 1.0125^{12}) + (25 \times (1.0125^{12}/.0125-1) \times 1.0125) = 3,525.14$$

Savings with percentage increments

Sometimes savings plans, notably insurance contracts, increase the deposit requirements by so much each year, often by an annual percentage lift – even if payments are monthly.

For example assuming a 10 years term at 10% annual rate with a 6% uplift on the payments each year and a required future value of £10,000.

What is the first deposit required – and what are the payments in each subsequent year?

Assume that a future bank balance of £10,000.00 is required at the end of 10 years and that the bank is giving 10% nominal interest.

If you decide to increase your payments each year by 6%. what is the first annual payment and the first monthly payment?

This is the type of calculation where a schedule is useful to see exactly "what happens to the money":

Schedule for Savings DUE:

452.91	x 1.10	= 498.20	1
498.20 + (452.91 x 1.06^1)	x 1.10	= 1,076.11	2
1,076.11 + (452.91 x 1.06^2)	x 1.10	= 1,743.50	3
1,743.50 + (452.91 x 1.06^3)	x 1.10	= 2,511.22	4
2,511.22 + (452.91 x 1.06^4)	x 1.10	= 3,391.31	5
3,391.31 + (452.91 x 1.06^5)	x 1.10	= 4,397.14	6
4,397.14 + (452.91 x 1.06^6)	x 1.10	= 5,543.57	7
5,543.57 + (452.91 x 1.06^7)	x 1.10	= 6,847.03	8
6,847.03 + (452.91 x 1.06^8)	x 1.10	= 8,325.79	9
8,325.79 + (452.91 x 1.06^9)	x 1.10	= 10,000.07	10

Schedule for savings ORD: (sinking funds)

(498.20 x 1.10)		= 548.02	1
(548.02 + (498.20 x 1.06)		= 1,076.11	2
(1,076.11 x ") + (528.09 x 1.06)		= 1,743.50	3
~ ~ ~ ~ ~ ~ ~ ~ ~ ~ ~ ~ ~ ~ ~ ~ ~		~ ~ ~ ~ ~ ~ ~ ~ ~ ~	
(6,847.03 x ") + (749.11 x 1.06)		= 8,325.78	9
(8,325.79 x ") + 841.70		= 10,000.05	10

First the conventional formula:

```
Where i = the annual interest rate as a decimal (.100000)
      j = the annual percentage increment as a decimal (.060000)
      f = [(1 + i)/(1 + j)] - 1                        (.037736)
```

$$\frac{FV}{S_{\overline{n}|} \text{ at } f\% \times (1 + j)^{-n}} = \text{1st payment}$$

$$\frac{10,000.00}{\frac{(1.03774^{10} - 1)}{0.03774} \times 1.03774 \times 1.06^{10}} = £452.91 \text{ 1st pmt DUE}$$

Monthly calculations with an annual percentage uplift

Above it was seen that the payments were annual, the 6% increment also being an annual lift, consequently, for monthly payments, the "j" factor must be calculated slightly differently: $((1 + 10/1200)^{12})/1.06) = 1.042182$ and this replaces the previous factor in the above formula.

$$\frac{FV}{\ddot{a}_{\overline{p}|} [\text{at } i/p)\%] \times (1 + j)^n \times S_{\overline{n}|} [\text{at } f\%]} = \text{first periodic deposit}$$

$$\frac{10,000.00}{\frac{(1 - 1.008333^{-12})}{.008333} \times 1.00833 \times 1.06^{10} \times \frac{(1.042182^{10} - 1)}{.042182} \times 1.042182}$$

$$= £10,000 \div 259.62 \qquad\qquad = £38.52$$

Example: You want to save around £2,000 at the end of two years. Your bank manager tells you that he will give you 12% nominal, with interest calculated monthly. You ask him how much would you need to deposit *monthly* to achieve this. After a slight hesitation he replies "£73.41, providing you make your deposits at the beginning of each month." "Alternatively," he continues, "if you prefer, you can start off the first year with £70 monthly deposits and then increase the monthly deposits to £77 next year."

– 83 –

Is your bank manager right? If you act on his alternative recommendation what will your balance be at the end of two years?

$$2000 \div (1.01^{24} - 1)/.01 \times 1.01 = \underline{73.41 \text{ Yes, correct.}}$$

$$77/70 = 1.10 = 10\% \text{ increment } \& \ 1.01^{12}/1.10 = 1.024386\% \ (1 + f)$$

$$70 \times (1 - 1.01^{-12})/.01 \times 1.01 \times 1.10^2$$
$$\times (1.024386^2 - 1)/.024386 \times 1.024386 = \underline{1,996.69 \text{ balance.}}$$

Below is a DCF calculation:

Investment   0.00
Cash flows 70 x ä___   x [1.01^{-1}]   * *   =   787.86
                12 |
            77 x ä___   x   1.01^{-13} =   769.10
                12 | _____
                                             NPV = 1,556.96
            1,556.96 x 1.01^{24} =   NFV = 1,976.93 ord
            1,976,93 x 1.01   =   NFV = 1,996.70 due

What would be the final balance if you decided to start with £70 but to pay £78 for the last 12 months?

$$70 \times (1 - 1.01^{-12})/.01 \times \ [1.01 \times 1.01^{-1}] = \ * *$$

70 x   11.255077   x   1.01 x 0.990099   =   787.86

$$78 \times (1 - 1.01^{-12})/.01 \times \ 1.01 \times 1.01^{-13} =$$

78 x   11.255077   x   1.01 x 0.878663   =   779.09
                                                 _____
                                             NPV = 1,566.94
            1,566.94 x 1.01^{24} =   NFV = 1,989.60 ord
            1,989.60 x 1.01   =   NFV = \underline{2,009.50 \text{ due}}

Admittedly the first cash flow series, above * *, could be shortened to annuities ordinary, with no discounting [bracketed above], but as explained in the DCF section earlier, the simplest format to remember is when the discounting exponents are always the sum of the periods already calculated, (in the above example 1 + 12 = 13).

Periodic percentage increments

Very occasionally the percentage increases relate to the periodic payments. Monthly increments to monthly payments would be unlikely, but with semi–annual instalments a depositor might care to increase each deposit. Assume a £10,000 required balance from 10% nominal, after 2 years of semi–annual deposits, with a 3% lift every six months. What is the first payment necessary?

The existing annual formula/equation can be used for semi–annual increments, by halving the investment rate and doubling the number of years.

Taking the "f" factor as 1.05/1.03 which equals 1.019417, and entering the values given in the above example, what is the first semi–annual payments required?

$$\frac{10,000 \times 1.03^{-4}}{(1.019417^4 - 1)/.019417 \times 1.019147} = 2,116.46$$

and the following schedule will demonstrate the semi–annual values:

```
2,116.46                              x 1.05 = 2,222.29
2,222.29 + (2,116.46 x 1.03^1)        x 1.05 = 4,622.35
4,622.35 + (2,116.46 x 1.03^2)        x 1.05 = 7,211.09
7,211.09 + (2,116.46 x 1.03^3)        x 1.05 = 9,999.99  QED.
```

A negative formula (f) rate

In the event that the percentage uplift (say, 12%) is higher than the investment rate (say, 10%) the "f" rate will inevitably be negative. Such an unusual working rate need cause no anxiety – use it!

$$1.10/1.12 = 0.982143$$
$$(0.982143 - 1) \times 100 = -1.7857714290\%$$

Inflation

A loan of £100 at 10% over 10 years will provide a future value of:

$$100 \times 1.10^{10} = 259.37$$

If inflation was running at 20% each year the future value in real terms would be:

$$100 \times 1.10^{10} \div 1/20^{10} = 41.89$$

But while mathematically correct, if applied to an indexed pension, for instance, the inflation factor would not be applicable until after the first year.

Therefore the correct method in that case is:

$$100 \times 1.10^{10} \div 1/20^{9} = 50.27$$

But what happens if the compounding is monthly, when the inflation rate is normally taken as an annual profile?

In this case we get a negative working rate, but no matter:

$$100 \times \frac{(1.10/1200)^{120}}{1.20^{9}} = 52.46$$

Consequently the true rate is:

$$((52.464278/100)^{1/10} - 1) \times 100 = -6.246742$$

And this rate can be used for any calculation where above parameters remain constant, in that the future value of, say, $50,000 is, therefore, at the end of 10 years:

$$50,000 \times (1 + -6.246742/1200^{120} = \$26,728.15$$

Remember, as inflation is usually considerd to be an annual factor it must be realised that a 1% monthly inflation rate is NOT 12% per annum rate but is:

$$(((1 + 1/100)^{12)} - 1) \times 100 = 12.682503$$

And a 12% annual rate finds a monthly inflation factor of:

$$(((1 + 12/100)^{1/12}) - 1) \times 100 = 0.948879$$

CHAPTER 6

Discounted Cash Flows Calculations
(DCF & DEDCF)

General

Discounted cash flow calculations are an essential part of any financial problem – and an invaluable part of the checking process to verify rate interest requirements etc.

Useful, too, when there appears to be no known method of finding rates, or other peripheral calculations, from an abnormal loan structure. Because of this, the writing of yet another one-off computer program can sometimes be avoided!

There are a variety of business-type calculators now on the market, and most have DCF programs incorporated, so many readers will already be fully conversant with both the concept and the working of this method of calculation. Nevertheless, before examining some slightly more sophisticated DCF, "decimal entry" DCFs (DEDCF) and a "modified" internal rate of return method (MIRR), it is worth including a few notes to bring the less familiar up to date.

Basically, discounted cash flow calculations consist of an *investment*, normally assumed to be negative, and a series of actual or projected cash flows (CFs) which, as they are received or disbursed, are discounted back to the present time, using a rate of interest which is called the internal rate of return (IRR).

As with other rate interest calculations the concept is that as soon as a cash flow is received it is immediately reinvested *at the current calculation interest rate.* And it is this method of reinvestment, as we shall see later, which causes some problems and which has some interesting counter measures.

All such repayments are assumed to be "in arrears". If there are any payments in advance they are subtracted from the "investment", and the number of cash flows in the term suitably adjusted. Each of the discounted cash flows is added to the (negative) investment to find the present value, or the *net present value (NPV)*, as it is called.

If various projected cash flows, over a number of years, are assumed and the required yield, or IRR, is used in the calculation a resulting positive NPV implies that the project is worth while, in that the required return has been exceeded. A negative NPV suggests that the project should be avoided like the plague! DCF calculations, naturally, have a variety of uses, project guessing being only one.

If the NPV is zero the inference is that the chosen rate is a precisely accurate reflection of the cash flows chosen, and in that case the interest rate *is* the IRR. And whereas, as we shall see later, the NPV can be found by calculations; without a DCF program, the IRR can only be deduced by lengthy interpolation. Computer and calculator programs, however, happily relieve the statistician of such worries.

It is important to remember that cash flows cannot be "mixed", they must *all* be annual, semi-annual, quarterly, monthly, weekly or even daily – *but never mixed*. Sometimes a mix may be necessary, where for instance the income (rent) is monthly and the tax (on the rent) quarterly. The problem can be overcome, as outlined later, but *not*, repeat *not*, by a CF mix. (This cannot be stressed too much, for time and time again I have been confronted by students who have forgotten this inflexible rule – some being quite convinced that their calculator is wrongly programmed!)

There are two types of entry, the single entry and the group, or multiple, entry. With computers, and indeed the modern calculators, providing extremely rapid calculating and retrieval time, it makes little difference which kind of entry is input.

But, as will be seen later, to calculate as opposed to compute the group entry can cause some problems.

Let us first take a simple type of cash flow calculation, where there is an "investment" of £50,000 and a number of single entry cash flows discounted each year at 11%.

						(£)
Investment						=-50,000.00

Cash flows	outgoings	income	total CF	discounting		
1	10,000	5,000	-5,000	x 1.11^{-1}	=-	4,504.50
2	5,000	10,000	5,000	x 1.11^{-2}	=	4,058.11
3	5,000	5,000	0	x 1.11^{-3}	=	0.00
4	0	15,000	15,000	x 1.11^{-4}	=	9,880.96
5	0	20,000	20,000	x 1.11^{-5}	=	11,869.03
6 investment sold	55,000	55,000	x 1.11^{-6}		=	29,405.25

$$NPV = 708.84$$
$$708.84 \times 1.11^{6} = NFV = 1,325.83$$

In this series of cash flows the required return was 11% each year and as the NPV was positive the return is well covered. A computer program will find the actual return, the IRR, as 11.28%, the NPV being zero. The reader might care to find the NPV for the above cash flows, if the required return was 12%. In this case the NPV should show a *negative* £1,732.30.

Looking at the series of cash flows above it will be evident that this type of DCF calculation is used extensively in property markets. Rents, rates, services, taxes etc are all known and can be discounted; and the resulting yield, or return, on a capital investment thus can be determined. Alternatively, given a required yield the DCF will show whether the investment stands up to scrutiny, i.e., whether the NPV is positive or negative.

Group discounting
If we had a series of five similar CFs all the same they would all be fairly easy to discount and to find the requisite balance if, perchance, the conventional payments had been rounded or even altered.

A simple example of a £1,000 repayment loan at 10% nominal, over 5 years, would require annual payments of £263.80:

– *89* –

```
1,000.00
263.80a___    at 10%
       5 |
                    -5
1,000 ÷ (1 - 1.10  )/.10 = 263.797481
```

If the payments were increased to £264.00 the final balance, due to fractional over-payments each year, would be £1.24, in other words the last payment would be £264 - 1.24 = £262.76, from $(1.000 \times 1.10^5) - (264 \times (1.10^5 - 1)/.10)) = -1.236400$

					(£)
Investment				=	-1,000.00
Cash flows					
264	x	1.10^{-1}		=	240.00
264	x	1.10^{-2}		=	218.18
264	x	1.10^{-3}		=	198.35
264	x	1.10^{-4}		=	180.32
264	x	1.10^{-5}		=	163.92
			NPV	=	.77
	Balance due	$.76770792 \times 1.10^5$ = NFV	=	1.24

But if this had been a series of 300 payments, to save time, they would be "grouped" together, and for £1,000 at 11% over 25 years the payments would be £118.84:

```
1,000.00
a___    at 11%
 25|
                     -25
1,000 ÷ (1 - 1.11   )/.11 = 118.740242
```

			(£)
Investment			= -1,000.00
Cash flows			
118.74 x ä___ = 1,109.997737 and x by 1.11^{-1}			= 1,000.00
25| (at full precision 999.997961487)			

Is this not interesting? That the capital value of all 25 groups could be found *on an annuity DUE basis* and then discounted by exponent ONE to provide the full investment?

Which leads us to suppose that this must be the method, or a variation of it, to provide group calculations.

So we could "formula-ise" this method by multiplying each cash flow, or group of cash flows, by the annuities DUE factor and then discounting by the interest rate powered to the <u>sum</u> number of groups required.

Formula:

$$\text{CFs } \ddot{a}_{\,\overline{g}|} \quad \times \quad (1 + i/p)^{-y} = \text{discounted cash flow for period g}$$

And doubtless the example below will clarify the formula above.

We already know that for a loan of £1,000 the annual payments are £118.74 at a interest rate of 11% over a term of 25 years. And although we have employed a DCF calculation to find the balance above we could have just as easily used conventional means. So why all the bother of employing a DCF calculation?

Consider a loan with a conventional structure but with a number of missed and made-up payments such as to make a conventional calculations almost impossible: and even if possible, the time taken and the thought required would hardly be worth all the trouble concerned. As we shall see below it is reasonably easy by worked DCF *calculation* and a matter of moments with a DCF computer or calculator program!

Suppose our £1,000 loan above was bedevilled with a series of missed and made-up payments: the 10th year's payment was missed and not made up until the 15th payment, and regrettably the 24th payment was missed entirely. In view of these irregularities what exactly is the balance due to the lender at the end of the 25th year?

The schedule of payments is: 9 made, 1 missed, 4 made, 1 payment + £200 made, 8 made, 1 missed, 1 made.

			(£)
<u>Investment</u>	at 11.00% discounting		= -1,000.00

<u>Cash Flows</u>

Pmts	x ä__	x $1.11^{-(1 + 0)}$	
	9			
0	x ä__	x $1.11^{-(1 + 9)}$	
	1			
Pmts	x ä__	x $1.11^{-(10 + 1)}$	
	4			
Pmts + 200	x ä__	x $1.11^{-(11 + 4)}$	
	1			
Pmts	x ä__	x $1.11^{-(15 + 1)}$	
	8			
0	x ä__	x $1.11^{-(16 + 8)}$	
	1			
Pmts	x ä__	x $1.11^{-(24 + 1)}$	
	1			

Now convert the above into an equation:

<u>Investment</u>			= -1,000.00

<u>Cash Flows</u>	at 11.00%		
118.74	x $(1 - 1.11^{-9})/.11$ x 1.11 x 1.11^{-1}	=	657.47
0.00	x $(1 - 1.11^{-1})/.11$ x 1.11 x 1.11^{-10}	=	0.00
118.74	x $(1 - 1.11^{-4})/.11$ x 1.11 x 1.11^{-11}	=	129.74
118.74 + 200	x $(1 - 1.11^{-1})/.11$ x 1.11 x 1.11^{-15}	=	66.62
118.74	x $(1 - 1.11^{-8})/.11$ x 1.11 x 1.11^{-16}	=	127.71
0.00	x $(1 - 1.11^{-1})/.11$ x 1.11 x 1.11^{-24}	=	0.00
118.74	x $(1 - 1.11^{-1})/.11$ x 1.11 x 1.11^{-25}	=	8.74
		NPV =	-9.72
	Balance due (to the lender) -9.72 x 1.11^{25} = NFV =		-132.07

Consequently, we can see how very valuable a discounted cash flow calculation is. But it has, in computer and calculator programs, one serious drawback, namely the inability to enter any value other than an integer. In fact decimal entries in the *middle* of a cash flow series are not required, what *is* required is a first entry the result of a decimal calculation, such as for an odd days calculation.

And equally useful, if not more important, would be to be able to "cash flow" fixed interest returns in the guise of bond yields. For, as we shall see later, the different calculations and structures of such loans can change the requirements with alarming rapidity, necessitating a number of different computer programs designed to provide the yields to redemption, prices, etc.

If in some way this drawback could be overcome then a host of useful calculations, previously impossible, would suddenly unfold, resulting in being able to check various calculations with an odd days content and many related problems could undoubtedly be solved.

Below the **DEDCF** method, the **DE** standing for a *Decimal Entry* and not, I hasten to add, the **de** Lisle DCF method – although I am aware that it is sometimes so called.

Decimal entry discounted cash flow (DEDCF)
The DEDCF method employs the same group entry input as outlined above, employing, as it did, the annuities *due* factor and by discounting each cash flow.

But instead of discounting by an integer, if the whole series of cash flows reflect an odd-days profile, the *first* exponent of the discount factor *includes a decimal*. Sometimes the exponent is a decimal fraction alone, at others an integer plus a fraction.

If the first cash flow represents a partial amount of the values input (as in the odd days interest for a bond yield calculation) then the exponent is a fraction only, otherwise the first exponent is 1 + fraction.

Once there is a fraction in the first exponent then all the subsequent discounting exponents must include the fraction, irrespective of the build-up of the integers, according to the number of cash flow entries.

For instance, in a later chapter on Bonds an example is given whereby payments (coupon) are made in 3 periods of half years over a term of 665 days (665/182,5 = 3.363836), and below are the relevant parameters:

		(£)
<u>Investment</u> at (7.777501/2)%		= −97.166952

$$\underline{\text{Cash Flows}}$$

$$\text{Pmts} \quad \times \ddot{a}_{\overline{1|}} \quad \times (1 + i/p)^{-(0 + \text{fraction})}$$

$$\text{Pmts} \quad \times \ddot{a}_{\overline{2|}} \quad \times (1 + i/p)^{-(0+1+\text{fraction})}$$

$$\text{Pmts} \times 100 \quad \times \ddot{a}_{\overline{1|}} \quad \times (1 + i/p)^{-(1+2+\text{fraction})}$$

and converted into an equation:

<u>Investment</u>		= −97.166952

$$\underline{\text{Cash Flows}}$$

$$2.75 \qquad\qquad \times (1.038888^{-(.643836)}$$

$$2.75 \qquad \times \ddot{a}_{\overline{2|}} \quad \times (1.038888^{-(1.643836)}$$

$$2.75 \times 100 \quad \times \ddot{a}_{\overline{1|}} \quad \times (1.038888^{-(3.643836)}$$

<u>Investment</u>		= −97.166952

$$\underline{\text{Cash Flows}}$$

$$\frac{2.75 \quad \times 1-1.038888^{-1}}{.038888} \times 1.038888 \times 1.038888^{-(0.643836)} = 2.683276$$

$$\frac{2.75 \quad \times 1-1.038888^{-2}}{.038888} \times 1.038888 \times 1.038888^{-(1.643836)} = 5.068991$$

$$\frac{102.75 \times 1-1.038888^{-1}}{.038888} \times 1.038888 \times 1.038888^{-(3.643836)} = \underline{89.414686}$$

$$\text{NPV} = 0.00$$

Assuming a £1,000 loan at 10%. If there are 18 odd days (base 360) the payments will be £172.32 each year for 10 years.

If the annual payments, however, were reduced to £170, find *by a DCF calculation* the balance due at the end of the 10 years.

Without a DEDCF program/calculation this cannot be determined: in other words the conventional DCF program, in computers or in many sophisticated calculators, cannot undertake an "odd days" calculation.

```
Investment   at 10%                                      = -1,000.00
Cash Flows
                    -10                          -1.60
170    x (1 - 1.10   )/.10 x 1.10 x 1.10              =      986.51
                                                NPV  =      -13.48
                                          10.6
             Balance due -13.482936 x 1.10       = NFV  =   -37.03
```

Could this balance be found by any means other than a DEDCF calculation? Yes and no.

Yes, if you knew the original annual *full precision* payments, namely £172.323425671; and to know that you would have had the use of an odd-days computer/calculator program, and if that facility was available then you have no need of anything else!

No, not accurately. If you knew only the *rounded* value of 172.32 you could find a fractionally inaccurate balance as follows:

$$((1 - 1.10^{-10})/.10 \times 172.32 \times 1.10^{10})$$
$$- (170.00 \times (1.10^{10} - 1)/.10) = 36.97$$

In other words, the 18 odd-days on top of the £1,000 increased the conventional payments from £162.75 to £172.32: and the first part of the equation above calculated what the loan amount would be, if the payments were £172.32 and there were no extra days.

We could, of course, do the same thing with monthly payments, which, with 18 odd days, would probably be more realistic in practice.

Assuming that the monthly payments are £13 the balance is:

```
                                                           (£)
Investment   at (10/12)%                              = -1,000.00
Cash Flows
                  -120
13 x (1-1.0083333    )/.008333 x 1.008333
                                       -1.60
                          x 1.008333           =      978.84
                                            NPV  =     -21.16
                                      120.6
        Balance due -21.160946 x 1.008333     = NFV  =   -57.57
```

Discounted cash flows with a differing periodic base

Above it was stressed that there can be no "mix" of the periods of the cash flows: but occasionally a mix is a must. Let us assume that here are 120 months of £135 cash flows representing income and an outgoing tax bill every quarter of £150.

If the required rate of return was 10% nominal what is the cost of the investment (the +/- NPV)?

Obviously, one could break the tax bill down to a monthly profile in that every third month the cash flow would be £135 – £150 but this would mean a total of 30 entries of £120 with 3 group entries and 30 single entries of a negative £30, in all a chore which most statisticians would baulk at!

$$
\begin{aligned}
135 &\quad x\ 1.008333^{-1} \\
135 &\quad x\ 1.008333^{-2} \\
(135 - 15) &\quad x\ 1.008333^{-3} \quad \text{and so on for a further 29 quarters!}
\end{aligned}
$$

An alternative method is to convert the *quarterly* payments to equate with the monthly rate interest and in that case we have:

$$
135\ x\ \frac{(1 - 1.008333^{-120})/.008333\ x\ 1.008333}{1.008333} = £10,215.61
$$

and as $1.008333^{12/4} = 1.025209$:

$$
150\ x\ \frac{(1 - 1.025209^{-40})/.025209\ x\ 1.025209}{1.025209} = £3,752.20
$$

consequently, £10,215.61 – £3,752.20 = NPV = £6,463.40
Investment cost

(the denominator is the same as multiplying by $(1 + i/p)^{-1}$)

Doubtless readers will have appreciated that, in this particular case, the same result could be found from:

$$
\underset{\substack{120| \\ (\text{at } 0.833333\%)}}{135s} \quad - \quad \underset{\substack{40\ | \\ (\text{at } 2.520891\%)}}{150s} \quad = £6,463.40
$$

Some drawbacks to the DCF concept and the counter measures

One of the drawbacks, unhappily, when using the traditional DCF calculations is to find an IRR is that just occasionally there may be more than one *mathematically* correct answer.

This should not mean that the statistician should lose confidence in the concept; for such abnormalities occur rarely and then only when the cash flows are quite out of the ordinary, unreasonable and unrealistic.

As the following example will go to prove.

An investment of £3,000, a positive cash flow of £1,700 for 5 months, a negative cash flow for the same amount also for the next 5 months, no payments for 9 months and in the last and 20th month the final cash flow is £3,400.

```
Investment   at (??)%                                    = -3,000.00
Cash Flows
                        -5
              (1 - (1 + i/p)  )/(i/p) x (1 + i/p)
  1,700    X  ───────────────────────────────────
                        (1 + i/p)^1

                        -5
              (1 - (1 + i/p)  )/(i/p) x (1 + i/p)
 -1,700    X  ───────────────────────────────────
                        (1 + i/p)^6

    0                 for nine months

                        -1
              (1 - (1 + i/p)  )/(i/p) x (1 + i/p)
  3,400    X  ───────────────────────────────────
                        (1 + i/p)^20
                                                 ──────────────
                                           NPV =     0.00
```

Some DCF computer/calculator may be unable to compete with these esoteric and completely unrealistic values, but should they be able to, they could find *three* different IRRs, all from the same CF inputs above!

```
Rate A will be  2.416119% monthly, converted to  28.99% nominal
Rate B will be 11.875489%    "         "    to 142.51%    "
Rate C will be 32.255423%    "         "    to 387.07%    "
```

Superimpose either of these rates in the above formula schedule and in all three cases the NPV will be a zero!

And of course as such they are all quite useless! For one must avoid the temptation to take the one which "seems sensible", 2.42% if the inputs were monthly or perhaps 11.88% if the inputs were annual.

If, therefore, there are a series of IRRs, all stemming from the same number of positive/negative abnormal cash flows the whole thing must be rejected and other methods sought.

In the Chapter following alternative methods of DCF calculations, the Modified Internal Rate of Return (MIRR) and the Financial Management Rate of Return (FMRR) both of which will, *inter alia*, overcome the problems of irregular positive and negative cash flows, are examined in detail: but before moving on to these slightly technical and sophisticated methods one last comment concerning series calculations.

Series compounding
Although it has little or nothing to do with discounted cash flow calculations it might be of interest to know how series *compounding* can be calculated in the same fashion as series discounting above. Consider:

$$
\begin{array}{ll}
10 \times 1.10^6 & = 17.72 \\
10 \times 1.10^7 & = 19.49 \\
10 \times 1.10^8 & = 21.44 \\
10 \times 1.10^9 & = \underline{23.58} \\
& = 82.22 \text{ Total}
\end{array}
$$

By series compounding $\text{pmts } s_{\overline{g}|} \times (1 + i/p)^y$

Where: g = the number of groups required (4)

y = the number of group periods (6)

$10 \ s_{\overline{4}|} \times 1.10^6 \qquad = 82.22$

$10 \times (1.10^4 - 1)/.10 \times 1.10^6 \qquad = 82.22$

CHAPTER 7

Modified IRR & Financial Management RR

General

Leaving aside, for the moment, the problem, outlined in the last chapter, of the very occasional multiple, and therefore inaccurate, answers: pray reflect on one further problem that so far we have had no reason to consider.

We have already seen the kind of projected cash flows that a property developer might well enter into his DCF computer program, and the IRR, thrown up from such calculations, might well range from 20% to 40%: a matter, perhaps, for congratulation – some years ago.

But not any more, for it then became apparent that in the calculations for discounted cash flows, repayment loans and the like, the whole concept depended on the interest, engendered in each period, being re-invested immediately *at the interest rate concerned*; indeed in the case of fixed interest bonds, so important is this concept thought to be that the yields to maturity are usually reduced fractionally if the bond is redeemed on a non-banking day – because reinvestment is not possible until the day following.

And that being the case how can any financially astute entrepreneur accept a project return on his forecast cash flows of 20% or 30% when he knows well that the "going rate" is far less than that?

Some Real Estate statisticians in the States reckoned that some sort of calculation should be made whereby this rather ridiculous disparity between a mathematical concept and the real world would no longer confuse the issue, and so the "Financial Management Rates of Return" came into being, closely followed by a "Modified" IRR calculation. employed,

The concepts are quite simple: there are two rates, the "safe" rate and the "risk" rate; the former being around the current bank rate or prime rate, the latter being a entrepreneurial rate; in other words a reasonable spread between, say, 10% and 25%

Notional rates
Before examining the methods of overcoming the reinvestmemt problem, two examples may be of interest, designed as they are to stress the difficulty of combining the the reinvestment IRR with practical current market rates.

	Investment A	Years	Investment B
Inv:	−5,000.00		−5,000.00
CFs	0.00	1	5.500.00
	0.00	2	0.00
	0.00	3	0.00
	0.00	4	0.00
	8.811.71	5	437.25

By DCF program the IRR will be found as 12% and 15% respectively.

Investment A	Investment B
$5{,}000 \times 1.12^5 = 8{,}811.71$	$5{,}500 \times 1.15^4 = 9{,}619.53$
	$\underline{\hphantom{9{,}61}437.25}$
	$10{,}056.78$

Consequently:

$$\text{A: } 100((\,8{,}811.71/5{,}000)^{1/5} - 1) = \text{IRR} = 12\%$$
$$\text{B: } 100((10{,}056.78/5{,}000)^{1/5} - 1) = \text{IRR} = 15\%$$

The investments appear similar for they both require the same capital amount, namely £5,000, both over a term of 5 years. Because of its higher IRR, at first glance, Investment B would seem far the better bet. But this is only because the calculation assumed that the £5,500 received in the first year was reinvested immediately at 15%. As £10,056 is greater than £8,812, based on the *notional* structure of interest rates, it is, indeed, difficult not to agree that investment B is the better investment.

But when the reinvestment rate employed falls into line with the current market rate of 10%, (as it was when this example was drafted!) the whole scenario changes:

<u>Investment B</u> $5{,}500 \times 1.10^4 = 8{,}052.55.$
$$\begin{array}{r} 437.25 \\ \hline 8{,}489.80 \end{array}$$

Investment A is now worth less than investment B, and so unless investment B can be can be serviced by a rate 5% above the going rate, which is unlikely, investment A in the real world, is a far better investment.

Although, I hope I have made my point, just one more example; two investments of $5,000 and $7500. At the end of 5 years, with no further income, the first investment is valued at $12,441.60 (on $5,000) whereas the second investment at the end of 5 years is worth $17,158.18 (on $7,500). The respective yields therefore are:

$\mathbf{X}$: $100((12{,}411.60/5{,}000)^{1/5} - 1) = $ IRR $= 20\%$
$\mathbf{Y}$: $100((17{,}158.18/7{,}500)^{1/5} - 1) = $ IRR $= 18\%$

Again, because of the higher yield, at first glance, Investment X looks the more attractive. But the initial investment of X was less than Investmemt Y, by some $2,500, so for true comparison purposes both investments must be "on all fours"; and to achieve this $2,500 must be invested by Investor X.

With the "going rate" of 10% this will produce, at the end of 5 years, only ($2,500 x 1.10^5), namely $4,026.28, and when added to the original future value of $12,441.60 we find that the yield of investment X is now *less* than investment Y:

$\mathbf{X}$: $100(((12{,}411.60 + 4{,}026.28)/7.500)^{1/5} - 1) = $ IRR $= 17.00\%$
                             — now less than investment Y's 18.00%

Financial management of the rate of interest (FMRR)
The FMRR method of calculation is to employ *two* rates, the "safe" rate (usually slightly below the market going rates) and

the "risk" rate (usually the sort of rate which an entrepreneur would expect to receive on his venture capital).

Below is the method employed to harness these two conflicting requirements, the safe and risk rates, to provide an NPV or an IRR nearer, it is thought, to reality in real estate projections.

A projected property developement, with the return adjusted by FMRR

	($)
Initial Investment	− 12,000.00
Projected cash flows:	
Year 1 (setting up costs)	− 25,000.00
2 (" " ")	− 25,000.00
3 (profits commmencing)	15,000.00
4 (expected losses + more investment costs)	− 10,000.00
5 (profitability returns)	15,000.00
6 (expectation of property sale)	125,000.00

Conventionally, the calculated return, after the property realisation, would be found as slightly in excess of 20% but as the current market investment rate is in the region of 12% management decided that for a FMRR calculation the safe rate should be taken as 10% and the risk rate 15%.

Taking these two rates as a guide, it was further decided that if the resulting FM rate of interest was *less than* 18.5% the project would be shelved.

The FMRR method
1. Discount all the *negative* CFs, at the *safe* rate, and add the result to the original investment.
2. Tidy up an anticipated periodic deficit by investing sufficient funds in the previous year "to cover" – again at the *safe* rate.
3. Having eliminated all the negative CFs find the future value *at the risk rate*.

In short, possibly a slight over-simplification, discount the negative cash flows at the safe rate, and compound the positive cash flows at the risk rate.

Taking the example above, and discounting the negative CFs by 10%:

$$\$12,000 + (25,000/1.10) + (25,000/1.10^2) = \underline{\$55,388.43 \text{ PV}}$$

In the fourth year there was a deficit of $10,000 and if we invested $9,090.91 in year 3 the cash flows for year 3 would be $15,000 – 9,090.91 and in the 4th year, $10,000 – 10,000, consequently to obtain the FV:

$$\$125,000 + (15,000 \times 1.15^1) + (0.00 \times 1.15^2) + (5.909.09 \times 1.15^3)$$
$$= \underline{\$151,236.99 \text{ FV}}$$

$$100 \left\{ \left\{ \frac{\text{future value}}{\text{present value}} \right\}^{1/n} - 1 \right\} = \text{FMRR\%}$$

$$100 \left\{ \left\{ \frac{151,236.99}{55,388.43} \right\}^{1/6} - 1 \right\} = 18.22\% \text{ FMRR}$$
$$\text{Project shelved}$$

The modified internal rate of return (MIRR)
Whereas the FMRR calculation overcomes the problem of the wisdom of reinvestment at the market rate, the modified IRR was designed to ensure that never could there be two or more answers, as seen in the previous chapter – even if those erroneous answers stemmed from cash flows seldom if ever employed in practical cicumstances.

The MIRR method also employs the two-rate concept, but in this case both the negative and positive CFs are discounted by the safe and risk rates respectively.

And to be frank, as the MIRR calculation, as we shall see, is a good deal simpler to calculate, and indeed program, and as it also uses the two-rate method many statisticians employ it in preference to the FMRR method, and who is to say that they are wrong!

For if the previous FMRR (18.22%) calculation had been done on a MIRR program the MIRR found would be 17.66%.

Moreover, if the safe rate had been raised from the original 10% above to the going rate of 12% (see current market investment rate above) and the entrepreneurial rate lifted from 15% to 25% the FMRR would equal 19.05% and the MIRR 19.11%.

The MIRR method

Discount the negative CFs by the safe rate and the positive CFs by the risk rate.

Bring the risk rate PV to its FV and, then in the same way as with the FMRR calculation, divide the FV by the PV, raised to the power 1/n.

Taking, therefore, the previous calculation:

Negative CFs discount 10%

		($)
Investment		$=\ -\ 12{,}000.00$

years	Cash Flows		
1	$-25{,}000 \times 1.10^{-1}$	$=$	$-\ 22{,}727.27$
2	$-25{,}000 \times 1.10^{-2}$	$=$	$-\ 20{,}661.16$
4	$-10{,}000 \times 1.10^{-4}$	$=$	$-\ \underline{6{,}830.13}$
		$PV\ =$	$-\ 62{,}218.56$

Positive CFs discount 15%

years	Cash Flows		
3	$15{,}000 \times 1.15^{-3}$	$=$	$9{,}862.74$
5	$15{,}000 \times 1.15^{-5}$	$=$	$7{,}457.65$
6	$125{,}000 \times 1.15^{-6}$	$=$	$\underline{54{,}040.95}$
		$PV\ =$	$71{,}361.34$
	$71{,}361.34 \times 1.15^{6}$	$FV\ =$	$165{,}063.13$

$$100 \left(\left\{ \frac{165{,}063.13}{62{,}218.56} \right\}^{1/6} - 1 \right) = 17.66\% \ \text{MIRR}$$

If a risk rate of 20% had been taken above then the IRR would be 18.11%

In the same way calculate the cash flows, in the previous chapter, which resulted in three erroneous answers:

Negative CFs discount (10/12)%

	(£)
Investment	= $-$ 3,000.00

Cash Flows

Months

(1– 5)   positive – ignore

(6–10) $-1{,}700 \times \ddot{a}\underset{5|}{} \times 1.008333^{-6}$ = $\underline{-\ 7{,}954{,}55}$

PV = $-10{,}954.55$

Positive CFs discount (15/12)%

Months

(1–5) $1{,}700 \times \ddot{a}\underset{5|}{} \times 1.012500^{-1}$ = 8,190.32

(6–10)   negative – ignore

(11–19)   "   "

(20) $3{,}400 \times 1.012500^{-20}$ = $\underline{2{,}652.03}$

PV = 10,842.35

$10{,}842.36 \times 1.0125^{20}$ FV = 13,900.24

$1200 \left\{ \dfrac{13{,}900.24}{10{,}954.55} \right\}^{1/20} - 1\} = 14.37\%$ MIRR

An alternative MIRR

There is yet another, and somewhat simpler alternative method, a modification of the above MIRR calculation, and one which may well commend itself to those who use a calculator with a DCF program.

This method is like the above calculation, save that the PV of the safe discounting becomes the "investment" and in this case alternative MIRR comes to 13.258855% nominal.

Investment   = $-$ 10,954.55

$1{,}700 \times \dfrac{(1 - 1.011049^{-5})/.011049 \times 1.011049}{1.011049}$ = 8,225.35

$3{,}400 \times 1.011049^{-20}$ = $\underline{2{,}729.20}$

NPV = 0.00

CHAPTER 8

UK Building Society Mortgage Calculations

General
It never ceases to surprise that there are so many borrowing from so many Building Societies, in the United Kingdom, that few mortgagors seem to know, or care, about how their mortgage accounts are reconciled and the calculations required to provide the legal requirements of disclosure.

Admittedly the building societies' computer controlled lending and borrowing accounts are accurate and usually available on demand, and that some of the calculations appear complex, nevertheless there is no reason why borrowers should not understand the somewhat unique methods employed by the building societies –and perhaps benefit from such knowledge.

With such a large part of the community borrowing from societies it is hardly surprising that sometimes they are the object of criticism, often from those who tend to forget the help which societies give to those who no fault of their own have temporary difficulty in meeting their monthly repayments; and from those who would be less inclined to criticise if they were more aware of the method which the societies employ to calculate their various requirements.

UK building society methods
The building societies require monthly repayments of capital and interest but, ignoring more conventional methods which make up the balances at the end of each month, building societies calculate their payments annually. These annual payments are then divided by 12 to determine the monthly payments – suitably rounded upward – and reconciliation occurs at the end of each year, when the annual days' interest due is compared with the amount derived from the total number of payments made.

A £25,000 loan over 25 years at 13% nominal would require £284.25 payments each year. Building societies calculate all their scale payments per £1,000 and so:

$$\frac{1000.00}{a\underline{}} \text{ at } 13\% = £136.43 \text{ annual payments}$$
$$25 \mid$$

$$1,000/(1 - (1.13^{-} 25))/.13 = £136.43$$
$$\div 12 = 11.368827$$
$$\text{rounded} = 11.37$$

These annual payments, divided by 12 and rounded upward to the nearest penny, provide the monthly payments per the basic £1,000, and thus, in the case of a £25,000 loan the £11.37 is multiplied by 25 to give £284.25.

The Interest Rate Cartel

Prior to 1983 nearly all building societies were members of the Building Society Association (BSA) who recommended current interest rates to all their members who invariably conformed. But around that time several societies broke away from the BSA and decided to go their own way, thus breaking the interest rate cartel.

Building Society Mortgage Repayment Tables

Although the BSA doesn't hold quite the same sway as it did in the past their scale payments book is still in use, the resultant payments, as per £1,000, differing very little from the calculation set out above to find the payments for a loan of £25,000. In fact nearly all societies calculate as above, taking the annual rate, dividing by 12 and then lifting the payments to a "suitable round up". The lift is obviously to taste.

The BSA repayment table method was to calculate in three sections. Taking a rate of 7.90% nominal over a term of 20 years the scale payments show as £8.43 on £1,000.

For a loan of £4,650 one would have thought that the payments would be, pro rata, namely £4,650/1,000 x 8.43 = 39.199500, rounded to £39.20

But the example given in the BSA repayment tables pamphlet:

```
4,000/1,000 x 8,43 = 33.720000 = 33.72
  600/1,000 x 8.43 =  5.058000 =  5.06
   50/1,000 x 8.43 =  0.421500 =   .43
                             39.21 BSA monthly payments
```

Nowadays, this somewhat pedantic method is usually ignored and unless the society concerned decided to lift the payments to £39.25 (as nowadays they might well do!) £39.20 would obtain. In the old days there was invariably much criticism that the BSA quoted rate was a good deal less than the true rate. But now no such problem exists; for, as will be seen below, all such rates must be disclosed as to their effective rate, or in fact the "APR", being the effective truncated to one place of decimals.

Disclosure for Building Societies
In the previous Chapter the 1974 Consumer Credit Act and its Regulations were discussed.

Just prior to the issue of the regulations, The Building Societies Association (the BSA) realised that, in certain circumstances, the Act would include some regulations with which it would be difficult to comply.

The complications arose from the method employed by building societies of reconciling their accounts at the end of each year. For it was realised that, since payments are always in arrears, if an advance was made during the month of December there would be no payment, that month, to offset the interest between the date of the advance and the year end.

In such a case the balance of the loan at the first year end after the advance might well be fractionally greater than the loan itself – and as the regulations required *all* the data be correct it appeared that quoted term might well be understated – and if so illegal.

The complication was of such proportions, in that some advertisements could become illegal under the new disclosure regulations, that the BSA were busily preparing a new pamphlet of their scale payments.

The Association reckoned that all their payments would have to be increased across the board; for example the scale payment for a £1,000 at 11% over 25 years was £9.90 and the "worst case scenario", as it was then called, was when the advance was made on the December 1 (30 days before year - end reconciliation).

Consequently, the new scale payments, for this particular example, were to become £9.90 x (1 + 31/365 x .11) = £9.99 monthly payments, making a difference of over £50 a year on a £50,000 mortgage. And this method would ensure that at no time would the term quotation be other than legally correct.

As this increase in payments was to be right across the board it was clear to the meanest intelligence that when the new payments were announced all mortgages would cost more.

A neatly timed letter in the Financial Times, however, a few days prior to the debate in Parliament pointing out the problem and the BSA's likely action, I believe, concentrated the minds of our MPs, and alerted them to an almost certain outcry – and in their wisdom they quickly decided that Building Societies and Local Government Authorities would be exempt from disclosure!

For many years some borrowers, who were unaware of the underlying reason for exemption, complained bitterly that building societies did not have to show their true rates!

The problem has some bearing, even today on how building societies currently calculate their accounts.

A BS £25,000 mortgage at 13%, over 25 years. If the loan was advanced on (say) December 1 then at reconciliation on December 31 the balance of the loan would stand at:

£25,000 x (1 + (13/100 x 31/365) = £25,276.03 year end balance

Incidentally, it is thirty-*one* days' interest because building societies require the "days to and from two dates" method, namely the "days between", plus one day.

With an increased end of year balance and with an unaltered quoted interest rate, the quoted term of the loan must inevitably be suspect.

Taking the monthly payment above, "annualised", namely (£284.25 x 12 = £3,411) and both the above year-end balance and the (annual) nominal rate of 13% the term becomes:

$$\frac{LOG \quad \frac{3,411}{.13} \div (\frac{3,411}{.13} - 25,276.03)}{LOG \quad 1.13} = \frac{27.2626780}{1.13}$$

$$= \frac{3.305519}{0.122218} = \underline{27.046168} \text{ term}$$

Some 10 years later, in 1985, a new finance act regularised the narrowing gap between banking and building societies' method of conducting business. Banks, much to their annoyance, were in future to conform to the long established practice of building societies, which repay interest to their lenders net of tax, and Building societies, to their equal annoyance, were no longer exempt from disclosing the Annual Percentage Rate of Charge (APR) and the Total Amount Paid (TAP).

As soon as building societies realised that exemption was no longer to be their protection against an illegal quotation the same crisis discussions took place, but this time instead of raising all the rates across the board, never a popular move, it was decided to ask those seeking a mortgage to pay the "accrued interest" for that period between the advance and the end of year reconciliation date.

The payment was to be up front at the time of the advance, in other words they would receive the loan, less the accrued interest although this contribution would be credited at the first reconciliation of the account.

The "excess"
Assuming that the above loan was advanced on February 1 it will be found that there are 333 days between the advance date and the year end and therefore 334 interest days (to conform to the societies' methods), and 10 payment periods to the year end (March-December); therefore, on a loan of £25,000 at 13% over 25 years, the *LOS*, the loan outstanding, at the first reconciliation at first glance is:

$$[25,000 \times (1 + (.13 \times 334/365))] - (284.25 \times 10) = £25,131.47$$
Consequently, the excess is $25,131.47 - 25,000 = £131.47$

The accrued interest
Before the necessity of repaying the accrued interest (a/i) front end arose everyone knew that the balance at the first year end was loan plus days' interest less any payments made, but few knew, or were required to know, the precise interest engendered. So what exactly is the accrued interest?

Scale payments are calculated assuming twelve repayments per year; but in the year of the advance, as payments are always in arrears, there cannot possibly be more than eleven off set payments.

Furthermore it must be remembered that the monthly repayments contain proportions of both interest and of capital.

To find the accrued interest, rounded, calculate as follows:

```
(25,000 x .13 x 334/365) - (25,000 x .13 x 10/12) = £265.64 (a/i)
(    daily interest    ) - ( monthly interest  ) = (accrued)
 25,000 x .13 x ((334 x 12/365)-10) ÷ 12            = £265.64
```

The rounding is necessary because, notionally, the accrued interest is paid cash across the counter at the advance date. Consequently the loan outstanding at the end of the first year's reconciliation is loan plus days interest *less* any payments made, *less* the accrued interest, *less* any front-end fees: £25,131.47 − 265.64 = £24,865.83.

Disclosure – requirements for quotations

There are two distinct requirements, the APR and TAP, for either a "typical case" quotation or a "specific" quotation involving detailed discussion of a particular mortgage.

Every society must decide when the first repayment is to be made, for this dictates the resulting calculation. Some require all repayments to be made on the same day of the month as the advance date, others favour the first calendar day of each month. Naturally the date of the first payment after the advance will affect the true rate and hence the APR.

If the method is to require payments to be made on the first day of each month then the first repayment is made on the first day of the month after the advance, providing the advance is made within the first three quarters of the month concerned – if not payment is postponed until the first day of the month following.

In the early days, when the disclosure regulations first applied various methods were employed for "general disclosure".

But nowadays, a "typical case" example is usually considered sufficient. A typical case, often being "half a year", namely 200 odd days and 6 months.

The normal method of calculating assumes that the first payment is made exactly one month after the advance.

If the advance was made on the first of the month and for some reason all payments are required to be made on, say, the 15th of each calendar month this means that, on paper, the borrower will owe a small amount of extra interest, some 15 days, on the *payments* – not the capital amount!

Alternatively, of course if the first payment for some reason was delayed by, say, 15 days then the borrower would be "in the money" for those 15 days interest

These extra days calculations affects *only* the APR and not the TAP – or for that matter any other related calculation.

Front-end fees

Front-end fees, legal and search fees, etc, must also be considered for disclosure.

If a society *always* makes certain charges then these must be become part of the "typical case scenario" and deducted from the loan, at the same time as the accrued interest is deducted, before the calculation is made to determine the periodic interest rate for the "typical case" disclosure.

Disclosure – typical case quotation

Taking a £25,000 loan at 13% nominal over a period of 25 years with monthly scale payments of £284.25, with fees of £150, and assume that the society concerned requires a "first of the month" payment.

Assuming a "mid year" advance as being a "typical case" quote June 15 to December 31 provides 199 + 1 interest days offset by 6 months payments.

In that case the year end balance, from which the advertised APR and TAP can be derived is:

```
£25,000 - (25,000 x .13 x 200/365)-(25,000 x .13 x 6/12 = 24,844.18
and allowing for £150 fees = 24,844.18 - 150          = 24,694.18
```

and with the rounded values it will be found, by computer/interpolation that:

$$\frac{24,694.18}{284.25a_{\overline{300}|}} = \text{monthly} = 1.108992\% \text{ per}$$

$$\begin{aligned} \text{x } 12 &= 13.307899\% \text{ nom} \\ &= 14.150376\% \text{ eff} \\ &14.1\% \qquad \text{APR} \end{aligned}$$

Disclosure – specific quotation

The only difference to the above is that for a specific quotation the precise date of the advance is known and from that premise the APR and TAP calculations are determined. Taking the original example, assume that the advance is made on February 1 which requires 334 interest days between the advance date and the first year end reconciliation. We know from a previous section that the accrued interest is £265.64

In the same manner as above the accrued interest will be found as £265.64 and from a present value of 25,000 - 265.64 less the fees of £150 we find a year end balance of £24,584.36, and by interpolation:

$$\frac{24{,}584.36}{284.25a\underline{}} = \text{monthly} = 1.114649\% \text{ per}$$

$$300|$$

$$\times 12 = 13.375792\% \text{ nom}$$
$$= 14.227050\% \text{ eff}$$
$$14.2\% \quad \text{APR}$$

The TAP
The Total Amount Paid is the total amount of the payments *plus* the a/i, *plus* any front-end fees. In this example the accrued is £265.64 and the fees are £150, together £415.64. Consequently: (284.25 x 300) + 415.64 = £85,690.64 TAP

To find balances
Sometimes it is necessary to find the balances at a certain time, either to redeem the loan or in case of a rate change. Always work to or from the year end reconciliation date.
To find the balance from a "loan outstanding":

`(LOS x (1 + nominal rate/1200 x days/365) - (months x pmts) = Balance`

Assume a balance of £5,430.25 *at the year end reconciliation* and it is required to find the loan outstanding on April 23rd next. The period between January 1 and April 23 is 112 days (+ one day) = 113 days interest, and 3 month's payments.

$(5{,}430.25 \times (1 + .13 \times 113/365)) - (3 \times 284.25) = £4{,}796.05$

To find a balance on April 23, 1989 from a loan outstanding of £6,661.25 on the June 15 1988: *first find the balance at Dec 31*, some 200 days interest and 6 month's payments. Then calculate, as above, for 113 days and 3 months. To calculate for 313 days interest, less 9 payments, would not provide the correct answer, remembering that societies always reconcile their accounts at the year end.

Endowment loans
The repayments for endowment loans are interest only, the capital sum being repaid at maturity. The above calculations

for the accrued interest and disclosure obtain and there is no need for the precise last payment method (see below).

Taking a loan of £25,000 over 25 years, advanced February 1, with a nominal rate of 13.50% the monthly payments, therefore, are 25,000 x 13.50/1200 = £281.25

The accrued interest is:
(25,000 x .135 x 334/365) – (25,000 x .135 x 10/12) = £275.86
and in this case, the year end balance is:
£25,000 – 275.86 – 150 = £24,574.14

But is it?

Endowment loans are repaid, theoretically, at the end of the term and so to find a true rate the capital sum must be discounted to the present time, *at that rate* – and subtracted from the capital balance. Consequently an interpolation calculation by a computer/calculator is required:

$$25{,}000 \times (1 + i/p)^{-300} = \text{the discounted amount}$$

$$\frac{24{,}574.14 - (25{,}000 \times 1.145170^{-300})}{281.25a_{\overline{300}|}} \quad \begin{array}{l} = 1.145170\% \text{ per} \\ \times 12 = 13.742037\% \text{ nom} \\ = 14.641476\% \text{ eff} \\ \quad 14.6\% \qquad \text{APR} \end{array}$$

And in this case TAP is (281.25 x 300) + 275.86 + 150 *and plus* the £25,000 = <u>£109.800.86</u>

The disclosure regulations, which were largely based on the Crowther Report (1972/3), were never intended to be applied to home loans. In fact Crowther specifically excluded them, from his recommendations. Consequently the TAP for home loans in general and endowment loans in particular are always somewhat horrifying – especially to new time buyers!

The insurance premiums, either for endowment loans or repayment mortgage protection, which are usually included in the monthly payments, do not have to be "disclosed" *unless* the lender is acting as the principal, rather than as an agent for an assurance company. In this case all fees, front end and/or monthly premiums must be included in the disclosure figures.

Even if all the endowment premiums are passed on, by the building society, directly to the assurance company the quoted rate for endowment loans is often slightly higher than for an equivalent repayment loan.

Maximum Advance Scheme (MAS)
This scheme is merely the accrued interest by another name. A simplified method employed by some societies to cover, without detailed explanation, the necessity for borrowers to pay the front-end accrued interest contribution!

Penalties for Early Redemption
Some lenders make a charge for the early redemption of a loan, and building societies are no exception.   But the practice varies and not all societies make such demands.

If penalties there are, naturally, they should conform to the Consumer Credit Act regulations, outlined in the section Rule of 78, which rule that for an early redemption, for a loan term of five years or under, two months' interest may be charged; for more than five years, one month's interest.

Tax Relief
The tax relief on home loans is at the basic rate of tax, subject to the capital value not being greater than £30,000 (1989). For loans above £30,000 the rebate is allowed on the first £30,000 only – the remainder receiving no further relief.

The borrower of a home loan repays both capital and interest, the annual interest being nominally income to the societies and thus subject to tax. Each borrower, whose payments are reported to the revenue, is given relief at the basic rate of tax. Should the borrower be subject to a higher rate appropriate adjustments will be made later.

This apparently somewhat unwieldy method has worked reasonably well for years, but delays in sorting out the correct claw-back sometimes occur, which can be inconvenient for the borrower and doubtless tiresome for the Revenue.

As a result an option was provided a few years ago whereby borrowers, instead of making gross payments and in due course having the tax rebate returned, could if they wished make net payments, the interest in effect being net of tax thus precluding any further Revenue interference – except for those whose personal tax is higher than the basic rate!

As readers will be aware this scheme is called Mortgage Interest Relief at Source, or MIRAS for short, and the method treats the nominal rate as net of tax. Assuming that the basic rate of tax was 25% then instead of the asking rate being 13% the net rate would be 13 x .75 = 9.75 per cent. Over 25 years for a loan of £1,000 the monthly payments would reduce from £11.37 gross to £9.00 net, or, on £25,000, from £284.25 to £225.00.

If that is the case why then are the calculations for all above examples, which are for loans under £30,000, outlined on a gross basis when in fact the borrower would treat the interest rate as net of tax and work out the payments, accrued interest, etc accordingly?

The answer lies in the "etc"!

The Inland Revenue has ruled, quite understandably, that the lower interest rates resulting from MIRAS cannot be allowed to create the illusion of reduced effective rates (hence the legally disclosed APRs) and the correct TAP. Consequently all the calculations above have been calculated in their gross form so that the "etc" calculations such as the APR, TAP, last payments, etcP are all understood and are legally correct.

In the above example, a £25,000 building society loan over 25 years at 13% nominal it will be recalled that the *gross* payments were £284.25 and the accrued interest was £265.64, based as it was on 334 days interest and 10 months payments from the advance date to the year-end reconciliation date.

In practice, assuming a basic tax rate of 25%, the gross rate of 13% becomes 13.00 x .75 = 9.75% net and the resulting monthly repayments would be £225 (*net*) and the borrower would consequently pay a *net* accrued interest of £199.23.

But remember, please, *this is the extent of the alterations* to the above calculations; for the remaining calculations, to take one instance, the "excess", are all employed to find the necessary *gross* values required for disclosure.

Where the loan is greater than the current (1989) relief of £30,000 then the gross calculations naturally obtain, the borrower making gross payments and his tax accountant, or the PAYE system, merely adjusting his tax for the relief, until such time as it is no longer applicable.

A refinement – the "last payment"
And now for the bad news! While the above methods of finding the APR and the TAP, for either a "typical" or specific quotation, is generally accepted as the conventional means for disclosure, a few elegant building societies have some reservations and prefer a yet more detailed approach. Namely the calculating of the amount of the last payment prior to finding the APR and TAP – irrespective of the fact that few home loans ever run the full term or that the quoted rate is unlikely to remain unchanged over the full term!

While other societies give little credence to this "precise" method it must be accepted as the ideal, although the APR is unlikely to differ from that found by the conventional method the TAP is only a few hundreds less – a minor saving which is unlikely to prevent the inevitable cardiac arrest suffered by any first time borrower. This method does, however, give accurate, rather than greatly inflated, values for the TAP when the payments, for some reason, are greater than the scale payments – as will be seen in the second of the examples that follow.

First the exact number of period payments due must be determined; then the balance at the end of that term; then the exact amount of the last payment.

As this last payment refinement does not apply to endowment loans we must take the above repayment loan as the example.

The calculation of APR and TAP

Assume a loan of £25,000 over a term of 25 years at 13%, advanced February 1 giving 334 interest days and 10 payments, of £284.25 monthly, to the year end reconciliation day.

The accrued interest is found as £265.64 and the excess as 131.47. Assume fees of £150.

(1) Balance less the accrued interest plus the excess, namely £25,000.00 – 265.64 + 131.47 = 24,865.83

(2) Employing an *annual* profile, calculate the final positive balance, some 25 or 24 years hence.

If when calculating the balance is found to be negative reduce the term by one.

$$24{,}865.83 \times 1.13^{25} - (284.25 \times 12) \times (1.13^{25} - 1)/.13 = -2{,}903.25$$
$$24{,}865.83 \times 1.13^{24} - (284.25 \times 12) \times (1.13^{24} - 1)/.13 = 449.335962$$

don't round

(3) From now onwards start thinking in terms of a *monthly* profile. Consider the term as we know it so far: 24 years x 12 = 288 months, plus the 10 months between advance and first reconciliation = 298 months plus one month according to the following interest calculations. A total of 299 months, which will be employed later, *inter alia* to calculate the TAP.

(4) If the last payment is divided by the payments it is clear that there is a "bit over". The interest therefore for the last two months must be 449.335962 x (1 + .13 x 2/12) = 459.07. Now divide this value by the payments 459.07/284.25 equals 1.615028 – and consider thereon only the *fraction*.

(5) Taking the *fraction* 0.615028 x 284.25 = 174.82 last pmt

The refined APR and TAP

The previous calculation to find the APR was as below:

$$\frac{24,584.36}{284.25a_{\overline{300|}}} = \text{monthly} = 1.114649\% \text{ per}$$

$$\text{x } 12 = 13.375792\% \text{ nom}$$
$$= 14.227050\% \text{ eff}$$
$$14.2\% \quad\quad \text{APR}$$

From the last calculation above, there is now a "last payment" of £174.82 to be considered. In fact this is a "future value" (FV) and as such must be discounted by, how many months? Why 299 of course – see notation section (3) above.

By computer interpolation the monthly rate is 1.114449% and the nominal 13.373392%. The effective rate is 14.224339% and the APR 14.2%, which is the same as that calculated for the specific quotation earlier.

$$\frac{24,58436 - (25,000 \text{ x } 1.114449^{-299})}{284.25a_{\overline{299|}}} = 1.114449\% \text{ per}$$

$$\text{x } 12 = 13.373392\% \text{ nom}$$
$$= 14.224339\% \text{ eff}$$
$$14.2\% \quad\quad \text{APR}$$

The TAP now has the addition of the last payment, but the number of payments had dropped from 300 to 299, namely 284.25 x 299 + 265.64 + 150 + 174.82 = £85,581.21, nearly £30,000 less than that stated in the specific quotation method, the method without the last payment refinement.

More about the last payments

In all the above last payment examples the convention is, and so is the assumption mentioned above, that "month's interest" has been taken for each of the last month's payment.

In the first "last payment" example above it will be recalled that the balance (the FV) was found as £449.335963 and the last two months interest provide the last payment:

```
449.335963 x  (1 + 13.00/100 x 2/12)  = 459.071576
and FRAC(              FV/pmts ) x pmts  = last pmt
     FRAC(459.0715786/284.25) x 284.25 = 174.82
```

But if a society, perhaps a little pedantically, required the actual number of days make up of those two months the calculation, for this example, would be:

```
Jan: 31 days, and Feb:, by convention, taken as 30 days = 61 days
FRAC((449.335963 x (1 + 13/100 x 61/365))/284.25) x 284.25 = £174.85
```

Alternatively, somewhat more complex, if it was required to have each month's interest by days:

```
449.34/284.25 = 1.58 = 1 month (Jan. 31 days) and .58 x365/12 = 18
days so,  449.34 x (1 + (13/100 x (31 + 18)/365) =  457.18
and, 457.18/284.25 = 1.61 and .61 x 284.25       = £172.93 last pmt
```

For the "typical case", 200 days and 6 months, the FV would be 1,457.69 and x $(1 + .13 \times 6/12)/284.25$ and the fraction x payments = a last payment of £131.19. For the days method: FRAC(1,457.69 x $(1 + .13 \times 184/365)$ x 284.25 = 131.97

As the differences are so small and the APR is unlikely to be affected, most societies simply employ the conventional "months" interest method and ignore the precise "days" methods outlined above.

Example: A building society (repayment) loan of £57,000 at 15.125% over a term of 25 years with monthly payments of £741.57. The front-end fee is £384.45. The advance date is the same as in the previous example.

Should the reader care to check his understanding of the foregoing the following data may be useful as his own calculations unfold:

Typical Case Method		*Last Payment Method*	
Accrued interest £	704.66	Accrued interest £	704.66
Excess	£ 473.3	Excess	£ 473.3
TAP	£223,560.11	TAP	£219,961.41
Nominal rate	15.584472%	Nominal rate	15.561031%
Effective rate	16.747280%	Effective rate	16.720267%
APR	16.7%	APR	16.7%

More about the accrued interest

I am somewhat hesitant in outlining the following, for I have no wish to confuse the reader; but, as he will probably have realised from reading this book, there is usually more than one way of doing things! No sooner has one outlined the correct, conventional and generally accepted method throughout an industry, you can be sure that some financial institution will come up with their own in-house method!

Looking back, it will be seen that the reason for having a front-end fee, the accrued interest, was to ensure that the quoted term would not lead to an illegal disclosure.

Should, therefore, a calculation be found to provide an accrued interest sufficient to achieve this object it must be acceptable – even if only one society uses it!

For a *Repayment Loan,* over 25 years, of £36,313.05 with a completion date giving 356 days to the year end (with 11 payments) a gross nominal rate of 12,75% the gross monthly payments will be £406.04

The society concerned calculated thus:

```
£36,313.05 x .1275 x 356/365 = £4,515.75 interest.
£36,313.05
+ 4,515.75
 40,828.80
- 4,466.44  (less 11 payments of 406.04)
£36,362.36  (projected balance)
```

$$36{,}362.36 - \cfrac{\cfrac{(406.04 \times 12)}{a}}{(300-11)/12|}$$

$$36{,}362.36 - \frac{4{,}872.48}{.135002} = \underline{270.56 \text{ accrued interest}}$$

And to check that the disclosure is not illegal: the loan plus the excess equals £36,362.36, and at 12.75% gross nominal and with annual payments of (12 x £406.04) the term is just under 25 years and 3 months – over the quoted 25 years.

But reducing the loan, plus the excess, by subtracting this a/i, we get £36,362.36 – 270.56 = £36,091.91 and with this value as the loan outstanding the term becomes a legal disclosure of 24 years and 1 month.

Out of interest the conventionally calculated accrued interest would be £271.66 – not a lot in it!

For *Endowment Loans*, because of the endowment interest structure, the accrued interest must be precisely the same as the conventional method, namely:

```
        13,350.25 x (13.25 x .7 ÷ 1200)   =  103.186307 net payments
and   (13,350.25 x 13.25/100 x 356/365)
    − (13,350.25 x 13.25/100 x 11/12)   =  103.79 gross a/i
                              x .7        =   72.65 net   a/1
```

As the parameters, for both the repayment loan above and endowment loan, were drawn from two "calculation sheets" kindly provided by the society concerned, I append their calculation below.

Their calculations for a repayment loan, over 25 years, of £13,350.25 with the same completion date as above, at a gross nominal rate of 13.25% with *net* monthly payments of £103.18, the basic tax rate of being 30%, are below:

```
        13,350.25 x (13.25 x .7 ÷ 1200)       =   103.186307
but the society concerned rounded to = £103.18 net       payments
                                      = £147.40 gross     payments
        £13,350.25 x 13.25/100 x 356/365 = £1,725.29 gross interest
                            at 30% tax = £1,207.70   net   interest
        £1,207.70 − (103.186307 x 11) = £ 72.65 net    a/i
                                      = £103.79 gross a/i
```

Mortgage Guarantee Premiums

Throughout the industry a guarantee premium is not unusual, the precise rate charged naturally being according to the individual bank or building society.

One such guarantee might well be 4% on the amount by which th loan exceeds 75% of the purchase price of the property (or the valuation, whichever is the lesser). The premium becomes a front-end fee and must be accounted for in the APR calculation, both for the specific and, if applicable, a typical case quotation.

The reason for a premium is simple; if the property is worth £65,000 and the loan was for £45,000, in the unhappy event of a foreclosure, there is substantial latitude between the possible realisation of the property and the loan amount. But if the loan agreed was for £63,000 then the room for manoeuvre reduces to almost dangerous proportions for the lender. The premium, in a small way, aims to reduce this discrepancy.

A loan for £55,000 on a property valued at £65,000 would require a premium of £90 if the guarantee rate was only 3% on an 80% excess. (55,000 – (65,000 x .80)) x .03 = 90.00

If a society charged 70% on the excess and a 4% premium the front-end fee would be £380, namely (55,000 – (65,000 x .70)) x .04 = 380.00

Obviously, no premium is required if the actual loan is less than the excess percentage; if, for example, the above loan was only for £50,000, the negative would be found as follows: 50,000 - (65,000 x .80) = – 2,000

Ex-gratia payments
Nowadays, most building societies accept ex gratia payments without demur: some credit the borrower's account the day they arrive, others at the same day as the borrower's payments are made.

It must be appreciated that some institutions, other than building societies, offer home loans in the same style as those offered by the societies but do not necessarily follow all their conventions. And it is these institutions that may delay the credit of ex-gratia payments for up to 3 months.

There is quite a reasonable explanation: we all know that

there is a "banker's turn", in that there is a difference between borrowing and lending.

Whereas when we lend at, say, 10% it will costs us 13% to borrow. When we have a mortgage and we are borrowing at 13% when we make an ex-gratia payment in effect what we are actually doing is to lend that money to the institution *at the borrowing rate!* And whether a large bank or small lender few care to give credit 2% or 3% higher than the going rate.

Why three months credit delay? This method is one which has been used over the years to iron out this disproportionate ex-gratia payment rate, and although not very scientific it is generally agreed that it works in practice. At least it used to, in the days when the turn was not more than 2% or 3% but even nowadays with a wider spread it still has some merit.

For if we assume an ex-gratia payment of £100 at a loan interest rate of 13% the interest at the end of 12 months is £13, but if the period was reduced to only 9 months the interest would become only 9.75%, consequently the turn is 3.25%. Alternatively, for a lending rate of 11% (against a borrowing rate of 8%, namely a 3% turn) a three months credit delay would reduce the 11% to 8.25%, a 2.75% turn.

As I said not very scientific but this is the method that some lenders use, even nowadays, to even things up.

MIRAS with constant payments
We have seen above the difference between the net and gross interest rates and realised that if the loan amount was over the statutory £30,000 the relief applicable was a matter between each borrower and the Revenue. It was not until after 1987 that arrangements were made whereby societies were able to accept some form of payments which took into account the net payments for the first £30,000 and the gross payments thereafter. To call these partly net and partly gross payments an "average" would be misleading, nor can they be described, or calculated, as a weighted mean.

There are two distinct methods of "constant" MIRAS payments; those that are truly constant throughout the whole term of the loan and those which are constant only up to the time when the current balance of the loan falls below the £30,000 tax relief.

The payments after that period rising each year commensurate with the amount that the tax relief falls. The schedules provided later will probably be more enlightening than a mass of explanation.

We have already shown that the Inland Revenue have ruled that the lower MIRAS interest rates cannot be allowed to create the illusion of a reduced effective rate, and that consequently all "disclosure". *must* be assessed on the *gross* values.

The value of these "constant" gross/net payments are not Revenue sponsored and the correct tax remit to the Revenue is the responsibility of individual societies.

The calculation of the "gross profile method" payments
The gross profile payment method, whereby payments are constant only while the loan outstanding is above the prescribed £30,000, is fairly easy to calculate.

$$\frac{\dfrac{Loan}{a_{\overline{n}|}} \text{ at a nominal rate\% – } annual \text{ calculations profile } - (30{,}000 \times rate\%/100 \times tax\%/100)}{12} = pmts$$

And taking an example of a £40,000 loan over 25 years at a nominal rate of 13.50%, and assuming the current basic tax rate is 25%:

$$\frac{40{,}000}{a_{\overline{25}|}} \text{ at } 13.50\% = 5{,}637.80072989 \text{ which divided by 12 and rounded} = \text{monthly payments of } 469.82$$

and $(5{,}637.80072989 - (30{,}000 \times 13.50/100 \times 25/100)) \div 12 = 385.44$
(note the unrounding above)   gross profile payments

In the above example the constant payments will obtain for the first 15 years, for it will be found that the balance at the beginning the 16th year falls below £30,000, namely £29,990.38 found by:

$$(40,000 \times 1.135^{(15-1)} - (5,637.80 \times (1.135^{(15-1)} - 1)/.135)$$
$$= 29,990.38$$

In each of the following 9 years the monthly payments will rise little by little every year until the 25th and last year's payments which will be such that the loan balance, at the end of the 300th month, will be zero; in this example £455.85.

How are these payments calculated?

Having found the balance, at which ever year end is required, multiply by the rate%/100 and the tax%/100 and then subtract that amount from the *annual* payments *(unrounded)*, – and then divide by 12.

In this example therefore the payments for the 16th and 25th years will be:

$$(5,637.80072989 - (29,990.38 \times .135 \times .25)) \div 12 = 385.47$$
$$(5,637.80072989 - (4,967.23 \times .135 \times .25)) \div 12 = 455.85$$

The other intermediate payments can be found in the same way (see schedule below).

It must be stressed that even if the payments are MIRAS constant the official disclosure, both the APR and TAP, must be based on the *gross* scenario, the gross rate and the gross payments.

Remember, too, the accrued interest must also be calculated gross, for disclosure purposes, even though it is paid net of tax if the account is MIRAS orientated.

Gross Profile Payments

Year	Balance (rounded)	Interest	Repayments annually	Monthly payment
1	40,000.00	4,387.50	4,625.30	385.44
2	39,762.20	4,355.40	"	"
3	39,492.30	4,318.96	"	"
4	39,185.95	4,277.60	"	"
5	38,838.26	4,230.66	"	"
6	38,443.62	4,177.39	"	"
7	37,995.71	4,116.92	"	"
8	37,487.33	4,048.29	"	"
9	36,910.32	3,970.39	"	"
10	36,255.41	3,881.98	"	"
11	35,512.09	3,781.63	"	"
12	34,668.42	3,667.74	"	"
13	33,710.86	3,538.47	"	"
14	32,624.02	3,391.74	"	"
15	31,390.47	3,225.21	"	"
~~				
16	29,990.38	3,036.53	4,625.63	385.47
17	28,401.28	2,875.63	4,679.26	389.94
18	26,597.65	2,693.01	4,740.13	395.01
19	24,550.53	2,485.74	4,809.22	400.77
20	22,227.06	2,250.49	4,887.64	407.30
21	19,589.91	1,983.48	4,976.64	414.72
22	16,596.74	1,680.42	5,077.66	423.14
23	13,199.50	1,336.45	5,192.32	432.69
24	9,343.64	946.04	5,322.45	443.54
25	4,967.23	502.93	5,470.16	455.85
26	0.00			

The calculations to find the schedule values before the cross over point and the required payments afterwards:

$(40,000.00 \times 1.135)$ — gross annual payments

$(40.000.00 \times 1.135) - 5,637.80072989 = 39,762.20$ et seq.

OR

$(\text{loan} \times 1 + i^{(n-1)}) - (\text{pmts} \times (1 + i^{(n-1)} - 1) \div i) = \text{bal}(n)$

$(40,000 \times 1.135^{24}) - (5,637.80072989 \times (1.135^{24} - 1) \div .135$

$$= 4,967.23 \text{ balance}$$
year 25

The calculation of the "constant" payments

How are the constant payments to be calculated?

The short answer is, not without difficulty! The trick is, first, to determine, by interpolation, the cross-over point (in years or months) where the different net/gross payments would notionally change if the payments were not constant. The formula is below:

```
Where:  A  = the loan amount
        R  = the relief limit        (at present £30,000)
        i  = the gross interest rate (as a decimal)
        j  = the net   interest rate (as a decimal)
        t  = the cross-over factor in years (or months optional)
```

Actuarially shown as:

$$\frac{(A - R)}{a_{\overline{t}|} \text{ at } i\%} + [R \times (j)] \quad \text{MUST equal} \quad \frac{R}{a_{\overline{n-t}|} \text{ at } j\%}$$

Taking the above example again, the gross monthly payments are £469.82, and as the tax is 25% basic then the net payments would fall to £352.36 – but of course only the first £30,000 is eligible for relief.

Consequently, if constant payments are to be made over the whole term they must be calculated in such a way as to allow for the tax rebate only on the first £30,000.

Obviously such payments will fall somewhere between those payments relevant to the net and gross values.

The formula, by interpolation, requires the calculation to be such that both sides of the equation are finally the same, the variable being the cross-over factor.

As the calculations are annually based both sides of the equation must finally be divided by 12 to provide *monthly* payments with the resulting equation being:

$$\frac{\dfrac{(A - R)}{[1 - (1 + i)^\wedge{-t}]/i} + [R \times (j)]}{12} = \frac{\dfrac{R}{[1 - (1 + j)^\wedge{-(n-t)}]/j}}{12}$$

As the whole point of the calculation is to determine the constant payments when the loan is greater than £30,000, or the current tax relief obtaining, so obviously when calculating the loan amount must be in excess of £30,000.

The interest rate taken is always the *gross* nominal rate, not the net rate.

Example: A loan of £40,000 at 13.50% nominal over 25 years. In this case at a basic rate of 25% and a net rate 10.125% (found from 13.50 x .75 = 10.125) the cross-over factor, (t), is 14.064855, accordingly (n – t) = 25 – 14.064855 = 10.935145

$$\frac{\dfrac{10,000.00}{(1 - (1.135^{-14.0649})/.135} + (30,000 \times .10125)}{12} \quad = \quad \frac{\dfrac{30,000.00}{(1 - 1.10125^{-10.9351})/.10125}}{12}$$

$$1,623.49 \quad + \quad 303705$$

$$4,660.99/12 \quad = \quad 4,660.99/12$$

$$388.42 \quad = \quad 388.42$$

Once the two sides of the equation balance the cross-over factor *must* be correct – as indeed so must the payments set out.

Schedule calculations

Unlike the gross profile schedule in the constant schedule below the balances of individual years cannot be found by formula/equation; each year's balance must therefore be calculated and recalculated until the balance for the required year is found - as per the schedule below.

This necessity of scheduling also applies to finding the balances at the cross over point.

Constant Net Payments

Year	Balance (unrounded)	Interest	Repayments annually	Monthly payment
1	40,000.00	4,387.50	4,661.04	388.42
2	39,726.46	4,350.57	"	"
3	39,415.99	4,308.66	"	"
4	39,063.61	4,261.09	"	"
5	38,663.66	4,207.09	"	"
6	38,209.71	4,145.81	"	"
7	37,694.48	4,076.26	"	"
8	37,109.70	3,997.31	"	"
9	36,445.97	3,907.71	"	"
10	35,692.63	3,806.01	"	"
11	34,837.60	3,690.58	"	"
12	33,867.14	3,559.56	"	"
13	32,765.66	3,410.86	"	"
14	31,515.48	3,242.09	"	"
15	30,096.53	3,050.53	"	"
~	~ ~ ~ ~ ~ ~	~ ~ ~ ~	~ ~ ~ ~ ~	~ ~ ~ ~
16	28,486.02	2,884.21	"	"
17	26,709.19	2,704.31	"	"
18	24,752.46	2,506.19	"	"
19	22,597.61	2,288.01	"	"
20	20,224.58	2,047.74	"	"
21	17,611.27	1,170.86	"	"
22	14,733.37	1,491.75	"	"
23	11,564.09	1,170.86	"	"
24	8,073.91	817.48	"	"
25	4,230.36	428.32	"	"
26	−2.36			

To find the schedule values, before and after the cross over:
```
40,000.00 + (((40,000.00–30,000)x.135) + (30,000 x .10125)) − 4,661.04
                                                     = 39,726.46
39,726.46 + (((39,726.46-30,000)x.135) + (30,000 x .10125)) − 4,661.04
                                                     = 39,415.99
```
and after the cross over point:
```
28,486.02 + (28,486.02 x .10125) − 4,661.04         = 26,709.19
26,709.19 + (26,709.19 x .10125) − 4,661.04         = 24,752.46
```

Some practicalities

We all know that theory and practice are often two different things! Above we have been quite happily calculating the last payments, 25 years ahead when we know that it is unlikely that the borrower will "stay in" for 25 years, and that the rate will remain unchanged to the same time.

Above we have been scheduling a loan with both constant and gross profile payments over 25 years when, again. it is highly unlikely that there will be no changes through the term

Let us therefore pretend, in order to test the following practice, that at the start of year 9 the "new" balance is £36,910.32 for a *gross profile account* and make a schedule for the remainder of the payments.

As the original loan was for 25 years in order to achieve the same period to redemption the calculation the new term is 17 years, derived from $25 - 9 + 1 = 17$.

So by taking, for test purposes, the precise value (£36,910.32) at the beginning of year 9 it is seen that remaining values are the same. Consequently, we know that the method of determining the number of future years is correct.

Now consider if there is a rate change to 12% from November 15, year 8. What is the balance and payments in the final, 25th, year of the original term or of the 17th year of the " new" loan arrangement?

There are 319 days from January 1 to November 15, and consequently $365 - 319 = 46$ days from November 15 to the year end reconciliation. So we have 13,5% for the first 10 months and 12% for the last 46 days.

And that is how we did it for conventional building society mortgages as outlined earlier. But in the case of these MIRAS constant related calculations it is more usual to work on an annual/monthly basis.

$$(37{,}487.33 \times (1 + 10/12 \times .135)) - (385.44 \times 10) = 38{,}850.25$$

and $(38{,}055.92 \times (1 + 2/12 \times .120)) - (385.44 \times 2) = 37{,}839.38$

It will be seen that the payments in the second portion of the year's loan have not decreased, this is because, until the next calculation the new payments can't be determined. So the old payments are employed, and the balance at reconciliation date is just that much less than it would be if the correct payments had been determined. Now with this new balance we can employ the gross profile calculation, and it will be found to balance in the last and 17th year is £4,744.98 and that the final gross profile payment is £431.00.

Turning to *Constant Payments* the same type of method is used as we employed for gross profile account, namely find the balance at the beginning of the year under reference and continue to find each balance for each year until the value is under £30,000 and then switch until the final balance is zero.

Doing a schedule test, as we did above for the gross profile calculations will not be quite as accurate, and this is due to the fractional differences in the x-over and constant payment calculations. For instance the correct constant payments are £388.42 but when the test is done it will be seen that the balance for the remaining 17 years finds the constant payments as £388.41, and this odd penny make a few pounds difference in the last payment 17 years ahead.

The required balance can be found, as before, by calculating the new balance at the beginning of any particular year, after that all that is required is to calculate a schedule, or if one has a computer or programmable calculator, to step through the succeeding balances before and after the cross over point.

I am greatly indebted to an old friend, Mr Stephen Perry, currently the Manager for Business Analysis, and Corporate Planning, with the Nationwide Anglia Building Society, for allowing me, on more than one occasion, to check with him some aspects of the MIRAS calculations above. I should add that none of the examples above are in any way connected with his Society.

CHAPTER 9

Hire Purchase and Leasing

General

The differences between hire purchase (HP) and leasing, apart from the nomenclature, is in the calculations and presentation. Whereas an HP contract is usually quoted with a simple interest rate, leasing is normally quoted with its true (amortised) compound rate.

Usually lenders (the hire purchase or leasing companies) require a deposit or some sort of advance payments by the borrower, to "show willing", and as we shall see this front-end requirement substantially affects the overall calculations.

Some instructional computer/calculator manuals point out that leasing calculations "typically use advance payments", but this implies one up-front payment only. In practice this is usually considered inadequate, the lender normally preferring three such payments. Where there is an advanced fee, whether an initial deposit or a series of advance payments, the subsequent payments are always "in arrears".

With hire purchase, as indeed the name implies, the goods are hired and are in fact deemed to have been fully purchased only when all the payments have been completed. Leasing, however, is a different concept in that the goods are leased and at all times remain the property of the lessor, the lessee returning the plant at the end of the term of the lease. In this case the plant can be written off as "scrap" (salvage), re—leased or sold "at best". In the latter case the leasing company will require the lessee to cover the sale value, called for contract purposes the "residual". If the residual was (say) £1,000 and the effective sale realised that amount, or more, the lessee would not be required to make any payments over and above his periodic (monthly or quarterly) instalments; but if the leasing company forecast the future sale value incorrectly then the lessee will be required to make up the difference.

The manuals often refer to the residual as "the option to purchase at the end of the leasing period", and if the lessee wishes to do so he can purchase the plant for the assumed residual value (on which the periodic payments were in part based) but, in the UK, it is unlikely that this action would appeal; for if the plant was purchased by the lessee at the end of the contract there would be no tax advantages.

I propose to delve no further into this aspect of the UK tax system as it relates to hiring and leasing (if indeed such a conglomeration of rates, concessions and liabilities can be called a system). Suffice it to say that providing, and only providing, such arrangements are kept at arms' length some useful tax concessions can be obtained. If tax concessions are sought it is illegal for the lessee to bid, or to instruct an agent to bid, at public auction for plant or vehicles recently leased.

Disclosure (of APR and TAP), while necessary for hire purchase, is not necessary for leasing between companies. But if the lessee is an individual then disclosure is normally required.

HIRE PURCHASE CALCULATIONS

The general mechanisms of hire purchase agreements are relatively simple and are probably well known to those using this often expensive method of acquiring capital goods. But there are one or two minor anomalies, such as balloon payments and front-end fees, which may complicate matters.

There are, in effect, three separate arrangements that must be considered, namely a conventional hire purchase calculation derived from the usual flat rate, or simple interest, quotation; the same with an insurance content and, lastly, a balloon payment with or without the extra month's breathing space before the residual must be paid at the end of the term. More detailed explanations are outlined below.

Having found the payments, the true rate, the effective rate and the TAP calculations can then be made.

If the payments are increased to cover a small insurance premium, as they are pro rata and as the capital content also is increased accordingly, the true rate and hence the APR remains unchanged.

Example
A high street purchase of (say) kitchen units for £764.71 with a 15% deposit and an HP contract over 24 months. If the quoted (flat) rate was 15% what are the monthly payments, the APR and TAP?

First find the deposit, namely 15% of £764.71 is 114.706500 and, consequently the capital value, for the calculation of the payments, becomes £764.71 – 114.71 = £650.

The payments, therefore, will become:

$$((650 \times 15/100 \times 2) + 650)/24 = 35.21 \text{ (rounded)}$$

and by computer interpolation the rate is found as 26.583356% nominal:

$$\dfrac{764.71 - 114.71}{35.21a\underline{\hspace{1em}}} \text{ at rate\%}$$
$$24 \mid$$

$$650.00 \div ((1 - (1 + 26.583356/1200)^{-24}) \div 26.583356/1200) = 35.21$$

and the effective rate becomes 30.073808%, consequently the APR is 30.0%, with a TAP of $(35.21 \times 24) + 114.71$ making £959.75.

Front-end fees
Front-end fees, being an extra charge, will affect the yield, and thus the APR. If the front-end fee was £65 in the above example *subtract* the £65 from £650.

Without altering the payments of 35.21 the new rate computes as 38.14% nominal, the effective as 41.63% and the APR consequently becomes 45.5%, with the £65 being added to the above TAP to make £1,024.75

I said earlier that HP could come expensive!

Occasionally the fees are covered by making them part of the payments. In this instance the new payments would become £35.21 + 65/24 = £37.92; and the effective rate would be calculated as 40.729787% effective = 40.7 APR.

Any small registration fee, usually around £10 – £5, required for high street HP is usually paid together with the deposit: subtract such fees from the loan when recalculating the APR. If, however, the front-end fee is paid together with the first payment, as is the case with the more expensive type of lending, see the last three paragraphs of the Insurance Premium section below for the correct method of calculation.

Early redemption
In H.P. the penalties for early redemption fall into same categories as outlined in an earlier section on Rule of 78.

VAT loading and Insurance premiums
For the more expensive types of HP it may be thought convenient to insure against the purchaser being unable to meet his monthly payments, owing to sickness or temporary unemployment. In that case a finance house, through the hire purchase company, will arrange a small additional premium, with a consequent slight increase in monthly payments. The amount of the premium is usually related to the term of the loan, the rate being, say, 6% for one year, or 8.50% for 3 years.

Example: Assume that a car is purchased for £6,250.00, and that there is no part exchange required but that there is an agreed 20% deposit, making a total required repayment of £6,250 – (6,250 x .20) = 6,250 – 1,250 = £5000.00. The quoted simple interest rate is 12% over the three years and so the payments are 5000 x (1 + (12/100 x 3)) = £6,800 and this amount, divided by 36 months, equals monthly payments of £188.89.

Without any insurance premium the true rate (and APR) and

the total charge for credit are found by computer interpolation as 21.20% nominal, an effective of 23.39% an APR of 23.3% and a TAP of £8,050.04:

$$\frac{5,000.00}{188.89a\underline{}} \quad \text{at rate\% = 21.200325\%}$$
$$36\ |$$

and

$$5000.00 \div ((1 - (1 + 21.200325/1200)^{-36}) \div 21.200325/1200) = 188.89$$

In the event that insurance was required, at an agreed rate of, say, 8.50% over a three year term, the new payments are found in the following manner:

$$£(188.8888889 \times 36) \times .085 \quad = 578.00 \ (\text{interim value})$$

$$\frac{5,000}{5,000 - 578} \quad = 1.130710 \ (\text{factor})$$

$$188.89 \times 1.130710 \quad = £213.58 \quad \text{new pmts (rounded)}$$
$$578.00 \times 1.130710 \quad = £653.55 \quad \text{premium}$$
$$5,000 + 653.55 \quad = £5,653.55 \ \text{new value}$$

An alternative method of finding the above factor:

$$\frac{1}{1 - (188.88888889 \times 36 \times .085/5,000)} = 1.130710$$

Providing there are no fees, the true rate, and consequently the APR, are the same whether or not there is an insurance element. For although the payments with the insurance content are higher so also is the capital value, namely cost *plus* the premium. In the above example £5,000 + 653.55.

If VAT, currently at 15%, is charged multiply the payments 1.15, here £188.89 x 1.15 = £217.22

Insurance rated payments, if loaded with VAT (here £213.58 x 1.15 = £245.62), will cost *a lessee who is not VAT registered*, that much more and the nominal and effective rates will be seen to rise accordingly. Should, therefore, new nominal and effective rates need to be calculated (here 31.80% and 37.87%), remember the *premium* (here £653.55) is NOT affected by the addition of VAT to the insurance payments.

But if there are any fees involved, then the true rate, the effective rate, and thus the APR, must be recalculated; for there will be a difference, albeit in some cases small. Paradoxically, the true rate is sometimes less with fees and insurance than with fees but without insurance.

The above is true provided, and only provided, that this fee is paid at the outset. Unfortunately the practice, with this type of contract, is that such fees are more often than not paid *with the first payment* - which, this being an HP contract, is always paid in arrears. Consequently the only *correct* method is to employ a discounted cash flow calculation.

The good news is, however, that the difference between the two methods is normally so small as not to affect the APR. Nevertheless, if in doubt, employ a DCF calculation.

Hire purchase balloon payments
When HP is related to the more expensive purchases, such as private cars, etc, as opposed to the conventional high street purchases, it greatly resembles a leasing profile, having a balloon or, in leasing terms a residual. But unlike a leasing contract the vehicle belongs to the purchaser at the conclusion of the agreement.

In this case because, with the motor trade in particular, leasing and hire purchase are inexorably linked and the financing interwoven, the repayment of the residual is sometimes delayed for one month after the end of the term; the reason being the necessity to assess the true worth of the residual.

With this type of hire/leasing the quotation is, or should be, at the true rate and the periodic payments can calculated by the conventional annuities ordinary amortisation formula.

However, should the quote be given (abnormally) as a flat rate, the flat rate *must* be converted to a true rate before there is any question of calculating the payments or considering the balloon factor.

Assume a £1,000 HP loan over a period of 24 months at a 20% true nominal rate (APR 21.9%) with a balloon payment (residual) of £100. Find the payments for the extra month.

$$\frac{1,000.00 - 100 \div (1 + 20/1200)^{25}}{a_{\overline{24}|} \quad \text{at } (20/12)\%} = 47.53 \text{ payments}$$

$$(1,000 - (100/1.016667^{25})) \div ((1 - 1.016667^{-24})/.016667) = 47.53$$

The section, entitled "The final payment option", under Leasing below, provides a somewhat fuller explanation as to why there is sometimes a requirement for a delay in the payment of the balloon, or the determination of the residual.

LEASING CALCULATIONS

The rate of interest for leasing contracts is usually quoted at the true nominal rate, seldom as simple interest – but see the Simple Interest Quote section below.

Only if a leasing contract is made with an individual member of the public, rather than to a company, is it necessary to provide the APR and TAP. If so, it is a simple matter to convert the quoted nominal rate to the effective (and hence, truncating to one place of decimals, to the APR).

In hire purchase agreements there is usually a reasonably substantial deposit required, indeed sometimes a front-end fee as well. The repayments, in consequence, are always in arrears. With leasing, however, the conventional calculation is for payments in advance, namely *one* advance payment only.

But since most lessors consider that a single payment in advance is a somewhat meagre form of deposit they prefer a larger initial payment. There is no conventional way of deciding the size of this initial payment, but the most fashionable arrangement appears to be "three payments in advance".

Having decided on (say) three advance payments then, because the norm for leasing contracts is one advance payment, it is clear that there will be two, <u>not</u> three, extra advance payments. As there will the same number of payment periods, irrespective of advance payments, there will be two, as opposed to three, non payment periods. The question is when are these non payment periods to occur in the life of the loan, at the beginning of the lease, *initial pause*, as it is called, or at the end of the lease, *terminal pause*, or whether the payments are *spread* over the whole term – with no pauses? Below are the various methods of calculation with examples.

Once the single conventional payment in advance is replaced by a number of advance payments all subsequent payments will be in arrears – for it would be absurd to demand a number of advance payments and then expect yet one more payment in advance merely because of the conventional method of calculating leases!

"In lieu" and deferred payment options
Some traders sometimes prefer to make a substantial initial down payment *in lieu* of a number of advance payments, others prefer to delay their initial payments for a few months.

But having become accustomed to the benefits arising from the various pause or spread modes they usually demand that there should be some non period payments. The lessor therefore has to calculate the methods of payment for either of these options, with an initial pause, a terminal pause or a spread.

The final payment option
Unhappily, there is still yet one further option! Suppose, for example, that the leasing arrangements were related to motor vehicles which the local garage was to sell to an individual purchaser. If terms were required the garage would probably take out an HP loan from a finance company, passing on the cost to the purchaser by means of a leasing contract. The purchaser now becomes the lessee. So far so good.

Readers will recall, from the general remarks made earlier, that if the residual was not calculated to the acceptable level the lessee might be required to make up the difference. The point is, when will the garage know whether or not the vehicle has achieved the stated residual value on resale?

The garage, receiving back the car at the end of the term, is likely to take a month to clean it up and take it to auction – and not until then will they know whether to ask the lessee for payment. Thus they could be "out of the money" for a period. "Charges" at this stage, on top of everything else, could be counter productive!

So what can be done?

The conventional way out of this dilemma is to assume that the vehicle is returned *one* month (or more) later. For example, at the end of the 36th month the residual will be calculated as if it is not due until the end of the 37th month (or more), which will increase the payments to an extent considered just sufficient to cover the lessor being out of the money by one month (or more).

In the terminal pause example below, instead of re-calculating the whole structure of the loan to ensure the "extra" residual month, the same payments would be due if the residual was reduced by £13.56.

Alternatively, if the residual was reduced by £50 the payments would rise by only £1.

One might wonder why any distributor bothered about the extra month's calculation in order to uplift the overall term payments by such a small sum. The difference, in the example being considered, is only 28 pence per month, or just over £10 for 36 months on a £10,000 contract.

However, if in the case of a large distributor moving 250 vehicles a month, every year, £10 a month x 250 x 12 months = £30,000 a year!

The required formulae are outlined below:

Where y = the number of advance payments required.

The Initial Pause

$$\frac{Cap - Res(1 + i/p)^{-np}}{a_{\underline{\quad\quad}}[\ np - y\ |\ x\ (1 + i/p)\wedge-(y-1)] + y} = Pmts_{\text{initial pause}}$$

In Lieu Options for Initial Pause

$$\frac{(Cap - in\ lieu\ pmts) - Res(1 + i/p)^{-np}}{a_{\underline{\quad\quad}}[\ np - y|\ x\ (1 + i/p)\wedge-(y-1)]} = Pmts_{\text{initial pauses}}$$

The Terminal Pause

$$\frac{Cap - Res(1 + i/p)^{-np}}{a_{\underline{\quad\quad}}np - y\ |\ + y} = Pmts_{\text{terminal pause}}$$

In Lieu Options for Terminal Pause

$$\frac{(Cap - in\ lieu\ pmts) - Res(1 + i/p)^{-np}}{a_{\underline{\quad\quad}}np - y|} = Pmts_{\text{terminal pauses}}$$

The Spread Method

$$\frac{Cap - Res(1 + i/p)^{-np}}{a_{\underline{\quad}}[\ np\ |\ x\ (1 + i/p)\ ] + (y-1)} = Pmts_{\text{spread}}$$

In Lieu Options for Spread Calculations

$$\frac{(Cap - in\ lieu\ pmts) - Res(1 + i/p)^{-np}}{a_{\underline{\quad}}np|} = Pmts_{\text{spread}}$$

To find the term

$$\frac{\text{LOG} \left[\frac{\text{pmts}}{i/p} \times (1 + i/p) - \text{res} \right] \times \left[1 \div (\frac{\text{pmts}}{i/p} \times (1 + i/p) - \text{loan}) \right]}{\text{LOG} \quad 1 + i/p}$$

The Example By taking *one simple example* throughout, and looking at all the various options, confusion should be avoided.

The example is a leasing contract for £10,000 with a £1,000 residual, commencing April 15th over a term of 36 months, at a true rate of 16.50%.

Three advance payments, or a £3,000 down-payment *in lieu* of advance payments, are required. It is assumed that there are no front-end deposits; if there are subtract the value from the capital amount.

The conventional method, (one payment in advance)

This assumes that there is *one* payment in advance to be paid on April 15th. The 35 following payments will then be made commencing a month later on May 15th, and on the 15th day of the 36th month the plant will be returned to the lessor – together with any residual payment applicable.

$$\frac{\text{Cap} - \text{Res}(1 + i/p)^{-np}}{\underset{[\, np \mid \, \times (1 + i/p) \,]}{a}} = \text{Pmts}_{\text{annuities due}}$$

$$\frac{10,000 - (1,000/1.013750^{36})}{(1 - 1.013750^{-36})/.013750 \times 1.013750} = 327.88$$

The initial pause (all subsequent payments in arrears)

This assumes that there are *three* payments in advance, made on April 15th. No payments will be made for the next two months and the subsequent 33 payments will commence on July 15th.

At the end of the 36th month the plant will be returned to the lessor – with any residual payment applicable.

$$\frac{Cap - Res(1 + i/p)^{-np}}{\underline{a}\atop[np - y \mid x (1 + i/p^-(y-1))] + y} = \text{Pmts} \atop \text{initial pause}$$

$$\frac{10,000 - (1,000/1.013750^{36})}{((1-1.013750^{-(36-3)})/.013750 \times 1.013750^{-(3-1)}) + 3} = 327.42$$

$$\frac{10,000.00 - 611.630001}{28.673967} = 327.42$$

$$\frac{9,388.369999}{28.673967} = 327.42$$

The "extra month" for the residual payment

If the requirement was an extra month's latitude for the payment of the residual, the residual must be discounted by 37 periods, instead of 36 in the equation above - i.e. 10,000 - (1,000 x 1.013750^-37) = £9,396.67 which, when divided by the denominator of 28.363967, makes the payments £327.71.

Payments "in lieu"

Any payments *in lieu* are merely deducted from the capital amount. If, above, the *in lieu* payment was £3,000 the capital amount would become 10,000 - 3,000 - 611.63 = £6,388.37

With *in lieu* payments there can be no other advance payments; that being so the "+ 3", in the factor above, are unnecessary and must be subtracted from the amortised factor of 28.673967. Consequently, with £3,000 *in lieu*, the payments will become £6,388.37 ÷ (28.673967 − 3) = £248.83.

And of course these payments would rise fractionally if, with the above requirement, an extended residual payment was also required. (9,396.67 − 3,000) ÷ (28.673967 − 3) = 249.15

The terminal pause (all subsequent payments in arrears)

This method, perhaps the most popular, is the converse of the initial pause, in that the non payment periods fall at the end of the term. The *three* advance payments are made on April

15th and the further 33 payments commence on May 15th. There are no payments for months 34 and 35 and the plant is returned to the lessor at the end of the 36th month, together with any residual amount if applicable.

$$\frac{\dfrac{Cap - Res(1 + i/p)^{-np}}{a}}{np - y \mid + y} = \text{Pmts terminal pause}$$

$$\frac{10,000 - (1,000/1.013750^{36})}{((1 - 1.013750^{-(36-3)})/.013750) + 3} = 319.50$$

In the same way as in the initial pause calculations, the extra residual month will require payments of £319.78 and if the *in lieu* was £3,000 the payments would reduce to: $(9,388.37 - 3,000) \div (29.384855 - 3) = £242.12$

The spread method (all subsequent payments in arrears)
This assumes that there are *three* payments in advance, made on April 15th. 35 payments are spread evenly over the full term commencing on May 15th: at the end of the 36th month the plant will be returned to the lessor, together with any residual amount applicable.

$$\frac{Cap - Res(1 + i/p)^{-np}}{[\,np \mid \times (1 + i/p)\,] + (y-1)} = \text{Pmts spread}$$

$$\frac{10,000 - (1,000/1.013750^{36})}{((1 - 1.013750^{-36})/.013750 \times 1.013750) + 2} = 306.47$$

But with a "spread" mode, with an up-front *in lieu* amount, all subsequent payments are in arrears. Consequently, with all the remaining periods "spread", the calculation required is, in effect, a simple annuities ordinary, in arrears: £9,388.37 – 3,000 divided by $(1 - 1.013750^{-36})/.013750 = £226.18$

Deferred Payments
Sometimes traders, for their own cash flow reasons, prefer to lease, and have the use of the plant *now*, but to begin the normal series of payments a few months later. In effect, this becomes a small additional loan, being calculated over the

period of delay at the quoted rate, and the extra amount is added to the original loan to become the new present value.

As the plant is being used from day one of the contract, irrespective of when the first payment is made, the plant must be returned, and the residual becomes due, on the same day *as if there had been no deferment.*

For example, assume that a lease had been agreed calling for plant to be delivered on Jan 1, 1989, the contract being for £5,000 over exactly 12 months at 16.50% with just one payment in advance – and no residual; the normal monthly payments would be £448.67.

In this case, as payments are in advance they will commence on Jan 1st and each of the eleven subsequent payments will be made on the first of each calendar month, the plant being returned to the lessor on the 31st December.

If, however, for some reason it was necessary to defer payments for, say, three months, this means, in effect, that there is a three months deferment period and a *nine* month leasing contract; for, as stressed above, the plant, being active from January 1, must be returned on December 31.

The capital value thus becomes the capital plus the interest value on the deferred three months' payments, namely:

$$£5,000 \times (1 + 16.5/1200)^3 = £5,209.10$$

Having been using the plant for 3 months, which in effect has cost him £209.10, the lessee could pay the interest of £209.10 together with his first payment.

Then, having reimbursed the lessor for his small "secondary" loan, have a nine month contract for a capital cost of the original £5,000 with payments of £586.38.

But the usual method it to let the debt stand over to be taken care of by higher payments, in this case a capital amount of

£5,209.10 for nine months, with £610.90 monthly payments.

An alternative method is to have lower payments based on the higher capital amount but for the term of the original contract *plus* the number of deferred periods, here some 15 months in all, in which case the payments will be £467.43.

However, if the alternative method is adopted the plant must still be returned at the end of the original term, namely, here, at the end of 12 months (and NOT at the end of the 15th month).

Theoretically, the last three payments for the 13th, 14th and 15th month must also continue to be paid after the plant has been returned, if the lessor is to get his full yield. In practice, of course, as neither lessee or lessor would contemplate payments continuing after the plant has been returned, a lump sum termination payment, equivalent to the value of the outstanding payments, is made, called sometimes an end payment fee or penalty.

Taking one of the above examples, namely a loan of £10,000 with a £1,000 residual at 16.50% for a term of 3 years in terminal pause mode with 3 advance and 6 deferred payments. The normal payments, with no variations, was £319.50. The new capital value consequently will be:

$$
\begin{array}{lll}
\text{Loan} \quad \text{x} & (1 + i/p)^6 & = \text{New Value} \\
£10{,}000 \quad \text{x} & (1 + 16.50/1200\ )^6 & = £10{,}853.88
\end{array}
$$

Employing the new capital value, it must appreciated that the term is 30 month payments and 6 months delayed payments, the plant being returned at the end of the 36th month.

$$
\frac{(\text{Cap} \times 1 + i/p)^{\text{Def'd}}) - \text{Res}(1 + i/p)^{-np}}{\underset{\displaystyle np - y\ |\ +\ y}{a}} = \text{Pmts terminal pause}
$$

$$
\frac{(10{,}000 \times 1.013750^6) - (1{,}000/1.013750^{30})}{((1 - 1.013750^{-(30-3)})/.013750) + 3} = 400.74
$$

$$
\frac{10{,}190.028537}{25.427747} = 400.74
$$

See the DCF calculation at the end of this section.

The alternative method would be mean lower payments and a termination fee at the end of 36 months of £2,091.36:

$$\frac{(Cap \times (1 + i/p)^{Def'd}) - Res(1 + i/p)^{-np}}{\dfrac{a}{np - y \mid + y}} = \begin{array}{l} Pmts \\ terminal\ pause \end{array}$$

$$\frac{(10,000 \times 1.013750^{6}) - (1,000/1.013750^{36})}{((1 - 1.013750^{-(36-3)})/.013750) + 3} = 348.56$$

$$\frac{10,242.254687}{29.384855} = 348.56$$

$$\underline{Termination\ fee}\quad (348.56 \times 6)\quad = 2,091.36$$

The termination payments are not discounted back from each individual month to the lump sum payment period, as a result the lessor's return increases fractionally, roughly an uplift of around a ¼ to ½ %.

Sometimes this slightly increased yield is not considered sufficient recompense for the lessor's good nature in permitting the lessee to delay his payments and if this is the case, the end payment penalty is increased commensurately.

But what the lessor must *not* do is treat the contract as the term plus the number of deferred payments and ask neither for any lump sum termination payment nor for the plant to be returned before the final payment.

For if this method is adopted the lessor's return will be very considerably less than the required (quoted) nominal rate.

In the above example, if the lessor did not insist on the return of the plant at the end of the 36th month, and the payments continued until the end of the 42nd month, the actual return would be 8.266357%, The verification is below:

$$\frac{(Cap \times 1 + i/p)^6) - Res(1 + i/p)^{-30}}{\underline{1a}} = \underset{\text{terminal pause}}{Pmts}$$
$$\overline{30 - 3| - 3}$$

$$\frac{10,000 \times (1 + 8.266357/1200)^6 - 1,000 \times 1.006889^{-30}}{((1 - 1.006889^{-27})/.006889) + 3}$$

$$\frac{10,420.501556 - 813.873459}{27.560902} = 348.56$$

$$\frac{9,606.628096}{27.560902} = 348.56$$

A DCF calculation of the correct values may be of interest:

```
Investment                              -10,000.00
Cash Flows                                   0.00   for 5 periods
              (400.74 x 3 advance pmts)  1,202.22        1
                                           400.74       27
                                             0.00        2
                                         1,000.00        1
I.R.R. = 1.374944 x 12 = 16.499324% (discrepancy due to rounded pmts)
```

Increasing the termination payments to lift the Yield

It will be clear by now that the correct method of calculating payments with a deferred element within the structure of the contract is to treat the term of the contract as being the same as the original, as if there had been no deferment, the plant being returned at the end of original loan term. In the above example at the end of 36 months.

It is, therefore, probably not particularly desirable to discuss various calculations connected with the *alternative* method, whereby the payments are less than those calculated by the conventional method but which have to be off-set at the end of the term by a termination payment or penalty fee.

But one cannot escape the possibility that if the alternative method is adopted the good natured lessor might well prefer a somewhat higher nominal return than that originally quoted.

If so how is the termination amount to be determined?

In the circumstances of a lessor wishing to increase his percentage return by increasing the penalty fees it must be appreciated that the required yield must only be related to the termination payment and not to the original payments.

In the above example it was seen that at 16.50% nominal the payments were calculated as £348.56, there being consequently a termination payment of £2,091.36 (348.56 x 6) at the end of the 36th month, at the same time as the plant had to be returned to the lessor.

A computer/interpolation will find the resulting nominal yield as 16.825039%. The lift from the quoted rate of 16.50% was entirely due to the fact that the lessor, instead of waiting to receive £348.56 for the months 37 through to the 42, would receive a lump sum at the end of the 36th month.

If, however, in the not improbable event that the lessor would prefer a yield of 20% what is the termination payment?

$$\frac{?}{((1 - 1.016667^{-(30-3)})/.016667) + 3} = 348.56$$

$$\frac{?}{24.600156} = 348.56$$

The calculation, in this example, then becomes:

$$(10,000 \times 1.016667^6) \times 1.016667^{30} - (348.56 \times 24.600156) \times 1.016667^{30}$$
$$= £4,052.27$$

As the original residual was £1,000 the lump sum, penalty, termination fee is £3,052.27

The same method of calculation can be used to check the comment above that, with the original six payments of £348.56, the yield increased by only a small amount, namely from a nominal rate of 16.50% to 16.825039%

$$\frac{?}{((1 - 1.014022^{-(30-3)})/.014022) + 3} = 348.56$$

$$\frac{?}{25.348761} = 348.56$$

Consequently:

$$(10{,}000 \times 1.014022^{6}) \times 1.014022^{30} - (348.56 \times 25.348761) \times 1.014022^{30}$$
$$= £3{,}091.36$$

As the residual was £1,000 the termination fee is £2,091.36, (check 2,091.36 ÷ 6 = 348.56).

Odd Days

Nowadays, when most a accounting is done by computers, it is an almost universal practice for institutions to require the individual payments from all their clients to arrive at their accounting office all on the same day, sometimes on the first or last day of each month, sometimes on the 15th day of each month. But while this may be an attractive method for the simplification of accounting practices, it may not always suit a client who, for reasons of his own, may wish to have his loan advanced on a day which is not an anniversary of one of the accounting dates prescribed by his particular lending or leasing Company. As a result "odd days" calculations, or "adjustments", are sometimes necessary.

If this is so with other forms of lending what about the odd days with leasing; for undoubtedly the plant leased will not always arrive on precisely the anniversary of the date required for payments.

The simple answer is that in practice no one bothers about the odd days where leasing is concerned. Before concluding that lessors are a benevolent lot it should be appreciated that the residual is in any event a "guess-estimate", and very often merely a percentage figure of the capital amount.

With competitive tendering the accuracy of the residual is all important, for if it is too high, to make the payments more attractive, it may well mean that the lessee must make up a payment at the end, something that is never popular. On the other hand if the residual is set too low the payments rise uncompetitively.

So whatever the payments/residual factor is, there is always a certain amount of latitude, and any odd days between getting the bull-dozer to the door on the 15th of the month and receiving the first instalment on the first of the next month, or 45 days later is really immaterial. For the additional interest engendered would increase the payments by such a small amount as to be not worth worrying about.

Finding the balances

It is often necessary to know how to find the balance at any one time, in case of a rate change or a requirement to redeem. For the sake of simplicity, the balances, shown below, are those for the 24th month for all the advance payment "modes".

The conventional method (with one payment in advance)

The payment is £327.88 monthly.

$$\frac{10,000 \times 1.013750^{24} - (327.88 \times 1.013750) \times (1.013750^{24} - 1)/.013750}{1.013750}$$

$$= £4,441.74$$

$$\text{Bal (24)}$$

The reason for dividing the payments by 1.01375 is to bring them to an annuities due profile, and the final division by the denominator is done because the reconciliation for annuities due is at the beginning of each period. If the division was not made the value would represent the balance at the end of the year/month/period.

It will be realised that any residual or balloon payment does not figure in the above calculation: for the simple reason that any balance drawn *includes* the value of any residual at the time of the reconciliation.

If the above calculation related to the 36th month, the final part of the above equation would be 1,000.050472/1.013750 and the balance would therefore, correctly, be £986.49, not £1,000 as many people might think.

But, remember, the mode is annuities due, *one* payment in arrears. For those still in doubt regarding the balance of £4,441.74 a discounted cash flow calculation will resolve the matter:

Investment	(10,000 – 327.88)	– 9,672.12	
Cash Flows		327.88	for 23 periods

If the I.R.R. is valued as 16.5/12 the NPV will be 3,244.46 and to obtain the Net <u>Future</u> Value multiply by $(1 + i/p)^{\wedge}(np-1)$ and in this case 3,244.46 x 1.013750^23 = 4,441.735049 or of course 3,244.46 x 1.013750^24 ÷ 1.013750 = 4,441.735049.

A DCF calculation over 36 months, or rather the capital less one payment and 35 subsequent payments, will provide an NPV of 611.660872 and an NFV of 986.49.

In the case of the remainder of the balances below, the above difficulties are unlikely to arise as they are calculated on the basis of payments in arrears.

The initial pause (**with three payments in advance**)
The monthly payments are 327.42 and the PV is therefore (327.42 x 3) − 10,000 = −9,017.74. There were two pause months before payments start, consequently with zero payments there are two periods of interest only − with no offset payments.

$$((10,000 - (327.42 \times 3)) \times 1.013750^2) \times 1.03750^{22})$$
$$- \frac{(327.42 \times (1.013750^{22} - 1)}{.013750}$$
$$= £4,170.14$$
$$BAL\ (24)$$

The terminal pause (**with three payments in advance**)
Subtract the *three* advance payments of £319.50, consequently the PV will be: (319.50 x 3) – 10,000 = –9,041.50

$$(10,000 - (319.50 \times 3)) \times 1.013750^{24} - (319.50x \; (1.013750^{24} - 1)$$
$$\overline{.013750}$$

$$= £3,536.10$$
$$\text{BAL (24)}$$

The spread method (with *three* payments in advance)

In this case the payments are £306.47 monthly and so with three payments in advance the capital sum, PV is (306.47 x 3) – 10,000 = –9,080.59

$$(10,000 - (306.47 \times 3)) \times 1.013750^{24} - (306.47 \times (1.013750^{24} - 1)$$
$$\overline{.013750}$$

$$= £3,957.89$$
$$\text{BAL (24)}$$

Balances for the extra "residual month"

Balances with the "extra" residual month pose no problem; for the slightly higher payments already take into account any difference in calculation. The terminal balance above of £3,536.10 becomes a balance of £3,527.04 from payments of £319.78

An example to find the capital amount

A company leases a machine for 4 years. The monthly payments are \$2,400 with two payments in advance with a residual of \$15,000 at the end of the leasing period, terminal mode. What is the capitalised value of the lease? The rate for borrowing is 18% nominal.

$$\frac{X - 15,000 \times 1.015^{48}}{((1 - 1.015^{-46})/.015) + 2} = 2,400$$

$$((((1 - 1.015^{-46})/.015)+2) \times 2,400)+(15,000 \times 1.015^{-48}) = \$91,476.00$$

When the compounding periods differ from the payment periods

When this occurs be clear which way round is the requirement. For example, the loan structure could either be Quarterly compounding with monthly payments, or monthly compounding with quarterly payments.

The tip is to find the *effective* rate of the period in which the *interest* is compounded and then convert that value back to the nominal rate based on the *payment* period. Subsequent calculations are precisely the same as if such conversion arrangements had never been made.

For example, taking the loan example above of £10,000 with a £1,000 residual over a term of 3 years, with 3 payments in advance, terminal mode. At a nominal rate of 16.50%, with monthly payments, and monthly compounding, the payments are £319.50.

$$\frac{Cap - Res(1 + i/p)^{-np}}{\dfrac{a}{np - y \mid + y}} = \text{Pmts terminal pause}$$

$$\frac{10{,}000 - (1{,}000/1.013750^{36})}{((1 - 1.013750^{-(36-3)})/.013750) + 3} = 319.50$$

If the structure of this contract was altered so that the compounding was to continue to be monthly but that the payments are made each quarter, what are the new payments?

First find the effective rate or monthly interest compounding:

$$(1 + 16.50000/1200)^{12} - 1) \times 100 =$$
$$1.17806813 \qquad = 17.806813\% \text{ effective}$$

Reconvert 17.806813 to it nominal format, based on quarterly payments:

$$(1 + 17.806813/100)^{\frac{1}{4}} - 1) \times 400 = 16.727915\% \text{ nominal}$$

Employing the converted rate of 16.727915% nominal, with *quarterly* payments and a *quarterly* working rate of 4.181979, the above equation would become:

$$\frac{10{,}000 - (1{,}000/1.0141820^{12})}{((1 - 1.0141820^{-(12-3)})/0.0141820) + 3} = 904.99$$

Alternatively, with quarterly compounding and monthly payments:

$$((((1 + 16.50/400)^4)^{1/12}) - 1) \times 1200 = 16.27815\%$$
$$\div 12 = 1.356515$$

$$\frac{10,000 - (1,000/1.013565^{36}}{((1 - 1.013565^{-(36-3)})/0.013565) + 3} = 318.54$$

A simple interest quote

Leasing quotations are usually at the true rate of interest, as indeed are all the examples above. But recently, with high rates of borrowing, some leasing companies have decided it makes commercial sense to quote their rates at simple interest, especially as hire purchase rates are so quoted and in the motor vehicle industry HP and leasing are inextricably intermixed. What difference does this make? Very little, save that the simple interest rates look somewhat more attractive – to the uninitiated!

Before any basic calculations are made the simple interest rate must be converted to it's true nominal rate, by finding the simple interest payments and finding the true rate thereof.

For example, a simple interest quote of 15% over a term of 3 years with monthly payments will find a true rate of nearly 26%, certainly a substantial rate of return to the lessor.

How is that rate determined? The simple interest payments can best be determined on the basis of £100, rather than the actual units of the loan amount of the contract lease.

$$\frac{100 + (100 \times .15 \times 3)}{3 \times 12} = 4.027778 \text{ pmts}$$

A computer interpolation will provide the true rate as:

$$\frac{100.00}{4.027778 \, a_{\overline{36|}}} = 2.164657\% = (x \ 12) = 25.975889\% \text{ nominal}$$

The lessor has two options, to quote a flat rate a little lower than the true "going rate" and collect a substantial return, or, the normal practice, to decide on the true return required and then calculate and quote a corresponding flat rate.

Whichever option is chosen, and the former method is unlikely to win friends, the working rate must always be the true rate, with the APR provided if necessary.

Making a factor list
A salesman, in a large firm of distributors discussing the various options available for a leasing contract with a client will probably have a PC on his desk to undertake the calculations outlined above. Other firms may provide their salesmen with programmable calculators, or bespoke calculators with specific leasing modules, especially if such salesmen are not necessarily desk-bound.

Some of the smaller firms, however, compete quite nicely with "factors". Instead of using a computer or calculator the salesman simply employs his factors list.

What exactly are these factors? A computer, or calculator, is initially used to fabricate them, but once they are listed all that is necessary is to indentify the relevant ones.

The basic value is taken as £1,000 and payments for a leasing contract are calculated at various rates, employing the various options outlined above. Assume that a 16½% rate over 36 months, with three advance payments, terminal type, was required. Employing the leasing formulae above the payments on £1,000 will be found as 34.0311356137. Dividing these payments by the capital value, the factor becomes 0.034031.

Do the same calculation with a £1,000 residual *but with no capital value*; and payments will be found as 20.8144635243. Divide by 1,000 to find 0.020814 as the next factor.

For payment accuracy the factors should correctly, be calculated to not less than 6 decimal places; but the industry usually reduces to 5 places, adding one penny to the resulting payments. For contracts over £100,000 the payments are generally rounded up/down to pounds only, the pence being ignored.

Now assume that a salesmen is discussing with a client the

cost of a £25,000 leasing contract with a £2,500 residual; having the same parameters as above, namely 16.50%, three payments in advance, over 36 months with a terminal pause.

Using the above factors in order to find the payments all he does is:

(0.03403 x 25,000 – 0.02081 x 2,500 = 798.73) + .01 = £798.74

Lists of factors can, therefore, be made by the above methods for any or all of the options outlined above.

Naturally a properly programmed computer can spew out pages of factor listings to cover any possible permutation that a salesman could possibly require.

A leasing scenario
A leasing company was telephoned one morning by an old and valued client requesting a quotation for the lease of a small garden-type £10,000 bulldozer over a period of the next five years.

The finance director figured that the commercial value of the type of dozer mentioned would, at the end of five years, be £1,000 and so treated this as the residual. The current arrangements for the leasing company were quarterly payments at a nominal rate of 15%. But as the client was well known to the firm it was decided not to charge any up-front payments but to arrange a conventional contract (annuities due – one payment only in advance). Reaching for his calculator the finance director worked out the payments required:

$$(10,000 - (1,000 \times 1.0375^{-20})) \div ((1 - 1.0375^{-20})/.0375) \times 1.0375$$
$$= \underline{660.39}$$

On telephoning to his opposite number in the client firm with this payment quotation, he met with some disappointment; for it appeared that his clients had also done some figuring as to what they reckoned the payments should be – and this was

£600 per quarter for the 5 years.

The finance director, privately wondering whether it was a try-on or if they had received a quotation elsewhere, replied that he'd "see what he could do and come back to them." Back to the drawing board. What percentage return would £600 give his firm?

Fortunately having a calculator/computer available he was able to find that with £600 per quarter the return would be only a nominal 10.85% (10.8617602247):

$$(10{,}000 - (1{,}000 \times 1.027154^{-20}) \div ((1 - 1.027154^{-20})/.027154)$$
$$\times 1.027154 = \underline{600.00}$$

The board would never wear that return: . . . . Timing?

Looking up at the ceiling he mentally reminded himself of the formula to find the number of quarters to cover his client's requirements:

$$\frac{\text{LOG}\ (((pmts/(i/p))\times 1+i/p)-res) \div (((pmts/(i/p)\times 1+i/p)-loan)}{\text{LOG}\ \ 1 + i/p}$$

$$\frac{\text{LOG}\ (((600/.0375)\times 1.0375)-1{,}000) \div (((600/.0375)\times 1.0375)-10{,}000)}{\text{LOG}\ \ 1.0375}$$

$$\frac{\text{LOG}\ (16{,}600.00 - 1{,}000.00) \div ((16{,}600.00 - 10{,}000.00))}{\text{LOG}\ \ 1.0375}$$

$$\frac{\text{LOG}\ \ 15{,}600.00 \div 60600.00}{\text{LOG}\ \ 1.0375}$$

$$\frac{\text{LOG}\ \ 2.363636}{\text{LOG}\ \ 1.0375}$$

$$\frac{0.860201}{0.036814} = \underline{23.366162\ \text{quarters}}$$

Telephoning his client again he was told somewhat acidly that if they'd wanted a term of nearly six years they've have asked for it in the first place. What about messing about with the residual? After all £1,000 was only an intelligent guess in the first instance:

$$(10,000 - (1,000 \times 1.0375^{-20}) \div ((1 - 1.0375^{-20})/.0375) \times 1.0375$$
$$= 660.39$$

$$((10,000 - (600 \times ((1 - 1.0375^{-20})/.0375) \times 1.0375)) \times 1.0375^{20}$$
$$= \underline{2,818.20}$$

Intelligent or not, thought the director, no one in his right mind could imagine that the dozer could sell for £2,800 after 5 years – not the way they treated their equipment.

The only other possibility would seem to be "advance payments": 4 payments?

$$(10,000 - (1,000 \times 1.0375^{-20}) \div (((1 - 1.0375^{-16})/.0375)) + 4)$$
$$= \underline{599.94}$$

Just as the finance director, not very hopefully, was about to ask his client if they'd wear an up–front payment of around of £2,400 one of his staff brought in a message from the dozer makers to say they had a six months old dozer of the type required, a bit scratched but otherwise as new, for £9,000. "And are you interested?"

The return? "Don't forget to adjust the residual", murmured the director to himself, 10% presumably?

After the necessary adjustment his computer/calculator provided him with a nominal rate of 15.42% (15.423626) – and verifying below:

$$(9,000 - (900 \times 1.038559^{-20}) \div ((1 - 1.038559^{-20})/.038559)$$
$$\times 1.038559 = \underline{600.00}$$

With the 15% required return what are the payments?

$$(9,000 - (900 \times 1.037500^{-20}) \div ((1 - 1.0375^{-20})/.0375) \times 1.0375$$
$$= \underline{594.35}$$

"Well", thought the director, "for their required £600 a quarter I'll ask if they'll accept the used dozer as suggested, and only if they are sticky will I mention the lower payments of £594.35."

Value Added Tax (currently 15%)
In some circumstances VAT may be due on the payments. Individual companies will be well aware if and when this applies to them.

If required, all that must be done is to add 15% to all the payments, and this would be calculated by:

Payments (gross) x 1.15 = payments including VAT.

The inevitable one-off
Assume a conventional small leasing contract of £1,000, over a term of 36 months, with one payment in advance (annuities due) at a nominal rate of 16.50%. There is no residual.

The 36 payments will be:

$$\frac{1,000.00}{ä_{\overline{36}|} \text{ at } (16.50/12)\%} = £34.92$$

The requirement is for the first payment to be reduced by 60% and the second payment to be reduced by 80% (from the original conventional payment) – and then for the remaining 34 payments to be even throughout.

The immediate reaction is to reduce the first payment to 34,92/1.60 = 21.83 and to find the balance at the end of the first month, namely £991.619838. Employing this balance and the next payment (34.92/1.80) of £19.40 the balance at the end of the second month is £985.587860.

The remaining payments would then appear to be;

$$\frac{985.58}{ä_{\overline{34}|} \text{ at } 116.50/12)\%} = £35.99$$

But if you rethink these payments you will realise that £35.99 less 60% is £24.59 and *not* £21.83 as taken above. To find the correct answer could mean a tiresome interpolation formula – which means working out a formula, checking and then loading into a computer.

The simplest way is to use a computer or calculator DCF program and manually interpolate there-in.

Before interpolation the investment would be 21.83 – 1,000 and the next payment 19.40 followed by 34 payments of 35.99. This provides, as would be expected, an IRR of 16.499504, the discrepancy being the result to rounding the payments.

By interpolation, not difficult and certainly not in this instance time consuming, the investment becomes –977.534184, (namely a first payment in advance of 22.465816) the next payment 19.969614 and the final 34 payments 35.945306 giving an IRR of 16.50%. But here again the payments must be rounded to 22.47, 19.97 and 35.95 respectively, with a consequent IRR of 16.509568%.

Early redemption
As leasing contracts are not considered to be "loans" *per se*, penalties for early redemption are not limited to the statutory rebate, for, from the lessor's point of view, early redemption can cause problems.

With hire purchase only the interest is taxed and the borrower can obtain capital allowances. With leasing, while the yearly written down allowances of 25% are permissible, the income and interest is taxed (currently) at 35%. The lessees' payments are allowable for tax, but in some cases the lessors' tax relief may be delayed as long as 20 months from the start of the lease; and as a consequence, for the first fiscal year, the lessors' books may well have to value the plant at, or even above, its purchase price.

Because of this, some banks stipulate that no terminations will be even entertained within the first two years of, say, a five year contract.

Others write into their contracts provision that, in the event of cancellation before the full term has expired, a *termination fee* will be charged.

The fee is usually at "a 5% discount on the outstanding payments" and the following schedule, end/starting and upward/working, will probably be more enlightening than this slightly obscure phrasing.

Penalties, imposed for whatever reason, are never popular, and while the problems facing banks and lending institutions are not always the subject of overriding sympathy, it should be appreciated that when such a penalty is charged it is usually to compensate for a situation which would otherwise result in a loss – and not simply to raise the lessors' return!

It must be remembered, too, that often the whole *raison d'etre* of some leasing contracts, and in particular the structure, is closely related to the tax benefits accruing to the lessee; and so, in the circumstances, penalties for early redemption are understandable, tiresome though they be.

Moreover, the method of a discounted 5% fee, outlined below, is not particularly swingeing when compared to the old fashioned yardstick of "three payments penalty"!

At the end of this chapter there is a short paragraph outlining the advantages of leasing, as opposed to outright purchase; and attention is drawn to the availability of certain UK tax concessions.

Below is a complete schedule of the 5% discounting process for a £10,000 loan over 24 months at a nominal rate of 16.50%

The monthly payments are £485.35 and there is one payment in advance.

Calculations are outlined to find an early redemption balance at the end of the 10th month and the termination fee.

Schedule for payments and 5% discounting

Loan £10,000 Term 24 months Nominal rate 16.50%

Payments £485.35   1 Advance payments

Month	Int — pmts	Balance	Discounts
		10,000–485.35	@ 5%
2 x 1.01375–485.35		9,160.13	10,668.03
3 x " "		8,800.73	10,225.11
4 x " "		8,436.39	9,780.34
5 x " "		8,067.04	9,333.72
6 x " "		7,692.61	8,885.24
7 x " "		7,313.03	8,434.89
8 x " "		6,928.24	7,982.66
9 x " "		6,538.15	7,528.55
10 x " "		6,142.70	**7,072.55
11 x " "		5,741.81	6,614.64
12 x " "		5,335.41	6,154.83
13 x " "		4,923.42	5,693.10
14 x " "		4,505.77	5,229.45
15 x " "		4,082.38	4,763.87
16 x " "		3,653.16	4,296.35
17 x " "		3,218.04	3,826.88
18 x " "		2,776.94	3,355.45
19 x " "		2,329.77	2,882.06
20 x " "		1,876.46	2,406.69
21 x " "		1,416.91	1,929.35
22 x " "		951.04	1,450.02 ↑
23 x " "		478.77	968.69 ↑
24 x 1.01375–485.35		−0.0014	485.35 ↑

The discounting:

485.35 ÷ (1 + 5/1200) + 485.35 =   968.69

(968.69 ÷ 1.004167)   + 485.35 = 1,450.02 et seq.

The balance calculation:

[(10,000 x 1.01375^10) −

(485.35 x ((1.01375^10/.01375)−1) x 1.01375)] ÷ 1.01375 = Bal(10)

[11,463.27 − 5,236.11] ÷ 1.01375 = 6,142.70

For early redemption at the end of the 10th month, the balance due (termination fee incl:) is £7,072.55:

The discounting calculation: (balance due)
Pmts   x (1 − 1.004167^−(n−t +1))/.004167 x 1.004167 = Bal(10)
485.35 x (1 − 1.004167^−(24−10+1))/.004167 x 1.004167 = 7,072.55

SKIPPED PAYMENT CALCULATIONS

When considering whether to lease or not, some companies realise that the plant they propose to hire cannot be used for parts of the year and that, irrespective of the resulting lack of cash flow, the monthly payments must be met on time.

For example, if a bulldozer was hired in October it might well be that the weather would prevent it being used during the three months commencing January. In that case the lessor might well agree that the payments for the months when the plant was out of action could be "skipped". How are the new payments, naturally somewhat greater than the normal payments spread over the whole year, to be determined?

Example: Assume a capital amount of £10,000 with a residual of £3,000 at a rate of 15% nominal with monthly payments over 5 years. The payments commence October and the months January – March (inclusive) are skipped.

October	– December	(3 months)
January	– March	(3 months) SKIPPED
April	– September	(6 months)

This means there are 3 months before the skipping starts and there are 6 payments after the skipping has finished.

Formula

$$\frac{(\text{loan} - (\text{res} \times (1 + i/p)^{-np})) \times ((1 + i/p)^{p} - 1)}{(s_{\underset{a|}{}} \times (1 + i/p)^{(p-a)}) + s_{\underset{b|}{}}} \times \frac{1}{1-(1 + i/p)^{-np}}$$

= pmts in arrears

Where (a) = # of pmts *before* skipping commences
      (b) = # of pmts *after* skipping concludes
      (p) = # of compounding periods in any one year
      (np) = # of periods in a *full term*

– *166* –

$$s\frac{}{np|} = \frac{(1 + i/p) - 1}{i/p} \quad \text{(savings ordinary)}$$

Taking the above monthly example:

$$\frac{(10,000-(3,000\times1.0125^{-60}))\times(1.0125^{12}-1)}{[((1.0125^{3}-1)/.0125)\times1.0125^{9}]+[(1.0125^{6}-1)/.0125]} \times \frac{1}{1-1.0125^{-60}}$$

$$= \text{pmts in arrears}$$

$$\frac{1,378.68}{9.587642} \times \frac{1}{0.525432} = 273.67 \text{ (ord)}$$

$$273.67/1.0125 = 270.30 \text{ (due)}$$

Quarterly payments

Substituting quarterly payments over a term of five years, with 1 quarter (Oct–Dec) before, and 2 quarters (Apr–Sep) after, skipping the payments required will be:

$$\frac{(10,000-(3,000\times1.0375^{-20}))\times(1.0375^{4}-1)}{[((1.0375^{1}-1)/.0375)\times1.0375^{3}]+[(1.0375^{2}-1)/.0375]} \times \frac{1}{1-1.0135^{-20}}$$

$$= \text{pmts in arrears}$$

$$\frac{1,358.57}{3.154271} \times \frac{1}{0.5211081} = 826.53 \text{ (ord)}$$

$$826.53/1.0375 = 796.65 \text{ (due)}$$

Payments in advance

With skipped payment structured contracts, a form of leasing, the payments are conventionally required to be in advance, namely one advance payment, annuities due. And the calculation to convert the ORD to DUE, as outlined on many occasions previously, is ORD $\div$ (1 + i/p) = DUE.

If a loan term was for, say, 48 months, when a single advanced payment is made, the number of subsequent payments are 47, a total thus of 48 payments in all.

Reverting to the monthly example above, the first series of monthly payments (in the first year) would therefore be 2, not 3 months. Not a problem *when there is just one advance payment*.

But as single up-front payments are not usually considered sufficient, an increased number of advance payments is usually required. Consequently, a snag arises for skipped contracts when the subsequent instalments are a mixture of made and missed payments. For any number of advanced payments, over one, would inevitably snarl up the whole of the skipping structure outlined above.

A number of advance payments
Below will be seen a practical example in which there are six advance payments required, with the structure of the loan having six non payment periods between the start of the contract and the first payment.

In such circumstances surely the sensible thing is not to expect the number of advance payments to be offset, later in the term, by a number of "pauses", as we have seen elsewhere, but to simply deduct the advance payments, whatever they are, from the capital sum and expect no missed payments later.

This method will not increase the indebtedness of the lessee, providing the payments are correctly calculated, for the original quoted nominal rate (or IRR) is retained.

The method merely reduces the capital value of the loan by the total amount of the advance payments concerned.

With the following example it will be seen that to apply the advance payments in any way other than that outlined above, would be, if not impossible, certainly inconvenient. For wherever in the term the payments were subtracted the original structure of skipped and missed payments would no longer obtain, and the whole object of the skipping procedure would, therefore, be negated.

For example, with capital equipment of £88,000 to yield 15.25%, a term of 4 years, monthly payments. and 6 advance payments required. Consequently, the 6 up front payments will be followed, here, by 48 payments (not 48 − 6).

The skipped payment structure required is as follows:

```
6 payments missed 6 payments made (year 1)
6 payments missed 6 payments made (year 2)
6 payments missed 6 payments made (year 3)
6 payments missed 6 payments made (year 4)
```

With no advance payments, with no payments before the skipping commences, six payments skipped and then six payments made, the equation will find *ord* payments of £5,114.20 and £5,050.02 if one advance payment, *due*, only is made. And when this calculation is made it will be found that the factor is 17.206985.

If 6 payments in advance are required then, in this example, the payments will become £3,791.96

How are these payments determined?

$$\frac{88,000}{6.193886 \times .454557 \times 6.111579} \times \frac{1}{} = \frac{88,000}{17.206984} = 5,114.20$$

$$\frac{88,000}{17.206985 + 6} = \frac{88,000}{23.206984} = 3,791.96 \ (ORD)$$

Obviously with more than one advance payment there can never be any question of dividing by (1 + i/p) to find the *due* payments.

What happens if there is a residual? No problem.

With a 10% residual of £8,800 merely discount this by the full term and subtract it from the capital amount of £88,000:

$$\frac{88,000 - (8,800 \times 1.012708^{-48})}{17.206985 + 6} = \frac{83,200.10}{23.206984} = 3,585.13 \ (ORD)$$

Deferred payments with a skipping scenario

Some say that deferring payments in a leasing contract which includes skipped payments should be resisted at all cost!

Two factors underline this reasoning. Having already accepted skipping facilities the lessor will hardly be impressed with the lessee's credit-worthiness if then asked to permit payments to be further delayed.

The second reason, equally cogent, is that if delayed payments become necessary, perhaps in order to accommodate a particularly valued client, and are suddenly superimposed on a skipping contract already agreed, the original structure of missed and paid periods is likely to be unacceptable and consequently must be reviewed.

In the first place it must be appreciate that the value of the payments must be based on the term *plus* the number of deferred payments, the plant being returned at the end of the original term (as if there were no delayed payments) and, at the same time, there will be a termination fee of not less that the payments multiplied by the number of delayed periods; the same system as the "alternative method" outlined earlier.

This being so, why is the original structure unacceptable and why must it be reviewed?

In the example which was outlined in the formula/equation above it will be seen that, having received the bulldozer in October (of 1989), the reason for skipping the payments from January to March (1990) was that the bulldozer could not be used in those months owing to the inclement weather and the lessee was thus unable, or at least unwilling for cash flow reasons, to make payments for those particular months.

If taking the above example the lessee required the payments to be deferred for three months why would it be *incorrect* merely to increase the above payments of £285.79 simply by adjusting the capital amount by $(1 + i/p)^{(\# \text{ def'd periods})}$?

Three deferred payments in this example would assume that

the first payments would be on January 1, 1990 – *just the very point at which skipping begins*.

The only recourse in these circumstances is for the lessee to make his payments as soon he can – when there is no skipping.

In this example, the earliest payment date is, therefore, April 1, 1990, and in consequence there will be *nine* payments (April – December inclusive) following; the new series of missed and made payments will *not* be 3 paid, 3 skipped and 6 paid (as in the equation above) but must be 9 paid (Apr – Dec) and 3 skipped (Jan – March).

Unhappily, one cannot lay down an "adjusting rule", and each problem must be thought out afresh.

For whereas the advance payments intruded on the skipping structure required above, in the second example above, where the payments were 6 skipped and 6 payments made, 3 deferred payments (or even 6 for that matter!) would in no way dislocate the required skipping structure.

Taking the first skipped payments example, but with three months deferred payments, the new capital value will thus become $10,000 \times (1 + 15/1200)^3 = 10,379.71$ and the new payments are found below:

$$\frac{(10,379.71 - (3,000 \times 1.0125^{-60})) \times (1.0125^{12} - 1)}{[((1.0125^0 - 1)/.0125) \times 1.0125^{12}] + [(1.0125^9 - 1)/.0125]} \times \frac{1}{1 - 1.0125^{-60}}$$

$$= \text{pmts in arrears}$$

$$\frac{1439.72}{9.463374} \times \frac{1}{0.525432} = 289.54 \text{ (ord)}$$

$$289.54/1.0125 = 285.97 \text{(due)}$$

When will the plant be returned and when will the termination fee of (3 x 289.54) £868.62 be made?

This method both achieves the object of permitting the lessee to obtain delayed payments as well as his skip requirements and preserves the original return (the quoted rate%) required by the lessor.

This latter point is important, for unless the lessor is convinced he can retain his required yield he most certainly will not permit the lessee to defer.

The old and new series of payments, with their respective cash flows, are:

invest:				*invest:*
-8,576.30				*-8,965.00*
C/flows	original	series	with 3 delayed pmts	C/flows
273.76	3 pmts Oct − Dec '89	1	3 defd Oct − Dec '89	
0.00	3 skip Jan − Mar '90	2	3 skip Jan − Mar '90	0.00
273.76	6 pmts Apr − Sep '90	3	6 pmts Apr − Sep '90	289.54
273.76	3 pmts Oct − Dec '90	4	3 pmts Oct − Dec '90	289.54
0.00	3 skip Jan − Mar '91	5	3 skip Jan − Mar '91	0.00
273.76	6 pmts Oct − Sep '91	6	6 pmts Oct − Sep '91	289.54
273.76	3 pmts Oct − Dec '91	7	3 pmts Oct − Dec '91	289.54
0.00	3 skip Jan − Mar '92	8	3 skip Jan − Mar '92	0.00
273.76	6 pmts Oct − Sep '92	9	6 pmts Oct − Sep '92	289.54
273.76	3 pmts Oct − Dec '92	10	3 pmts Oct − Dec '92	289.54
0.00	3 skip Jan − Mar '93	11	3 skip Jan − Mar '93	0.00
273.76	6 pmts Apr − Sep '93	12	6 pmts Apr − Sep '93	289.54
273.76	3 pmts Oct − Sep '93	13	3 pmts Oct − Sep '93	289.54
0.00	3 skip Jan − Mar '94	14	3 skip Jan − Mar '94	0.00
273.76	6 pmts Apr − <u>Sep '94</u>	15	6 pmts Apr − <u>Sep '94</u>	289.54
	to return plant		to return plant	<u>+868.62</u>
			namely 3 pmts termination fee	
(Nominal IRR 15%)			(Nominal IRR 15.02%)	

Some institutions may possibly succeed in finding other in-house methods of preserving their yields, but I have yet to meet them.

In the event of *quarterly* payments and, as above, three months deferred payments, namely ONE quarter, the first payment would fall on January 1, 1990 and because this is a "no pay" period the first payment will be April 1st. Thus the series of payments will then be 3 paid quarters (Apr–Dec) followed by 1 missed quarter (Jan–Mar) and the new payments, in these circumstances, will be £873.91

$$\frac{((10{,}000 \times 1.0375) - (3{,}000 \times 1.0375^{-20})) \times (1.0375^{4} - 1)}{[((1.0375^{0} - 1)/.0375) \times 1.0375^{4}] + [(1.0375^{3} - 1)/.0375]} \times \frac{1}{1 - 1.0375^{-20}}$$

$$= \text{pmts in arrears}$$

$$\frac{1{,}418.07}{3.113906} \times \frac{1}{0.5211081} = 873.91 \ (\text{ord})$$

$$873.91/1.0375 = 842.32 \ (\text{due})$$

The plant will have to be returned on exactly the same date, at the end of September 1994, as if there had not been any deferred payments, and the termination fee, in this case, will be not less than one quarter's payment, namely £873.91.

Conversely, it will be appreciated that if the first payment due, after a deferment, does not fall in a skipping period no reorganisation need take place. For consider, in the latter example, the contract was for £88,000 at 15.25% over 48 months, with 6 advance payments, with payments calculated above of £3,791.96. If some 6 deferred payments were now superimposed on that particular skip payment structure the only alteration would be an increase of payments to £4,090.44 simply by the increase of the £88,000 x 1.012708^6. And so taking the values from the related equation a few pages back:

$$\frac{88{,}000}{17.206985 + 6} = \frac{88{,}000}{23.206984} = 3{,}791.96 \ (\text{ord})$$

$$\frac{88{,}000 \times 1.012708^{6}}{17.206985 + 6} = \frac{94{,}926.83}{23.206984} = 4{,}090.44 \ (\text{ord})$$

The termination fee, in this case, will be nearly £25,000!

Penalty payments for early redemption

Early redemption for a skippped payments contract produces the same problems for the lessor, as was outlined above for conventional leasing.

Schedule for payments and 5% discounting

Loan £88,000 Term 48 months Nominal rate 15.25%
Payments £3,791.96 6 Advance payments

Month	Payments	Balance	Discounts
		65,248.24	
1	0.00	66,077.44	81,640.89
6	0.00	70,384.19	83,355.98
7	3,791.96	67,486.69	83,703.29
12	3,791.96	52,437.44	69,263.59
13	0.00	53,103.83	62,731.93
18	0.00	56,565.00	64,049.78
19	3,791.96	53,491.88	64,316.65
24	3,791.96	37,530.49	46,469.68
25	0.00	38,007.43	42,855.54
30	0.00	40,484.66	43,755.83
31	3,791.96	37,207.19	43,938.15
36	3,791.96	20,184.40	25,665.07
37**	0.00	20,440.91	21,962.24
42	0.00	21,773.19	22,423.62
43	3,791.96	18,257.93	22,517.05
48	3,791.96	.08	3,791.96

The balances are found conventionally:

$$\text{Balance}_1 \times (1 + i/p) - \text{payments} = \text{Balance}_2 \downarrow$$
$$\text{Balance}_2 \times \quad '' \quad - \quad '' \quad = \text{Balance}_3 \downarrow$$

and the discounting is as follows:

$$3{,}791.98 \div (1 + 5/1200) + 3{,}701.98 = 7{,}568.19 \; \text{month}_{47}$$

From the 42nd month the upward discounting would become:

$$22{,}423.62 \div 1.004167 + 0.00 = 22{,}330.57$$
$$22{,}330.57 \div 1.004167 + 0.00 = 22{,}237.91$$

Or for the 42nd month back to the 37th month:

$$22{,}423.62 \times 1.004167^{-5} = 21{,}962.24$$

In the event, for redemption at the end of the 37th month, the lessee would be required to pay £21,962.24, namely the balance due of £20,440.91, plus a termination fee of £1,521.33

For the periods where there are repayments:

$$\text{balance}_2 \times (1 + i/p)^{-6} + \text{Pmts} \; ä \frac{}{6\,|} = \text{balance}_1$$

For the 13th month (62,731.9257627) back to the 7th month:

$$62{,}731.93 \times 1.004167^{-6} + (3{,}791.96 \times (1 - 1.004167^{-6})/.004167$$
$$\times 1.004167)$$
$$61{,}186.25 + 22{,}517.05 = 83{,}703.29$$

If the written down balance is greater than the discount value the greater sum will apply.

Leasing postscript

Individuals or companies who need to borrow money are, I suspect, often bewildered by the various permutations available. Which option is the most suitable, an overdraft, a hire purchase or leasing contract, or just a straight loan?

Unhappily, certainly in the UK, the decision is often largely dependent, ultimately, on the tax benefits available.

I have so far avoided any detailed comment on taxation for the calculations are universal and taxation differs from country to country. However it would, perhaps, be a little remiss to ignore completely the advantages of leasing as opposed to outright purchase.

For example, office equipment can tie up a company's capital in an asset which is depreciating and, perhaps equally important, in an asset which may soon be obsolescent; whereas leasing, instead of purchase, will release the capital and allow later updating of the equipment for any new state-of-the-art upgrade.

Bank loans are usually dependent on the fluctuations of the current interest rate; with leasing the rates are normally constant during the term of the contract.

In the UK, for instance, if a company is paying Corporation Tax the leasing payments may be deducted from the taxable profits. Perhaps more significant is the fact that whereas the written down allowances on equipment purchased is 25% each year on the reducing balance, leasing payments are 100% allowable against tax – often perhaps even before the rental payments have actually come on stream. So in many cases VAT and CGT will need to be considered, as will the "going rate of lending".

Could the leasing company find a better return if invested elsewhere, the gilt market for instance?

All these, and often many more complex calculations, are usually made at the company's head office to determine the *true return* which, because of the above allowances etc, are often 2 or 3 points above the quoted rate. Each individual or company requirement must be studied on its own merits but some of the possible advantages of leasing, as opposed to other forms of borrowing should be not be ignored.

I am greatly indebted to T.V., a leasing manager, experienced in both European and North American markets for his kindness in checking some of the more esoteric calculations above. Naturally, any comments are mine alone.

CHAPTER 10

Statistics and Depreciation

Weighted mean
Most people know how to calculate an average, the sum of the data divided by the number of data items. But when there are different levels, or different bases, for various parameters then the data must be "weighted" to take the variations into consideration.

In Part II, in a section concerning split coupons and convertible bonds, one of the requirements is to determine the gross yield.

Because there is more than one coupon, a short weighted mean calculation is necessary before the conventional calculation of (coupon x 100)/price can be performed.

Assuming that there are two coupons, one for 8% over a term of four and a half years, the other for 12% over sixteen years, the weighted mean calculation is as follows:

$$\frac{(8 \times 4.5) + (12 \times 16)}{(4.5 + 16)} = \frac{228.00}{20.50} = 11.121951 \text{ average coupon}$$

Assume that your broker has different levels of commission charged for different cost levels of stock purchased, and you wish to determine the average commission paid:

	£	%
For amounts up to and between:	7,000 the commission charged is	2.5
	93,000	1.5
	150,000	1.0
	500,000	.5
	1,000,000	.25

Calculate as follows:

```
2.5  x      7,000  =  17,500
1.5  x     93,000  = 139,500
1.0  x    150,000  = 150,000
 .5  x    500,000  = 250,000
.25  x  1,000,000  = 250,000
5.75    1,750,000    807,000
```

and   807,000/1,750,000 = .461143
average commission level   = .46%

To be frank, to attempt to hand calculate a massive number of values for a weighted mean requirement is hardly cost effective, especially when, nowadays, most medium priced calculators have a WM key, and all that is then necessary is to enter the variables and finally press the key concerned.

In the next chapter there is a somewhat light hearted aside, which may be of interest to the statistician. concerning board voting which requires the employment of a weighted mean calculation.

Moving averages

There are various methods employed by statisticians to forecast future trends based on past results; one of the simpler methods is the *average*, but because this method sometimes appears unrealistic a better means is the *moving average*.

This method is achieved by substitution of the "oldest" value by the "latest" value, after the passing of a certain number of periods. If we had the following values

Days	1.	2.	3.	4.	5.	6.	7.	8.
Data	125	183	207	222	198	240	225	200

and if we took a *four* day moving average the calculations would go as follows:

$$\frac{125 + 183 + 207 + 222}{4} = 184.25 \quad \text{(base mean)}$$

$$184.25 + ((198 - 125)/4) = 202.50 \ [5]$$
$$202.50 + ((240 - 183)/4) = 216.75 \ [6]$$
$$216.75 + ((225 - 207)/4) = 221.25 \ [7]$$
$$221.25 + ((200 - 222)/4) = 215.75 \ [8] \ \text{and so on}$$

This method is often used to forecast possible future trends by comparing, say, a 10 – 20 days moving average with a 60 – 240 days moving average of a stock exchange index of daily share prices.

If the lead indicator for the lower (10 days) moving average is greater that for a higher (20 days) moving average the market is considered to be on a bull (rising) trend (c.f., the UK FTSE or the US Dow Jones Index). The converse is, of course, equally true; if a 240 day m/a is greater than a 60 day m/a the market would be considered to be on a "bear" tack.

But this is not quite the whole story. For if the first calculation, the base mean, (184.25 above) was chosen on a day when it was considered that the general trend was "out of line" (a "blip" as one chancellor liked to think!) it could affect all subsequent calculations.

Consequently, some statisticians often track back by at least 100 historic data values, which are evaluated before the mean base is determined and the "next day's" price selected.

If, for example, it is proposed to plot the day-to-day price of a particular stock exchange share, commencing January 1st, then the past historic prices might well be found from September 23rd of the previous year (100 days!).

I hold no brief, for or against, the use to which such methods are put, or the conclusions drawn – but merely outline the calculations required.

Exponential smoothing

Another popular method of analysing trends is the exponential smoothing method which, incidentally, belies its somewhat esoteric nomenclature, the calculations being extremely simple, quick, and needing little or no historic data.

The smoothing is executed by choosing an exponential factor of (say) 5% and employing the decimal fraction together with (1 – the decimal fraction) calculating as follows:

```
(data A x .95) + (data B x .05)  = data 1
(data 1 x .95) + (data C x .05)  = data 2
(data 2 x .95) + (data D x .05)  = data 3   and so on...
```

Taking the date prices as, say, 100, 98, 110:

```
(100.00 x .95) + ( 98.00 x .05) =  99.90
( 99.90 x .95) + (110.00 x .05) = 109.41 et seq.
```

Although some historic data should be evaluated, this method does not need the long back data which is desirable for the m/a method and it will be found ideal for indices, stock exchange and commodity prices, and any such requirements which have only moderate day to day movement.

Most statisticians have their own pet methods of averaging and smoothing out the peaks and troughs to make the perspective more presentable, and more understandable. My own view is that the 5% method above with, say, a fortnight's historical back up is an excellent method which has the great advantage of being simple to calculate day to day without a calculator.

Trend analysis

The above methods of smoothing index lines are usefully employed for a variety of requirements, but no one would suggest that such methods can be used to calculate the value of, say, a share on a certain day in the future.

But a chart could be made and to simplify the calculations, which I fear are complex enough, let us assume that the requirement is not stocks and shares but is sales per month.

Month	1	2	3	4	5	6
Sales	100	200	300	400	500	600

It would, obviously, be hardly be necessary to chart the above variables for it can be seen that the "lift" is a constant 100 units per month, nor would our intelligence be stretched to recognise that, if the trend continued, the unit of sales in the 7th month would be 700.

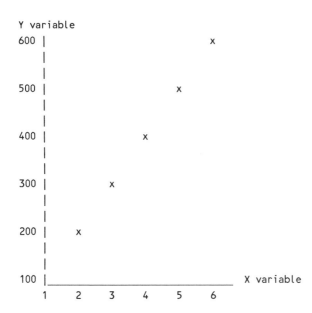

But if the sales picture was completely different, as below:

Month	1	2	3	4	5	6
Sales	300	410	420	320	330	500

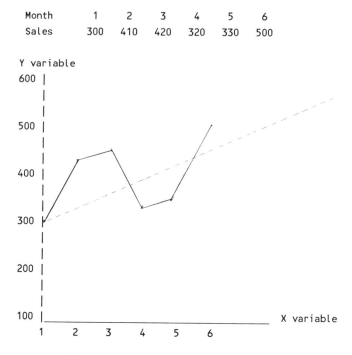

It is just possible that with the finest graph paper, the thinest of pencil points, and taking into account the uncertainty of the human hand, a clever chartist, *providing he could find the correct trend line*, should be able to read off the integer values, the sales units, for the 7th, 8th, and 9th months ahead.

By calculation, however, the precise estimate can be made as 446, 464.86, and 483.71 respectively.

How do we arrive at these figures? Frankly, without the aid of a computer or programmed calculator, with the greatest difficulty!

There are two basic formulae, for there are two variables the X and Y values; and there are two main options, either the values given provide a LINE, "linear trend analysis", or the variables are such that the future values tend to CURVE – "curve to fit" as it is called.

The short sales example above, would appear to be a straight line trend, i.e., a line drawn down the centre of the data values, would be a straight line rather than a curve.

But if the line had curved up or down then the "curve to fit" method would need to be employed and in that case the entry would be a log value not, for instance, 300 but logs (natural) 300, namely LN 300 = 5.703782.

How would we know which to use, normal or log entry?

Going "by sight" would be inexact, and later we will see that one part of our calculations concerns the "coefficient of determination", usually called the "fit", and designated "r".

To process the "X" variables

(1) The sum of the X factors
$$1 + 2 + 3 + 4 + 5 + 6 \qquad = \qquad 21.00 \ (\Sigma X)$$
(2) The sum of the squares of the X factors
$$1^2 + 2^2 + 3^2 + 4^2 + 5^2 + 6^2 \qquad = \qquad 91.00 \ (\Sigma X^2)$$
(3) The mean of X
$$21/6 \qquad = \qquad 3.50 \ (\overline{X})$$

To process the "Y" variables

(1) The sum of the Y factors
$$300 + 410 + 420 + 320 + 330 + 500 \qquad = \qquad 2,280.00 \ (\Sigma Y)$$
(2) The sum of the squares of the Y factors
$$300^2 + 410^2 + 420^2 + 320^2 + 330^2 + 500^2 \qquad = 895,800.00 \ (\Sigma Y^2)$$
(3) The mean of Y
$$2,280/6 \qquad = \qquad 380.00 \ (\overline{Y})$$

To process jointly X and Y (line)

$$(1 + 300) + (2 \times 410) + (3 \times 420) + (4 \times 320) + (5 \times 330) + (6 \times 500) = \qquad 8310.00 \ (\Sigma X_n Y_n)$$

Linear Regression

(a) $\dfrac{\Sigma X_n Y_n - \bar{X} \times \Sigma Y}{\Sigma X^2 - (\Sigma X)^2/n}$ = Gradient (G)
(the dotted line slope)

(b) $Y - XG$ = Intercept

(a) $\dfrac{8{,}310 - (3.5 \times 2{,}280)}{91 - (21^2/6}$ = 18.85714286
= 18.86 gradient

(b) $380 - (18.876 \times 3.5)$ = 314.00 intercept

Projections (linear) Sales Forecast

```
Intercept + (gradient x n) = projection (n)
  314     + ( 18.86  x 7) = 446.00 (7th month — see above)
  314     + ( 18.86  x 8) = 464.86 (8th month — see above)
  314     + ( 18.86  x 9) = 483.71 (9th month — see above)
```

Curve to fit calculations

The calculations above were correct; for the parameters given were in fact a trend LINE;. Below (with apologies to the purist), in order to save yet another example, let us assume that the data values above transformed themselves into values suitable for a curve fitting. Incidentally, although *logs* are employed in the curve fitting calculations they are known as the *exponential* curve fit (and not the "logarithmic" fit – which is again something a little different).

The X values remain unaltered as above but Y variables are logged (LN), thus 300 now becomes LN 300 = 5.703782 et seq

(1) $5.70 + 6.02 + 6.04 + 5.77 + 5.80 + 6.21 = 35.542216$ (ΣY)

(2) $5.70^2 + 6.02^2 + 6.04^2 + 5.77^2 + 5.80^2 + 6.21^2 = 210.74$ (Σy^2)

(3) $35.542216/6$ = 5.923703 (Υ)

To process jointly X and Y (curve)

```
(1x5.70)+(2x6.02)(3x6.04)+(4x5.77)+(5x5.80)+(6x6.21) = 125.213257
```
$$(\Sigma X_n Y_n)$$

$$\frac{125.21 - (3.50 \times 35.54)}{17.50} = \frac{.815500}{17.50} = \underline{.046600 \text{ gradient}}$$
(remains in log form)

$$5.923703 - (.046600 \times 3.50) = 5.760603$$

$$e^{5.760603} = 2.71828182846^{5.760603} = \underline{317.539619 \text{ intercept}}$$

Projections (curve to fit) Sales Forecast

```
Exp [LN intercept + (gradient x n)]  = projection (n)
Exp [LN 317.54    + (.046600  x 7)]  =
Exp [5.760603     + (.046600  x 7)]  =
Anti/log 6.086802763                 =  440.01 month 7
```

Coefficient of Fit

$$\frac{(\Sigma X_n Y_n - (\bar{X} \times \Sigma Y))^2}{(\Sigma X^2 - \frac{\Sigma X^2}{n}) \times (\Sigma Y^2 - \frac{\Sigma Y^2}{n})} =$$

$$\frac{330^2}{(91 - \frac{21^2}{6}) \times (895{,}800 - \frac{2{,}280^2}{6})}$$

linear

= .211662 r^2 = .460067 r

curve

THE ABOVE IN LOG FORMAT   = .195090 r^2 = .441690 r
(exponential)

The comparisons

The rule is that the "fit" factor nearest to integer 1 is the correct choice. In the above example .460067 (the linear fit) is slightly nearer to 1 than .441690 (the curve fit) so the correct calculation to determine future values is LINEAR.

Annual growth rates

Sometimes the growth rates of various parameters are required, and the calculations are slightly different depending on whether the fit is line or curve. And taking values from the above example:

Linear

$$100 \times [\, (\frac{\text{projection } 12}{\text{projection } 1})^{1/12} - 1] = \text{growth rate}$$
$$\text{(line)}$$

$$100 \times [\, (\frac{314 + (18.86 \times 12)}{314 + (18.86 \times 1)})^{1/12} - 1] =$$

$$100 \times [\, (\frac{540.32}{332.86})^{.0833} - 1] = 4.12\%$$

Curve to fit

The annual growth rate for a curve fit is somewhat simpler, merely a/log the gradient, less 1 and multiply by 100:

$$100 \times (\, ^{\text{gradient}} - 1) = \text{growth rate}$$
$$100 \times ((2.718282^{.046600}) - 1) = \text{(curve)}$$
$$100 \times (\, 1.047703 - 1) = 4.77\%$$

Missing data

Taking the above example values, suppose that the 4th data value was missing the *fourth* calculation would thus be ignored, the input running from 420 (3) and 330 (5). Do NOT treat a missing period as a zero – it is NOT 0 (4).

In this event it will be found that the intercept (linear) is 319.65 and the gradient 21.28 and consequently, in this example, the 7th month's sales projected forward would be 468.60 and the 12th month 575 precisely (instead of 447 and 540.29 respectively).

Stock Exchange prices

The following is largely theoretical, for while it is useful to be able to project a price forward *on past results* this takes no account of the rises or falls in the Market generally (the Index) over the time period under review.

Assume a company has the following end of year price data:

Year	Price
1986	50.00
1987	54.00
1988	56.64
1989	80.82
1990	155.00
1991	200.00
1992	?

The first thing to check is whether it is a line or curve calculation, and it will be found that the coefficient is .912969 for line and .944788 for curve (exponential).

Therefore the calculation to find (a) the value in 1992 and (b) the annual growth rate, will be the exponentional curve to fit mode; and (a) should be found as 242.33 (£2.42) and (b) as 34.79%

Alternative requirements
In the foregoing we have always taken the X variable to represent the time factor, i.e., months or years rising in correct chronological order 1 – 6.

But there is no reason why the X factor cannot represent values other than time.

For instance, in property calculations, square footage (or nowadays metres!) against cost, or in (say) tonnages calculations against freight cost, would be very normal forecast calculations.

If, for example, in a variable list of commodities some 4,500 tons cost $100, another 3,500 tons cost $200 and a further 10,000 tons cost $320, readers may care to calculate the tonnage per value of $250.

They should find the answer as 7125 tons.

Depreciation
Accountants employ various methods to assess the depreciation, over the years, of capital assets.

UK tax requirement reducing balance method
The UK tax system for writing down assets for tax purposes used to be the simple one of reducing the cost by one quarter of the asset value each year – thus achieving a complete write off in four years. But this method was recently changed by legislation to one of reducing the asset value by 25% each year – which may sound the same but isn't! For by this method the total amount never quite disappears.

In the old days an office copier, costing, say, £2,000 was written down by £500 each year until, by the end of the fourth year, it was totally written off. But nowadays for write down tax purposes the calculation is simply:

```
£2,000    less 25% = value end year 1.
2,000    - 500     = £1,500
£1,500    less 25% = value end year 2.
1,500    - 375     = £1,125
£1,125    less 25% = value end year 3.
1,125    - 281.25 = £ 843.75
£  845.75 less 25% = value end year 4.
845.75 - 210.94 = £ 632.81
```
– which is a very different ball-game!

The value of any year can always be found from:
$$\text{cost} \times [1 - (25/100)]^y = \text{book value}$$
For example year$_4$

or by calculator $\quad$ £2,000 $\times [1 - (25/100)]^4 = $ £632.8125

keystrokes: $\quad$ 1 [-] 25 [%] [=] [y^x] 4 [x] 2000 [=] 632.8125

The book value at the end of year 25 would be £2,000 x .75^25 = 1.51 and to write the asset value down to *one penny* would take:

$$\frac{\text{LOG} \quad .01/2000}{\text{LOG} \quad .75} = 42.43 \text{ years Logs, LOG or LN are equally suitable}$$

Check: $\dfrac{\text{LOG} (632.81/2000)}{\text{LOG} \quad .75} = 4.00 \text{ years (see example above)}$

Three main methods of calculating depreciation

Assume the cost (or capital value) is £10,000, with a salvage or scrap value (at the end of the period under review) of £500. Taking the term of the review as 5 years (n) find the depreciation and book value at the end of 3 years (y).

The Declining Balances

The declining factor (df) is calculated as follows:

```
Cost   x (1 - df÷n)^y-1 x df÷n  = depreciation for year₃
10,000 x (1 -  2÷5)^2   x  2÷5  = 1,440.00
(10,000 x (1 -  2÷5)^3) -  500  = 1,660.00 book value year₃
```

The Straight Line method

This is conceptually simple and is usually employed when the asset is not expected to depreciate greatly over the short term – it is applied to warehouses, buildings and property in general.

```
(Cost   - salvage)÷n        = depreciation each year
(10,000 - 500)     ÷5       = 1,900
(10,000 - 500) - (1,900 x 3) = 3,800 book value year₃
```

The Sum of the Digits method

```
(Cost - scrap) x ((n - y) + 1)/SOYD  (where SOYD = (n+(n+1))/2
                                            = (5+6)/2 = 15)
(10,000 - 500) x ((5 - 3) + 1)/15    = 1,900 depreciation year₃
1,900/2 x (5 - 3)                    = 1,900 book value year₃
```

The beta coefficient

The age-old argument over whether investment decisions are best made by "feel", experience and knowledge of a particular market, or by various "measurement of risk" formulae will probably never be fully resolved. In the States, where "flying by the seat of one's pants" plays little or no part in investment policy, there is a plethora of risk formulae of every kind and description. One such is the beta coefficient measure of market risk. This method considers the dispersion of the value around the mean value resulting from the general ebb and flow of market fluctuations: the stock or portfolio being compared to an index of choice.

The beta coefficient, therefore, is a measure of risk of a stock or portfolio. When the beta coefficient equals 0 the rate of return is considered to be "without risk"; whereas a beta of 1 equates to the normal investment risk in a diversified portfolio of stocks. The higher the beta, above 1, the greater the assumed risk.

Comparisons are made between a "riskless" market investment, such as, in the States, a short-dated US Treasury Bill and the rate of return shown by an index of choice, such as the Standard & Poor's 500.

Given that the anticipated annual return of a stock is 15%, if the current risk-free yield on a US 91-day T Bill is 5.52% and the estimated return on the Standard & Poor's 500 index is 13.25%, what is the beta coefficient of the stock in question?

The short formula is:

$$\frac{Yield\% - T\ Bill\ rate\%}{Index\% - T\ Bill\ rate\%} = Beta$$

$$\frac{15 - 5.52}{13.25 - 5.52} = 1.23$$

The premium paid for the above risk is, of course, simply the risk value (the index rate) minus the riskless value (the T Bill), here 13.25 – 5.52 = 7.73 premium.

CHAPTER 11

Pensions, Handshakes, Elections and Boardroom Voting

General

In many books there is one chapter the contents of which becomes a bit of a rag bag; this book is no exception in that the golden handshakes, voting at elections or in the board rooms have only a tenuous connection with financial calculations as such – but nevertheless it was thought that they may be of some interest to readers.

Indexed pensions

Indexed pensions are now part of our social scene, mainly for those in the public sector, civil servants, judges, the services and the like, and naturally those in receipt consider it is their due right. Those in the private sector are not so sure! For it is obvious that the likelihood of their pensions being indexed is problematical to say the least.

Certainly back in 1979 when the indexing was mooted many thought, and incidentally still do, that the country could not afford such luxuries; and two reports, one by the Actuary's Department (1979) and the Chown report of 1980, both addressed to the Prime Minister of the time, sped back and forth between Government Departments and their ministers.

Because the purely factual Actuary's report was drafted by civil servants who could themselves look forward to such pensions, some considered that they would naturally favour indexing, because, to quote a remark now enshrined in our legal history, "they would, wouldn't they"!

The official view was that civil servants, or so they said, had foregone many perks enjoyed by those in the private sector, in order to have a comfortable pension on retirement, and that unless indexing was introduced the pressure on wages would continue unabated and become so great that the standard of living of pensioners would inevitably become unfairly eroded.

Others totally disagreed, the trouble being that there was a woeful lack of useful data available to assess such arcane matters as the long term cost of pensions in general, in both the public and private sectors.

Unlike the private sector the Government does not need to "fund" pensions, but pays them year by year from the annual contributions we all make, often under protest, to the Revenue authorities!

The private sector, save for a few minor exceptions, quickly realised that indexation, even if desirable, was totally outside their funding potential.

Without employing the highly sophisticated actuarial methods for assessing survival, expectation of life etc, the following calculations below, while not actuarially precise, may be useful in providing some rough costings.

Our Civil Servant
A civil servant after 30 useful years of active service retires aged 60. His last appointment carries a salary scale of £20,000, including emoluments etc.

On retirement he will receive a "lump sum", tax free which is determined by the formula of 3/80th x the number of years service x the last salary scale, here 3/80 x 30 x 20,000 = £22,500

His pension, as opposed to the tax-free capital gift, is 1/3 of the lump sum, here £7,500, paid quarterly in arrears.

As a rough assessment, let us assume that, unlike governments, we have to "fund" this pension; and taking a 20 year expectation of life and a 12% nominal rate of interest we would have to deposit a capital sum of around £60,000 in order to "cover" the annual pension.

$$(7,500/4)a\underline{\quad} \quad \text{at } 100 \times ((1 + 12/100)^{1/4} - 1)\%$$
$$4 \mid \text{ at } 2,873735\%$$
$$1,875a\underline{\quad}$$
$$4 \mid \text{ at } 2,873735\% \quad = £\ 6,990.65 \text{ (PV)}$$
$$\text{and} \quad 6,990.65a\underline{\quad}$$
$$20\mid \text{ at } 12\% \text{ nominal} = \underline{£58,482.26}$$

(not indexed funded)

Now let's do the whole of the above calculation again, but this time taking into account inflation when we find the cost of funding.

The above values were valid at the time the discussion concerning indexing was rife; and inflation was running at 20% and rising. However, assuming, optimistically, that it would fall, an arbitary figure of 16% was taken as the future index value, purely for calculation purposes.

This then gives us a negative working rate, negative because the inflation rate is higher than the 12% going rate above, which becomes 1.12/1.16 = .965517 and – 1, x 100 = –3.45%

$$6,990.65a\underline{\quad}$$
$$20\mid \text{ at } -3.45\% \text{ nominal} = \text{indexed funding}$$

$$6,990.65 \times ((1 - 0.965517^{-20})/- 0.034483) \times 0.965517 = \underline{£199,150.84}$$

(index funded)

and there are many more civil servants retiring each year. . . .

The Golden Handshake
Often much of the controversy regarding the amounts due to be paid for the loss of office (be it for the low paid worker or for top management) stems from a failure to understand the mathematics and the concept behind such payouts.

If a company executive, at whatever level, having a contract to be retained by the company for certain number of years, is suddenly dismissed from that company through no fault of his or her own, the company, in all fairness, is liable to pay some compensation.

– *193* –

It is the amount of compensation due for the loss of office which is often open to question.

The generally accepted concept is that the amount of compensation paid should *if invested* represent, and be equivalent to, the amount of the pay and emoluments which the executive would have received annually if he or she had not been dismissed.

The legal arguments usually revolve round two issues: namely the amount of extra emoluments, apart from the basic pay, which the executive enjoyed during his time with the company *and* the rate of return (the percentage) on the (hypothetical) investment. Paradoxically, the higher the rate the lower the compensation, consequently the company will usually argue for the rate to be "near the banks' lending rate", the opposing view probably being "about 5%". Why is this?

Assume that a middle level executive is receiving, say, £50,000 per year, which includes all extras such as attractive mortgage rates, cars, BUPA, etc, and that he has a service agreement contract which ties him to the company for 5 years. Through no fault of his own, he is suddenly dismissed after 2 years.

The compensation must therefore be such that he can invest the cash, whatever it is, immediately on receipt, in order to receive £50,000 for the next three years.

The calculation is quite simply a "repayment loan" over a term, the pay and emoluments being treated as the "payments" and the compensation amount as the "loan amount". As the investment must necessarily be immediate as soon as the compensation is received the calculation must be payments in advance, annuities *due*, and paradoxically the lower the rate the greater the compensation.

$$50,000 \ddot{a}_{\overline{3}|} \text{ at } 10\% = 50,000 \times (1 - 1.10^{-3})/.10 \times 1.10 = £136,777$$

$$50,000 \ddot{a}_{\overline{3}|} \text{ at } 5\% = 50,000 \times (1 - 1.05^{-3})/.05 \times 1.05 = £142,971$$

The astronomical compensation sums, sometimes reported in the financial press, for the loss of office of top management, caused in many cases by take overs and mergers, are of course subject to capital gains tax, at the tax level of the recipient. Smaller sums, for junior grades, are tax free up to £30,000.

Election voting
Unhappily, elections, whether Local Government or Parliamentary, cannot fail to have some impact on markets in general and sometimes on commerce in particular; thus at election time even the busiest of executives has a passing interest in the results.

Sooner or later political commentators refer to "the percentage swing required" for either one party or the other, to gain or lose this or that seat. To be factually correct the term should be "any percentage swing greater than. . . ." but this colloquialism is generally accepted and will be used below without any amending qualifications.

The results of a previous election, or bye-election, or the existing composition of a chamber must, of course, be known before any swing can be calculated.

Last election voting figures

(PARTY A – PARTY B) ÷ TOTAL VOTES CAST x 50 = PERCENTAGE

(required for a change)

Present election voting figures

(PARTY A – PARTY B) ÷ TOTAL VOTES CAST x 50 = PERCENTAGE

(if negative a change has occured)

LAST ELECTION % SWING – PRESENT % SWING = PERCENTAGE SWING

Taking the simple example of a small Parish Council with just 10 members. Party A has 6 members, Party B has 4. At a bye election it will require an x% swing if Party B is to gain power:

$$\frac{6 - 4}{10} \times 50 = 10\% \text{ required for a change of party}$$

In the event Party B gained 7 seats against Party A. The result of the voting produced a swing of x% for the change in question:

$$\frac{3 - 7}{10} \text{ x } 50 = -20\% \text{ actual percentage}$$

And consequently the total swing to produce the final result of a changed Chamber is 10% – (-20%) = 30% percentage swing

One vital thing to remember is that the order of setting out the two parties must be the same for both calculations – and the "winner comes first" syndrome must be resisted!

In March 1982 one of the greatest Parliamentary bye-election upsets took place at Hillside (Glasgow) when the new SDP Party, in lieu of the old Liberal Party, defeated the well settled Conservative member who had a large majority.

In the *previous* General Election (May 1979) the Conservative votes were 12,368 against the Liberal figures of 4,349, and the total votes cast were 30,113; consequently the "swing required" for the SDP to take over from the Conservative would be:

$$\frac{12,365 - 4,349}{30,133} \text{ x } 50 = 13.3\% \text{ required for a change of party}$$

And in the event the SDP obtained 10,106 votes against the sitting member's 8,068:

$$\frac{8,068 - 10,106}{30,289} \text{ x } 50 = -3.4\% \text{ actual percentage}$$
$$\text{(negative – CHANGE)}$$

The *percentage swing* being 13.3% – (-3.4) = 16.7%

Board room voting – an idea !
It has often been argued that there is no such thing as a good or bad decision, only good or bad methods of making such decisions. If that is so, then surely some present day methods of decision making must come under severe scrutiny.

The democratic method of one man one vote may be a perfectly valid way, in a board room, of deciding whether the next AGM should be held at the Savoy, or the pub next door.

But is it really sound, and the best way, when the possible outlay of substantial funding, for a highly technical project, say, is under discussion, funding which almost certainly will affect the future of the company, those working in it, and the Shareholders?

For consider; board members are humans, with human failings, often subject to personal lobbying where departmental matters are concerned.

"I'll vote for your item 3 if you'll support my item 6", is not unheard of; nor the cry "Well, I'll go along with that, Chairman" by someone whom you well know hasn't bothered to acquaint himself with the brief supplied!

But more important, I much doubt if, on some subjects under discussion, the contribution of all members is equally valuable, and, consequently, whether all votes are equally valuable.

For example, for the last six months the managing director and his finance director have spent days, and some sleepless nights, working out how best to reorganising their somewhat ancient in-house main frame computer complex, changing to an up-to-date desktop networking profile.

The project cost would probably be in the nature of £500,000 and if mistakes are made, in cost or technical support, the consequence for this medium sized company could be disastrous: but it would perhaps be even more disastrous if nothing was done and the present mess was allowed to continue.

The MD and finance director, steeped in all the various options available, have now decided what is best, in their opinion, for the company – and a presentation for approval is being made at their next board meeting.

It so happens that, for many reasons, it appears that the decision will be a "close run thing".

Apart from different departments, and their directors, preferring the funding available to be passed to their own individual projects, there are some "out of town directors", entitled to vote on such an undertaking.

One such is Bloggins, now living in semi-retirement in Devon, tending his roses, whose visits to board meetings are rare and largely conditioned by whether his wife wishes to see the latest production at Drury lane. His elevation to the board was made many years ago as a mark of respect and gratitude for his loyalty to the company in looking after their ground nuts scheme in an African colony just after World War II.

The company secretary is convinced that on this occasion he will attend, and is equally certain that his vote will be against the project; ". . . never had these newfangled things in Africa, got on perfectly well without them, complete waste of money – spend it on something sensible".

Now is it really sensible, democratic and all that, for Bloggins' vote to nullify the finance director's vote? For assuredly, this is what it means.

It may be argued that nowadays board rooms are not like this, but it cannot be denied that not every member reads all his papers with diligence or that there is no personal lobbying.

So why could not, *for certain agenda items only,* the voting be according to "expertise and interest", and if this was thought desirable how could it be best achieved?

In the table below, there are two separate categories, namely "qualifications" and "strength of feeling". The latter category would be stated when the vote was cast, in secret if thought desirable.

The qualification vote could hardly be left to individual preference, for most would give themselves full marks; so this category would be decided by the Chairman and/or Company Secretary *and annotated against the related agenda item.*

Thus there would be a right of challenge, if necessary – and adjustment by agreement. In the above scenario Bloggins could hardly expect a high qualification vote, whereas the finance director's would be, for this issue, the highest; but in the event of discussions on irrigation matters in deepest Africa, Bloggins could score over the finance director who had to seek help from an atlas to find the area concerned!

The two categories of votes cast, as below, become the "percentage of the margin", by a weighted mean calculation – in effect quite a simple calculation determined by the company secretary on a simple calculator as the votes unfold.

Qualifications		Strength of Feeling		
		0.	100%	AGAINST
		1.	very strongly	"
1.	none	2.	strongly	"
2.	few	3.	moderately	"
3.	some	4.	on balance	"
4.	good	5.	NO VIEWS	abstention
5.	very good	6.	on balance	FOR
6.	highest	7.	moderately	"
		8.	strongly	"
		9.	very strongly	"
		10.	100%	"

If 6 directors voted by conventional means 3 against, 2 for, with 1 abstention, the motion would be lost.

But by employing the suggested method assume that the categories fell as below:

Director	Calculation	
A's qualification is 3 and he voted 4	4 x 3	3
B's " " 4 " " " 5	abstention	
C's qualification is 5 and he voted 6	6 x 5	5
D's qualification is 5 and he voted 7	7 x 5	5
E's qualification is 7 and he voted 4	4 x 6	6
F's qualification is 3 and he voted 4	4 x 3	3
	113	22

The formula to find the new type vote:

$$100 \times \frac{\text{weighted mean} - \text{median}}{\text{median}} = \text{percentage of the margin}$$

ROUND TO INTEGER

$$100 \times \frac{(113/22) - 5}{5} = 3\% \text{ motion agreed}$$

A negative result would mean that the motion is lost, a zero would require the Chairman's casting vote.

As set out the 100% categories are rarely used, being in effect almost a resigning matter if the vote goes against the director concerned.

There is no reason why the categories cannot be reduced in number if wished, but remember the "strength of feeling" must be an uneven number, in order to permit a median (the abstention vote) for calculation purposes.

Doubtless others will be able to provide scenarios from their own experiences; if so they will find that in those cases where the items are relatively unimportant the result of the two types of vote casting will be the same, but in controversial matters the results may well be illuminating!

You may tell me, of course, that the whole scenario is ridiculous and that there are no Bloggins' on company boards nowadays; I can only hope that you are right, but I am not yet convinced.

PART II

CHAPTER 12

Fixed Interest Loans – Bonds

Fixed Interest Loans

In Part I a variety of loans and savings arrangements were examined, the common factor being that in all cases the periodic interest due varied. In particular whereas compound interest calculations produced "interest on interest", in the case of repayment loan calculations it was seen that in each payment period the interest on such loans fell as the capital reduced.

In Part II we shall be dealing exclusively with fixed interest-bearing obligations, where the interest received by the lender is, in general terms, the same at each interest payment period.

In Part I, although the point was never specifically made, the tendency, was to regard the scenario from the perspective of the borrower. In Part II the opposite will obtain and when the examples are outlined it will usually be assumed that the reader is the lender.

Interest rolled up and paid per compounding period

A £100 loan at 10% compound interest over a term of 10 years will provide you with a future value £259.37. In this case the interest of £159.37 was derived from the interest for each of the ten years being "rolled-up", instead of being paid to the lender each year.

If, however, the lender wished to spend the interest due each year on wine, women and song he would have to accept that at the end of the term, when the loan has fully "matured", all he could expect to receive as the "redemption amount" would be the repayment of his original £100.

You cannot have it both ways, either the interest is rolled up and you get a substantial (capital and interest) lump sum payment at the end of the term, or you receive the interest every so often, and your loan amount returned intact at the end.

In effect, this latter arrangement is the basis of all fixed interest loans, and obviously there is nothing difficult about the calculations. And yet "Bond Yield" calculations are often considered complicated and only for the experts. Which is nonsense! For all the difficulties, the various ways of calculating this or that type of bond are merely man-made variations on this simple theme – as we shall see!

The creep-up
In the above example, with a 10% gross return on £100 you would expect to receive £10 each year, or more likely £5 each half year, while the loan was running (10 years or 20 half years) and your £100 returned at maturity. This fixed interest loan could be a personal loan to a friend or a loan by a member of the public to an industrial company wishing to raise funds for further development by the "issue" of a debenture loan.

A debenture is simply a promise by the borrower to repay the original loan at a fixed time in the future and an agreement to pay a fixed amount of interest every half year until the loan is fully matured. Governments make the same type of arrangements, save that their issues pay somewhat less than industrial debentures for, however elegant the company, the credit worthiness of governments is thought to be just that much more secure. Bonds are usually issued in multiples of 100 or 1,000; the former being the custom in the UK and both methods being employed in the USA, depending on the type of loan required.

If, for example, you purchased £100 of 5% Government Stock at Issue, in effect lending that sum to the Government, and the term of the issue was, say 20 years you would expect to receive £5 every half year for your holding.

During the term of the loan you may well see the price of your stock fluctuate according to the vicissitudes of the market; but if you had invested in order to obtain the interest either annually or semi-annually you will know that at the end of the loan term you will be assured of receiving the par value (£100).

Suppose you purchased the £100 worth of stock when it was priced at 80 points with 10 years to run to maturity; apart from receiving the half annual interest you would know that at the end of 10 years you would receive £100. In other words you would have a capital gain of 20 points over the 10 years, or looking at it a different way, a lift of 2 points each year.

The conventional gross yield of 10 x 100/80 = 12.50% takes no account of the capital lift, and as such is of little use as an investment tool.

What is required is some sort of a yield which reflects both the annual interest *and* the capital lift. And this yield is called the "Yield to Maturity" or shortly the YTM%

The Coupon and the Call
As we shall be using the term *coupon* throughout the following chapters, it should perhaps be explained at this point. The term denotes the *nominal* interest payment rate of the bond. When the interest on bonds is paid semi-annually, as most are, the statistician automatically always divides the coupon rate by half to determine the semi-annual interest payments. The term itself derives from the coupon, attached to bearer bonds which, when detached and presented to any authorised bank, permits the holder to draw his or her periodic interest – a method unremarkable in most countries, but less well known in the United Kingdom. For UK bearer bonds are not usually issued and, save in a few rather exceptional circumstances, are seldom held privately by UK nationals.

The term *call* is in many cases used instead of RV or redemption or maturity value, and means the amount returned to the lender at the end of the term. The terminology derives from the practice, especially in the USA, of a borrower "calling" its debenture, or part of its loan, to be repaid at a price higher than par, earlier than the normal maturity date. There is no problem in finding the price or the yield to call for all that is necessary is to alter the RV from 100 to the call price.

The Calendars

As we well know, there are two calendars used in financial calculations and bond yield calculations are no exception. Various markets have their own conventions; in the UK, for example, the 365 actual calendar is always employed, in the States one class of bond employs the actual calendar while others use the 30/360 financial calendar. EuroBonds always employ the 30/360 method.

When calculating the accrued interest with the 30/360 calendar the first day's payment is counted but settlement day is NOT. Also note that:

```
1st - 30th of the same month       = 29 elapsed days
1st - 31st of the same month       = 30 elapsed days
1st -  1st of the following month = 30 elapsed days
1st - 28th of February             = 27 elapsed days
```

When interest is payable on the 30th or 31st:

```
to  1st of the following month   =  1 day's interest
to 30th of the following month   = 30 days' interest
to 31st of the following month   = 30 days' interest
```

As will be seen in the Appendices, finding the number of days between two dates is a matter of calculating a date factor; but nowadays a calculator with date facilities is the best answer!

Redemption Dates

An Issue of stock, whether a Government Issue or an Industrial Debenture, will state, inter alia, the dates on which the interest will be paid, which may be annually, semi–annually, or very occasionally quarterly. Also the date on which the stock will be redeemed, that is the date on which the capital previously borrowed will be repaid to the person holding of the bond certificate at the time of maturity.

In the UK sometimes there are two redemption dates stated and this means that the "borrower", the Government or Corporation, *can* repay the loan amount on the first or earlier date but *must* pay on, or before, the last named date.

The rule for all calculation purposes is to take the *last* date providing the *clean* price of the bond stands below the "call" or redemption value.   If the clean price exceeds the call the converse is true.

The logic behind this thinking is that the only reason why a stock will stand above par is that the current lending rates must have fallen since the original issue, there being thus more buyers than sellers for the, now, high income bonds. In that case the borrower will wish to redeem his existing loan at the earliest opportunity in order to borrow more cheaply by making another loan issue with a (lower) coupon more in line with the "going" rates.

Sunday Redemption
Some statisticians consider that if maturity falls on a Sunday the yield should be reduced fractionally to compensate for the fact that reinvestment, theoretically, cannot be immediate but must wait for the banks to open the following day.

$$(\text{YTM\% x days life}) \div (\text{days life} + 1) = \text{YTM\% (adjusted)}$$

and assuming the YTM is 10% and that the days life is 665 days, with redemption date on a Sunday:

$$10 \quad x \quad 665 \quad \div \quad 666 \quad = 9.98\% \text{ adjusted YTM}$$

Divide by *one* extra day only; it is *not* legitimate to calculate an adjusted YTM by YTM x days/(days + 2).

Settlement
It has already been mentioned that there is a difference between the actual date of settlement and the date of purchase.

Settlement can be a trap for the unwary, for different markets, and indeed sometimes different stocks within those markets, have different rules for the time allowed before the value of the purchase has to be paid.

For instance, in the UK Government Securities, and Local Government bonds are settled the day following purchase. But for "Industrial Debentures" (Corporate Bonds) Settlement, (which previously related to the London Stock Exchange fortnightly "accounts" system), is now 7 days after purchase – to equate with the Eurobond market.

Leap Days
The lender receives a fixed amount of interest each half year, irrespective of how many days there are in that half year, consequently the leap days are ignored in bond yield calculations – unlike the calculations of bank deposits and other commercial paper which, when discounted, include interest for the total number of days in the interest period.

Accrued Interest
When using the financial calendar the total number of days between settlement and maturity is divided by 360 or 180 to determine the (n + k) factor. And the a/i days can be found by the factor (1 - k), which when multiplied by the previous divisor provides the number of a/i days. Naturally these days are an integer.

But for UK stocks where the base is conventionally 182.5 this (1 - k) method must NOT be used: for, depending on the part of the year, sometimes the value found by the (1 - k) method will contain a half day – and accrued interest calculated with "days plus a half" is not acceptable to the market.

Consequently for all UK calculations the precise number of calendar days between settlement date and the previous payment date *must* be found. To save time, if the (1 - k) x 182.5 comes to an integer that value can be used. But for any type of computer program the correct number of accrued calendar days *must* be found.

What happens if there is a leap day in the a/i days?

As seen above, for YTM calculations leap days are ignored *but* convention dictates that the market pays the extra day's interest for the accrued interest. So you can take your choice as how you determine the YTM - either taking the a/i with or without the leap day intervening.

Ex-dividends
With no system for "bearer stocks", half annual dividends are paid by the Bank of England to the registered holders of individual bonds. To avoid making payments to holders who have sold before the next due payment but too late for re-registration to be effected, the Bank rules that all such securities shall be deemed to be ex-dividend 37 days before the payment date following. (If declaration day falls on a Saturday, Sunday or Bank Holiday then D-day falls on the next day for dealing i.e., 35 or 36 days prior). Consequently, an investor making a purchase between the EX date and next payment date will not receive any accrued interest due. Ex-dividend payment also applies to Industrial Debentures, (corporate stocks) and the same limitations obtain.

Gross Yields
The gross yields are simply calculated as:

```
Nominal Coupon x 100/Clean Price   = Gross Yield
If the CP was 95, then 10 x 100/95 = 10.53%
```

Abridged YTM calculations
In terms of the repayment loans discussed in Part I, the cost of the bond corresponds to the loan amount and the redemption value (RV) to the balloon or balance. The repayments made on a loan, however, cannot truly be compared to the interest payments on a bond, for there is no capital components in the semi-annual bond payments, which cover interest only. Unhappily, just as for repayment loans, the interest rate, or with bonds the YTM%, has to be found by the usual guess and guess again interpolation - or more sensibly by computer or calculator program.

With a cost of 80 points, an RV of 100, and an annual "coupon" (or interest payment) of £10 the interest *rate*, or *yield to maturity* computes as 13.80515861%, as opposed to the gross yield, above, of 12.50%. This YTM was derived from:

$$\frac{80 - (100 \times 1.138052^{-10})}{10a\overline{}} = 1.00$$
$$10|$$

Consequently,

$$(100 \times 1.138052^{-10}) + 10(1 - 1.138052^{-10})/.138052 = cost$$
$$27.439773 + 52.560227 \qquad\qquad = 80.00$$

I need hardly say that the above is the simplest form of bond price/yield calculations.

The odd days
The calculation above was said to be in its "simplest form" because the term was *exactly* 10 years; in practice an integer term is only valid at issue, or in the rare event that the bond is bought and paid for on the precise date that an interest payment is due. The usual term is a number of periods, or more usually semi-annual periods, plus a number of odd days – and it is this that causes most of our difficulties, the man-made difficulties I mentioned above. For different markets, indeed often different statisticians, have different methods of making the calculations related to these "odd days".

Discounting maturity values back to the present time
To start with, for the sake of simplicity, let us make certain assumptions – which will be discussed in detail later. Assume that one unit of £100 of a 5.50% coupon bond has been bought for a price of 96 3/16th (96.1875), with a term of 665 days between purchase and maturity. The gross yield, usually expressed to 2 decimals places, is 5.50 x 100/96.1875 = 5.72%

As the purchase price is 96.1875 there is clearly a maturity lift of 3.81 points (100 – 96.1875) – so a YTM is obviously required. Since the payments are semi-annual the "life of the stock", in terms of half annual periods and odd days, is 665/182.5 = 3.643836 – or 3 half years and 117.5 odd days (.643836 x 182.5). At this stage don't worry about the half day.

The resultant (here 3.643836) of the division of a total number of life days by the "base factor" (here 182.5) is more than often referred to as the (n + k) factor (see below) the "n" being the periods (here half years) and the "k" being the odd days as a decimal fraction.

From the original prospectus we would know the coupon value and the redemption date or call when the full capital loan amount is due for repayment. We would naturally know when the stock was bought and consequently the number of days between purchase and maturity – and thus the n + k.

Given the YTM%, to find the cost (price) we must discount the maturity value *and* each semi-annual payment back to the present time, namely the purchase period – or rather the settlement date for, as we shall see later, there is often some latitude between settlement, when payment is actually made, and the actual purchase date.

Taking the above example, and a YTM of 7.777501% (always quoted as a nominal rate) the i/p will be $1 + 7.777501/200$ and a discount schedule will therefore look like this:

```
(RV    +    pmts)  x  (1  + i/p)⁻¹              =  discounting
(100   +    2.75)  x  1.0388875⁻¹              =  98.903875
(98.91 +    2.75)  x  1.0388875⁻¹              =  97.848780
(97.85 +    2.75)  x  1.0388875⁻¹              =  96.833179
```

What about the odd days?

```
(96.83 +    2.75)  x  1.0388875⁻ᵏ              =
(96.83 +    2.75)  x  1.0388875^-(117.5/182.5) =
   "         "     x     "    ^-0.643836       =  97.166952
```

The above was calculated by compound interest, but sometimes the requirement is for *simple interest discounting*; in that case only the *odd-days portion* is so calculated, the remaining part of the discounting process being unaltered.

In the above calculation, therefore, the last item of the schedule above would be:

```
96.83 + 2.75 x 1/(1 +          (i/p x k))          =
96.83 + 2.75 x 1/(1 + (.0388875   x .643836)) = 97.150799 (SI)
```

It will be appreciated that if simple interest was required and the price to be met was, as above, 96.1875 the i/p would be fractionally different, in this case 0.038838, namely a YTM of 7.767606%

But surely, the price to be found is 96.1875 – and not 97.166952 which is the result of the schedule just outlined.

True, but the 97.166952, if you look at the schedule carefully, *includes* the interest between the last payment date and the final redemption date. The price *plus* the *accrued interest* is usually known colloquially as the "dirty price", to differentiate it from the (rather obvious) "clean price" denoting a price clean of the accrued interest.

The accrued interest
The accrued interest, or a/i, is an integral part of any bond yield calculation. The bond formulae are always designed to find the dirty price, which must be cleaned to find the price less any accrued interest, for all quotations nowadays are given as prices clean of any a/i.

With bearer bonds, or those *cum-div* bonds which always pay any interest due to the purchaser, the a/i is *subtracted* from the dirty price (DP) to find the clean price (CP). But in those markets, notably the UK, when stocks are sold ex-dividend (i.e., at prices without any a/i due to the purchaser) the reverse is true and the a/i is then *added* to the price to find the clean *ex-div* price.

Consequently, to clean the above price of 97.1667952 we must subtract the accrued interest, found from the accrued interest days multiplied by the coupon/base – the accrued interest days being those days between the last interest payment date and settlement date. If our odd days above were 117.5 then the a/i days would be 182.5 – 117.5 = 65.

Consequently, the clean price would become:

```
97.166952 - (5.50/365 x 65)  =  96.1875
97.166952 - .979452          =    "
```

More usually one would find the amount to be deducted from the dirty price by:

```
5.50/2 = 2.75 and 2.75/182.5 x 65 = .979452
```

This method is reckoned to be less confusing when the "base" is different to 182.5 – as it often is! Indeed, we are, quite understandably, trying to run before we can walk and there are many facets to base methods and the application of accrued interest which will unfold later.

Indeed, one such matter is the question of the odd half day; suffice it to say, for the moment, that some markets and some statisticians will accept a half day in the calculations for the odd-days structure while others will not.

Irrespective of how the odd-days are calculated, the number of a/i days must be actual (integer) days and no half days; for the accrued interest is part of the financial accounting, whereas the odd days value is only part of a yield calculation, a subtle but important difference.

While the accrued interest is calculated to the full precision of the computer/calculator used and the convention is that the a/i will *not* be rounded, except in EuroBonds which always find their accrued to 2 places of decimals.

The formulae for bond/yield calculations
The chart below may help to clarify what, to some, often appears a little complicated.

In other words, what the previous schedule did and what the formula following will do.

Assuming the above example but with the dates filled in, namely settlement (SD) being on January 1, 1990 and maturity on October 28, 1991 the respective payment and redemption dates (RD) are shown below.

```
    SD- - - - - - - - - 665 days - - - - - - - - - - RD
      1.011990 4.281990      10.281990     4.281991      10.281991
    2.75—|————2.75————2.75————2.75————102.75
    pmts  |         pmts          pmts           pmts        RV + pmts
     a/i days odd  |                |              |            |
      65 | 117.5   |    (182.5)  |    (182.5)  |   (182.5)  |
         SD- - - - - - - -n + k = 3.643836- - - - - - - RD
```

The discounted value, namely the cost, for calculation purposes, is always the dirty price the price *plus* the accrued interest (price *less* the a/i for ex-div (see later) calculations).

The purchaser of this stock, who settled on January 1, 1989, and who was quickly registered as the owner of the stock, will be paid £2.75 on April 28,1990.

But as he is only entitled to 117.5 days interest he must return 65 days interest, the "accrued interest", to the previous holder. In fact, the value of the payment on April 28 1990 is 2.75 – (65 x 2.75/182.5) = £1.77, the accrued interest of 65 x 2.75/182.5 = .979452 = .98 being returned to the original holder.

In this example a yield to maturity of 7.777501% provides a price, "*clean* of accrued interest", of 96 3/16th; and consequently the price, including the a/i, namely the *dirty price*, is 96.1875 + .979452 = 97.166952.

The actuarial formula
The basic concept of discounting the redemption value, and each periodic payment, back to settlement applies to all bonds the world over. Any differences arise out of the peripheral calculations and do not affect the main concept.

$$\frac{RV(1 + i/p)^{-n} + Da_{\overline{n}|} + D}{(1 + i/p)^{k}} = DP$$

For "Simple Interest Calculations" the denominator is 1 + (i/p x k)

Where:

the "actuarial amortisation" equals

$$a_{\overline{n}|} = (1 - (1 + i/p)^{-n})/(i/p)$$

i   = the YTM% as a decimal
      If 10% = YTM then i = 10/100 = 0.10

p   = periods per year
      If semi-annual p = 2 (i/p at 10% = 10/200 = 0.05)

RV = Redemption Value, referred to as the "call" by many

DP = Dirty Price, namely Clean Price + Accrued Interest

D   = the half coupon for semi-annual calculations
      (n + k) = the total number of days between settlement
      and maturity (less any leap days) divided by "base"

Base = 365 for "actual" calendar
           semi-annual 182.5, 181, 182, 183, 184 (dependent)
      360 for 30/360
           semi-annual 180

Taking the example above with a yield to maturity of 7.77750137982/2 = 3.888750698991% semi-annual, a redemption vale of 100, a semi-annual coupon of 2.75% with a life of 665 days, providing an n + k of 665/182.5 = 3.64383561644. The values given here are calculated at full precision throughout, but are suitably reduced for display purposes below.

$$\frac{(100 \times 1.039^{-3}) + (2.75 \times (1 - 1.039^{-3})/.039) + 2.75}{1.039^{0.6438}} =$$

$$\frac{89.185536 \quad + \quad 7.646420 \quad + \quad 2.75}{1.024867}$$

= DP
= 97.166952

DP   - (a/i days ÷ 182.5 x coupon) =   DP   -   a/i   = CP
97.167 - (65   ÷ 182.5 x 2.75) = 97.167 - .979452 = 96.1875

Computer Scheduling

Scheduling could doubtless be used for all bond yield calculations, and in the old days at least one "jobber" on the London Market did indeed schedule Government "Shorts", that is stock with under 5 years to run to redemption. But this always seemed to me to be somewhat academic, for a schedule, as we have just seen, can be easily converted to a formula which provides precisely the same answers, namely yields to maturity or prices, the prices being dirty, but suitable for instant "cleaning".

As seen above, the convention with bond yield calculations is to ignore any leap days intervening, but those scheduling the "shorts" *include* any leap days, as well as the precise number of days within each payment period. The difference between this method and a formula is, frankly, negligible.

Bonds with less than 1 period (Per <1) to maturity
In the price/YTM formulae above, where there were several payment periods between settlement and maturity, plus some odd days, it was necessary to compute the YTM.

But when the remaining life of a bond is so short that there are no payments due before redemption a shortened formula is available which can find the YTM or price without the necessity to interpolate. If you have already written your own computer program for the conventional formulae, outlined above, the "short shorts" will work on your program and there is no need to write-in any of the "short" formulae below.

The compound interest discounting formulae:

$$\frac{RV + D}{(1 + i/p)^k} = DP(\text{Compound Interest})$$

$$100 \times p \times \left(\left(\frac{RV + D}{DP}\right)^{1/k} - 1\right) = YTM\%(\text{Compound Interest})$$

$$\frac{RV + D}{1 + (i/p \times k)} = DP(\text{Simple Interest})$$

$$100 \times p \times \left(\left(\frac{RV + D}{DP} - 1\right) \times 1/k\right) = YTM\%(\text{Simple Interest})$$

Take the example of a 4.75% Government bond with a clean price of 99 28/32nds (99.875) which is settled on February 7, 1988 and is redeemed for 100 on May 15, some 98 days later.

For these "short short" bonds, although there is no convention or rule, the most usual method is to calculate by simple interest mode and employ a base derived from the number of days between the payment date before settlement and the redemption date (in this example 182, consequently the a/i days here is 182 – 98 = 84).

What is the YTM?

$$200 \times \left(\frac{100 + (4.75/2)}{99.875 + 84/364 \times 4.75} - 1\right) \times \frac{182}{98} = \underline{5.164134 \text{ YTM(SI)}\%}$$

To find the odd-days

Admittedly this is a rare requirement, nevertheless it is set out below. Taking the original example, already covered by both schedule and formula:

$$\frac{\text{LOG } (RV(1 + i/p)^{-n} + D\underset{n \mid}{a} + D)/DP}{\text{LOG} \quad 1 + i/p} \times 182.5 = \text{odd-days}$$

$$\frac{\text{LOG } ((100 \times 1.03889^{-3}) + (2.75(\frac{1-1.03889^{-3}}{.03889})) + 2.75) \div 97.167}{\text{LOG} \quad 1.038887507} \times 182.5$$

$$\frac{\text{LOG} \quad 1.0024867}{\text{LOG} \quad 1.038887507} \times 182.5 = 117.5 \text{ odd-days}$$

Alternatively, the shortened compound interest calculated example:

$$\frac{\text{LOG } (100 + 2.375)/100.971154}{\text{LOG} \quad 1 + (5.164134/200)} \times 182 = 98 \text{ odd-days}$$

All the calculations above were at full precision although the display values have in some cases been abridged.

Approximate YTMs

There are two reasons why an *approximate* YTM formula is desirable. The main one, of course, being that as a computer or calculator program is necessary to find a YTM a quick "back of an envelope" check is obviously extremely useful, and secondly when writing a program which requires looping it saves much computer time if the start of the loop can be a reasonable approximation of what is finally required.

There are of course many methods of starting a loop approximation and doubtless each statistician will have his own pet method, and I would not presume to prescribe any particular way as being better than any other.

Nonetheless, the approximation I always use myself is one the Japanese use to calculate bond yields and which is an excellent approximation of the actuarial method.

$$[cpn + \frac{(call - clean\ price) \times 365}{life\ in\ days}] \times \frac{call}{clean\ price} = Yield$$

$$\frac{(cpn \times call/yield\%) + (365 \times call/life\ days \times call/yield\%)}{(call/yield\% \times 365/life\ days) + 1} = Price$$

The life is usually assumed not to include leap days, and while it is customary to calculate on an "actual" (365) basis there is no reason why the 30/360 calendar cannot be used if required.

And employing our above example with 665 life days:

$(((100 - 96.1875) \times 365 \div 665) + 5.5) \times 100 \div 96.1875 = 7.893515$

When a UK settlement date fringes a payment date

With computer or calculator programs, as opposed to normal mental agility, problems sometimes arise. One of these is as follows.

Assume a bond settlement is on November 14, 1988 and maturity November 15 1991. In the UK such a bond is treated as an ex-dividend calculation for obviously the purchase was made one day prior to the next payment date, namely November 15.

It will be found that there are 1096 "days between" and consequently there are $(1096/182.5 = 6.005479)$, some 6 half annual periods and 1 day $(.005479 \times 182.5)$. Now if maturity was moved one half year earlier, namely May 15 1991, one could confidently expect that there would be 5 periods and one day – and the new $(n + k)$ would be 5.005479.

Unhappily, if 912 (the number of days between settlement and the new advanced maturity date) is divided by 182.5 the $(n + k)$ factor becomes 4.997260 – and therefore if this $(n + k)$ factor is not recognised to be erroneous, and left unadjusted, the whole calculation will be inaccurate.

For example if the erroneous $(n + k)$ factor and the ex–dividend mode obtain the resulting incorrect calculation (based on a 12% YTM) would result:

$$\frac{100 \times 1.06^{-4} + 5(1 - 1.06^{-4}/.06)}{1.06^{.997260}} = 91.085195 \text{ XD DP}$$

```
1 day to pmt day = a/i of 1 x 5/182.5 =    .027397 a/i
                   91.08595 + .027397 = 91.11 incorrect price
```

There are two cures; the first is to switch, as soon as this situation is realised, to the correct $(n + k)$ factor, as above, of 5.005479 and employing the accrued as $1/182.5 \times 5 = .027397$

$$\frac{100 \times 1.06^{-5} + 5(1 - 1.06^{-5}/.06)}{1.06^{.005479}} = 95.757058 \text{ XD DP}$$

```
                95.757058 + .027397 = 95.784455 XD clean price
```

The alternative is to retain the *incorrect* $(n + k)$ factor of $912/182.5$, namely 4.997260 but to treat the remaining calculation as being in cum-div mode, retaining the original accrued of .027397 but of course, conventionally, in the case of a cum-div calculation *subtracting* the a/i from the dirty price to obtain the clean price..

But if the above is recalculated as a **cum**-div calculation:

$$\frac{100 \times 1.06^{-4} + 5(1 - 1.06^{-4}/.06) + 5}{1.06^{\wedge}.997260} = 95.802929 \text{ DP}$$

$$95.802929 - .027397 = 95.78 \text{ clean price}$$
$$\text{(XD calc cum-div)}$$

It is not uninteresting that calculating by the US quasi-coupon method (outlined in the next chapter) which does not recognise ex–dividend calculations also finds a clean cum–div price of exactly 95.78.

Here the (n + k) factor is 5 periods plus 1 day divided by 184 (which is the number of days in the coupon period in which settlement occured), namely 5.005435 and the accrued becomes 5 x 183/184 = 4.972826

$$\frac{100 \times 1.06^{-5} + 5(1 - 1.06^{-5}/.06) + 5}{1.06^{\wedge}.005435} = 100.755724 - 4.972826$$
$$= 95.78 \text{ clean price}$$

An Alternative Problem
The converse of the above is when a bond is purchased one day *after* the last payment date. For example, a 12.50% Bond with clean price of 102.125, a call of 100, with semi–annual payments, Settlement March 15 1988 and Maturity September 14 1997. Payment dates are 14 March/September. (Yes, I *know* Maturity is a Sunday but this is a mathematical *example* only – we are not trading!).

The required days between settlement and maturity are 3,468 which, when divided by 182.5, finds an erroneous (n + k) factor of 19.002740. For in fact there are only 18 payment periods due between settlement and maturity and indeed this is confirmed if settlement was one day later (3,467/182.5 = 18.997260). In other words we have the same difficulty as before – but in reverse.

The cure is the same as the above, in reverse. Either correct the inaccurate (n + k) factor, or use the quasi coupon method as above, or treat this **cum-div example** as an **ex–div calculation**. Each will find the YTM as 12.12%.

The simplest method for a computer program, as soon as it realises the inconsistency, is to retain all the parameters *and switch to the opposite mode*, cum–div to ex–div or ex–div to cum–div.

The Validity Test
But how can a computer program determine whether inconsistency obtains or not, and ensure that such erroneous values do not go unnoticed?

To test if settlement was *before* the next payment day, as in the first ex–dividend example above, add .005 to the $(n + k)$ value. If this changes the integer then action must be taken to adjust the calculation.

Above 912 "days between" divided by 182.5 = 4.997260 and 4.997260 + .005 = 5.002260 – integer changed.

Whereas the addition of .005 to one day more or less, namely $(913/182.5) + .005$ or $(915/182.5) + .005$ will be seen not to affect the integer.

For settlement *after* the previous payment date the solution will be the converse, namely the subtraction of .005. Taking, for example, a life of 3468 days divided by 182.5, adding .005 changes the integer, whereas subtracting .005 from "days between" of 3467 or 3469 will not affect the respective integers.

Both these rather irritating and tiresome problems are, unhappily, not alleviated by calculating, as some statisticians and computer programs do, the exact number of odd days between settlement and the next payment date.

By this method, in the first example, a computer program would correctly find some 18 periods but would then be faced with 183 (March 15 1988 – September 14 1988) days being divided by 182.5, and this added to the above 18 periods provides the same erroneous $(n + k)$ factor we had above!

Taxation Requirements

A recent change in the UK market practice is that when calculating net yields, apart from the interest payments being treated as net of tax, the *accrued interest* will be also so treated, as indeed has long been the practice in the USA. The accrued interest due *includes* the interest for any leap day intervening but it is optional whether this arrangement is used in calculating the yields.

Example Take a cum-div 5.50% Government Bond, with a clean price of 96.1875, a Redemption Value of 100, a term of 665 days, and a YTM% of 7.78%. If the tax rate is 25% and the net YTM% is 6.37% (the grossed up net being 6.37/.75 = 8.59%). There are 65 a/i days. Find the clean price.

The net coupon is 5.50 x .75 = 4.125, consequently the net accrued is 65/182.5 x 4.125/2 = .734589

$$\frac{100 \times 1.031850^{-3} + 2.0625(1 - 1.031850^{-3}/.031850) + 2.0625}{1.031850^{\wedge}.643836} = DP$$

$$= 96.922254 - .734589 = 96.1877 = CP$$

```
The gross yield =   5.50 x 100/96.1875 = 5.72%
Net gross yield =   5.72 x .75          = 4.29%
```

Assume that the above example now has a "small company" Corporation tax requirement of 25% Find the net YTM%

This is equivalent to a Capital Gains Tax (CGT) of 25% and as the reader will be aware such a tax affects the gain (or loss) between purchase and sale, and in the context of net YTMs the "sale" is of course the redemption value (RV), or the "call" price.

The tax is applied to the difference between purchase and the RV and the formula is:

$$call - (tax/100 \times (call - cost)) = call^{t}$$

In the above formula the "call" value is employed, rather than the RV, for although the normal maturity value is 100 sometimes (see the US section in the previous chapter) the "call" or RV is different to 100, and so in the above example:

$$\text{call} - (\text{tax}/100 \times (\text{call} - \text{cost})) = \text{call}^t \text{ or } \text{RV}^t_t$$
$$100 - (25/100 \times (100 - 96.1875)) = 99.046875 \text{ RV}^t$$

Taking the same example, with a YTM of exactly 6.37%, find the price, with a CGT of 25%:

$$\frac{99.046875 \times 1.031850^{-3} + 2.0625(1 - 1.031850^{-3}/.031850) + 2.0625}{1.031850^{.643836}}$$

$$= 96.072030 - .0734589 = 95.337441 \text{ CP}$$

To Find a PRICE from a YTM% with a CGT Content
Now we have a problem. Suppose that with a 25% overall tax rate for a small company you are asked to find the clean *price* from a *net* YTM of 5.94%, a gross coupon of 5.5%, a call of 100 and a term of 665 days.

How can this be calculated – when the conventional method is to net the redemption value (call) by subtracting the price from the call? For, surely, it is the price which we need to find.

In other words, you can't subtract and then multiply a factor if you don't first know what it is. Some statisticians avoid the issue by saying that such a requirement is seldom if ever needed!

First it is necessary to find a *Notional Call* or RV by:

$$\text{CALL} - (\text{call} \times \text{tax}/100) = \text{notional RV}^n$$
$$100 - (100 \times .25) = 75$$

In this case the notional call appears to be an obvious 75, namely 100 – 25: but *never* mentally "short circuit" the calculation outlined above; for if the original call was 102 the notional call would *not* be 77 but would be 76.5   Try it and see!

The values for the net coupon, 4.125% and the a/i of .734589 obtain. With this notional RV find the notional *dirty* price:

$$\frac{75 \times 1.029700^{-3} + 2.0635(1 - 1.029700^{-3}/.029700) + 2.0635}{1.029700^{.643836}}$$

$$= 75.165699 \text{ DP}$$

This DP **must** be "cleaned" 75.1765699 − .734589 = 74.431110

The trick is to now to find a factor which will convert the notional clean price of 74.431110 to a true **clean price.**

```
Notional price ÷ (1 − ((CGT/100) x (1 + i/p)^−n + k))   =  Price

   74.431110   ÷ (1 − (   .25   x 1.029700^−3.6438360)) =   "

   74.431110   ÷ (1 − (   .25   x     0.898844   )   =   "

   74.431110   ÷ (1 − .224711)                       =   "

   74.431110   ÷     0.775289              96.004337 CP
```

To check: 100 − .25(100 − 96.004337) = 99.001084 RV^t

$$\frac{99.001084 \times 1.029700^{-3} + 2.0635(1 - 1.029700^{-3}/.029700) + 2.0635}{1.029700^{.643836}}$$

$$96.738926 - .734589 = \underline{96.004337}$$

Q.E.D.

The above is the conventional compound interest discounting for a bond life where there are more than one period payment between settlement and maturity (per > 1).

For *simple interest discounting* the denominator would thus be 1 + (.029700 x .643836).

Below is a complete set of formulae for both compound interest (CI) and simple interest (SI) calculations and for both a number of payments periods after settlement (per > 1) and when there are none (per < 1).

Per >1 (CI)

$$\frac{RV^t(1 + i/p)^{-n} + Da\underline{} + D}{(1 + i/p)^k} = NP\ (DP) - a/i = NP\ (CP)\ldots\ldots$$

$$\text{divided by}\quad 1 - \frac{CGT/100}{(1 + i/p)^{n+k}} = CP$$

Per >1 (SI)

$$\frac{RV^t(1 + i/p)^{-n} + Da\underline{} + D}{(1 + i/p)^k} = NP\ (DP) - a/i = NP\ (CP)\ldots\ldots$$

$$\text{divided by}\quad 1 - \frac{CGT/100}{(1+i/p)^n \times (1+(i/p \times k))} = CP$$

Per <1 (CI)

$$\frac{RV^t + D}{(1 + i/p)^k} = NP\ (DP) - a/i = NP\ (CP)\ldots\ldots$$

$$\text{divided by}\quad 1 - \frac{CGT/100}{(1 + i/p)^k} = CP$$

Per <1 (SI)

$$\frac{RV^t + D}{1 +(i/p \times k)} = NP\ (DP) - a/i = NP\ (CP)\ldots\ldots$$

$$\text{divided by}\quad 1 - \frac{CGT/100}{1 + (i/p \times k)} = CP$$

Where:

RV^t = Taxed Redemption Value or call

NP = Notional Price

$a\underline{}_{n|}$ = $1 - (1 + i/p)^{-n}/(i/p)$

CI = Compound Interest

SI = Simple Interest

per<1 = More than 1 period payment to come after settlement

per>1 = Less " " " " " " " "

C = Coupon

D = ½ Coupon

For ex–div calculations delete + D from the above numerators,

Conversions

In earlier chapters the conversion of nominal to effective rates was discussed at length as was, in less detail, the necessary conversion of semi–annual Eurobonds to the "norm" of nominal rating. A semi–annual based Eurobond with a 10% YTM must be converted to 10.25% (see Euro Section below), the reason being that if the "norm" is annual interest payments, a semi–annual interest rate stock must be worth more: the conversion is $(1 + 10/200)^2$ and then subtract one and multiply by 100 to equal 10.25%.

Sometimes, rarely, there are stocks with four interest payments per year and, logically following on from the above calculation, one would have thought that the "adjustment" for (say) 12.50% would be $(1 + 12.50/400)^4 - 1 \times 100 = 13.10\%$

But in the UK, brokers' statisticians tend to consider the semi-annual interest payments as the "norm", so when they meet quarterly payments they convert the rate somewhat unconventionally by $(1 + 12.50/400)^2 - 1 \times 200 = 12.70\%$

A UK stock which has these characteristics is a UK Government stock, namely 2.50% Consols (*undated* – no redemption value!) and conversion when necessary would take place on the lines above. If, therefore, the stock stood at 20 points the *gross* yield would be $2.50 \times 100/20 = 12.50$ but shown as 12.70%

Incidentally, before the ease of computer working many statisticians used the "800 rule":

Gross yield x (1 + gross yield/800) = Flat yield adjusted

$$12.50 \times (1 + 12.50/800) = 12.70\% \text{ Flat}$$

("Flat", because, being "undated", there is no redemption value and therefore no yield to maturity).

For the inquiring mind it should be added that the above is merely a simple transposition of:

$$200 \times ((1 + \frac{12.50}{400})^2 - 1) = 12.70$$

$$200 \times (\frac{12.50}{200} + \frac{12.50^2}{160,000}) = 12.70$$

$$12.50 \times (1 + \frac{12.50}{800}) = 12.70$$

The calculations with quarterly payments present no difficulty in that the nominal coupon is divided by 4, and the i/p multiplied by 400 presents the YTM%.

The accrued is found by normal means, with the a/i days being found by the calendar, for the (1 - k) method must never be used.

An alternative adjustment for a Call

In previous examples it was seen that for an early "call" the life of the bond between settlement day and the call date became the [n + k] and the RV naturally became the call amount. The RV was also adjusted by virtue of levy on capital gains, or corporation tax.

This method of altering the value of the RV, from par (100) to the requisite amount, would appear so simple that an alternative method would seem superfluous.

But a few years ago a well known small programmable calculator was introduced which had an in-built bond program with one drawback. For reasons best known to themselves the makers wrote a *constant* call value of 100 into the program, so anyone wishing to deal with a capital gains problem or an early call price was unable to do so.

The associated Manuals contained no advice on how to overcome this lack – probably because, at that time, the manufacturers were unaware of the disastrous oversight which they had, presumably, unwittingly, perpetrated!

The wails of frustrated statisticians in some banking and broking offices were in fact totally unnecessary, for the answer is simple.

The tip is to "adjust" both the price and the coupon by multiplying each by 100 and dividing by the value of the required RV (the call). If the call was 101, the coupon 10% and the price 90 the coupon would become 10 x 100/101 = 9.900990 and the price will become 90 x 100/101 = 89.11

For example, if the life between Settlement and the Call date is 665 days, giving an [n + k] of 3.64383561644, and if the coupon is 5½% the accrued would be 65 x 5.50/365 = 0.97945205480. If the call price was 104 and the clean price exactly 90 the YTM calculates as 13.8909111618.

Precisely the same YTM would be found if the RV reverted to its conventional par value of 100 and the coupon, the price *and the accrued* were all multiplied by 100 and divided by the call value, here 104.

If, on the contrary, a price was required from the YTM, the price found will be the *dirty* price which, in this example, would need to be multiplied by 104, divided by 100 and then have the a/i subtracted to provide the clean price.

Returning to the main example in this chapter, a 5.50% bond with a 665 day life, with 65 a/i days, a clean price of 96.1875 and a yield to maturity of 7.777501%, and the call value conventionally at par (100). To demonstrate the *capital* gains *tax procedure* assume that with a 25% income tax *and* a 25% CGT and to find the NET YTM% the coupon is brought to net (5.5 x .75 = 4.125) and the RV becomes:

$$100 - .25(100 - 96.1875) = 99.046875 \text{ (RV*)}$$

and employing a *net* YTM of 5.854256% the equation below will validate to a clean price of 96.1875

$$\frac{(99.046875 \times 1.029271^{-3}) + 2.0625(1-1.029271^{-3}/.029271) + 2.0625}{1.029271^{.643836}}$$
$$= 96.922089 - .734589 = 96.1875 \text{ CP}$$

If the call value was a constant 100, however, and could not consequently be adjusted, multiply both the price and the net coupon by 100 and divide by the RV* of 99.046875.

If we recalculate the above equation with these new factors, using the same i/p of .029271 and the RV as 100 the price found should (must) be as above – 96.1875. Adjusting the half net coupon of 2.0625 by 100/99.046875 equals 2.082347 and the CP before being "reconstituted", should come to 97.854767:

$$\frac{(97.854767 - (2.082347 \times 65/182.5)) \times \ 99.046875/100 = 96.1875}{(100.00 \times 1.029271^{-3}) + 2.082347(1-1.029271^{-3}/0.029271) + 2.082347}$$
$$1.029271^{\wedge}.643836$$

$$
\begin{aligned}
&= 97.854767 \\
97.854767 - (2.082347 \times 65/182.5) &= 97.113109 \\
97.113107 \times 99.046875/100 &= \underline{96.1875} \quad \text{Q.E.D}
\end{aligned}
$$

Duration and volatility

The duration of a loan is the weighted average of the life of the bond; the mean of the number of payment periods, which (except for zero coupon bonds) is always shorter than the normal [n + k] term of the loan. Because of the natural market fluctuations, the loan duration is sometimes considered to be a useful measurement of the risk factor. Indeed some consider that it is a better benchmark than the conventional YTM%. The duration value must be determined first if volatility is required; for the volatility is merely the duration value divided by 1 + (YTM% ÷ (p x 100)).

The volatility calculation, or elasticity as it is sometimes called, can be used to determine the new price of a bond after an increase or decrease of the YTM%. Although the resulting prices are not precise they are reasonably accurate and for a quick listing can often save the labour of a full calculation.

There are two ways of calculating the new prices using the volatility factor, depending on how you address the latter calculation. For the change in YTM values can be expressed

as the difference between the old and new values or as
an increased or decreased percentage.

```
Expressed as a difference, duration ÷ (1 + i/p)          = volatility
Expressed as a percentage, duration ÷ (1 + i/p) x (i/p) = volatility
```

The duration calculation is one of discounting each payment
period and takes into account the call or redemption amount;
in all a fairly simple schedule.

Assume a price is 96.1875, a coupon of 5.5%, and a call 100.
Assume, too, that the life and YTM have been calculated as
665 days and 7.777501%, respectively, (although to be precise
it always best to work out the full precision, of the YTM).

Cpn	YTM discounting		Denominator		Life		Numerator
2.75 x	1.038888	− .643836 −1.643836	= 2.683276	x	.643836	=	1.727588
" x	"	−2.643836	= 2.582836	x	1.643836	=	4.245757
" x	"	−3.643836	= 2.486155	x	2.643836	=	6.572986
" x	"	−3.643836	= 2.393094	x	3.643836	=	8.720040
100 x	"		= 87.021592	x	3.643836	=	317.092378

97.16695	338.358749
(the DP)	

(the minor decimal discrepancies stem from the abridged YTM)

$$\frac{338.\ 358749/97.1667}{2} = \underline{1.741121\ Duration}$$

and   1.741121/1.038888 = <u>1.675947 Volatility</u>

Using the volatility method of calculation, what would be the
new price if the YTM was raised by a *difference* of .16, namely
a lift from 7.778 to 7.938%?

```
(1 − (Volatility ÷ 100 x Difference)) x  Price   = Converted Price
(1 − (1.675947   ÷ 100 x    .16     )) x 96.1875 = 95.3296 or 95 15/16
```

And if the difference is *less* than the existing YTM?

Don't forget, the higher the YTM, the lower the price; so the
difference, here, must be *negative* in the calculation below:

```
(1 - (Volatility ÷ 100 x Difference)) x  Price  = Converted Price
(1 - (1.675947  ÷ 100 x  - .16  )) x 96.1875 = 96.445 or 96 7/16
```

Such calculated prices are not precise, but can be considered accurate to 2 places of decimals. Employing the BONDS formula/equation it will be found that the new yield of 7.777501 + .16, namely 7.937501%, will find a clean price of 95.927405.

An ex-div calculation
Assume a 6% bond, semi–annual, ex-div, with a YTM of 15% and a call of 100. The days between settlement and maturity are 4019 with 4 a/i days. Find the duration and volatility.

In this case the first odd-days discounting is ignored and, of course, this series of discountings will be for 22 periods instead of the much shorter cum-div calculation above. In this calculation the numerator will be found as 725.431103 and denominator 52.139927 (the DP) which finds an ex-div duration value of 725.431103/52.139927 x 2) = 6.956580 and the volatility there is 6.956580/(1 + 15/200) = 6.471237

Computer programming
As this type of calculation is pure "scheduling" there is little difficulty in programming a "step type" coding, for instance, in BASIC for a computer or for, say, a small Hewlett-Packard 12C Business Calculator; but should you have to fit such a program into Lotus 1-2-3 or any other type of spread sheet coding then the only method is to employ geometric progression instead of scheduling. And should the reader require further information on this exceedingly complex and tiresome calculation may I suggest he obtains a copy of my *Programs for Financial calculations* (a solutions book for the Hewlett-Packard 17B and 19B Business Calculators).

Duration and volatility with a tax element
There is no problem when income, corporation and/or capital gains tax are part of the requirements. The coupon and accrued interest must be brought to net values and the RV, when CGT or corporation tax applies, is adjusted normally.

The forward projected price

Reminding ourselves of the earlier example of a 5.50% Bond with a term of 665 days a price of 96.1875 and a found YTM of 7.777501%.

The above presupposes that if the yield to maturity is 7.777501% in 665 days time the price will be 96.1875; and we have already appreciated that there is a capital lift of 100 – 96.1875 between settlement and redemption – irrespective of any price variations being traded in the market.

One could say, therefore that half way between settlement and maturity the *notional price* would be $(100 - 96.1975) \div 2 = 1.9$ and so around 332 days *back from maturity* the notional price would be roughly $96.1975 + 1.90 = 98$ points, again quite irrespective of market forces.

There are a variety of reasons why finding a notional price is useful; for valuation purposes, for example, or to discover whether the current price on a certain day has "beaten the index" — that is whether it is standing above or below the creep up price.

Such a calculation is usually called the *forward projected price* which although correct, in essence, can lead to a misunderstanding.

For, in fact, all such calculations must stem from the maturity date being discounted *back* to the required date.

If, therefore, the owner of the above bond wanted to know the notional price some 500 days after settlement the $(m + k)$ would become $(665 - 500)/182.5 = .904110$ and as the term is less than one full period we can find the forward projected price by using original YTM and the abridged formula, namely:

$$\frac{100 + 2.75}{1.03889^{.904110}} = 99.27 \text{ dirty} - \text{FPP}$$

To clean the above we can, *for once*, use the $(1 - k)$ method, instead of correctly finding the precise number of days in the so-called a/i period – for the whole calculation is a useful aid, but not necessarily an exact science.

$$99.27 - ((1 - .904110) \times 2.75) = 99.00 \text{ clean} - FPP$$

This particular procedure was a valuable basis for the calculation of *net optimum yields* which were used in the UK to find the best time to sell Government Stock which, in days long ago, was gains taxed if sold within one year of purchase.

The astute investor, resisting the obvious desire to sell as soon as a possible, namely after a year and a day and then reinvest elsewhere, reasoned that it was best to delay his sale until the stock was "full of accrued interest".

YTMs a guide only
Before turning to individual markets there are two points worth mentioning. In the olden days before computers, when the guess and guess again interpolation method had to be used to find the YTMs the values were usually quantified in quarters of one per cent, namely 11% – 11.25% – 11.50% and so on. Not withstanding that such values were quantified they were looked upon as a useful guide, an investment tool, in general terms.

But since the advent of computers, with the invaluable facility of being able to find the YTM of any bond in microseconds to 15 places of decimals, far too many people, in my view, have gone completely overboard about YTM calculations.

Too many statisticians appear to be concerned not with the true reason for using YTMs, as a general guide to investment, but with new ways of calculating and recalculating YTMs in different guises in different modes – as we shall see, to our cost, when we come to the different market methods.

Furthermore, everyone seems to be so besotted with yields to maturity, as viewed from settlement day, that they seem to forget that different expenses required, over and above the normal purchase payments, will considerably affect their yield returns – worth thinking about perhaps!

Press Listings

When checking bond yield formula and calculations there is a natural tendency to check with the listings in the financial pages of the world's newspapers. Such quotations should be treated with considerable reserve. For the data provided to the press, by various market consultants, brokers etc, are rarely calculated daily, being interpolated, averaged and/or calculated by the volatility method.

For instance, when settlement is one day after purchase the date for yield calculations is always the next market day. But for a Friday listing the day taken for calculations *should* be the following Monday – but in the financial press it seldom is!

CHAPTER 13

The Various Bond Markets

The basic actuarial procedures

The reader glancing back at the section *The actuarial formula* in the previous Chapter, will see that both the bond yield formula and the basic concept of discounting the redemption value and each of the periodic payments back to the settlement date apply to all such calculations the world over.

Why then are there different bond markets as implied by the chapter heading above?

The simple answer is that the markets, while all employing the basic discounting process, use different calendars and, in some cases, provide a different number of periodic interest payments each year. Consequently, there are various permutations.

The financial calendar (30/360), with either annual or semi-annual interest payments, as employed in Eurobond calculations.

The "actual" calendar (365), with semi-annual interest payments, as employed in the London market for UK stock (or with quarterly payments, as sometimes in Australia).

A mixture of the above two methods, each method being applied to different types of stock, is employed in the United States.

Below, the three markets Euro, US, and UK, their methods of calculation, their differences and any problems peculiar to the individual market concerned, will be examined in detail. As these three markets and their methods cover in one way or another all the actuarial permutations we can be assured that lesser markets must conform. Thus, when dealing on other exchanges (and with present day communications, dominated by modem and facsimile, this is an everyday occurrence) all that is necessary is to discover the ground rules of that particular market. Having first established the calendar and the method of interest payments employed one can then discover the purely parochial requirements, such as the latitude permitted between purchase and settlement days etc.

Readers will recall that the Japanese use a formula which is *not* actuarially based, it is in fact an "averaging" formula and was used in the previous chapter as a good "back of an envelope" calculation – and one which is could be usefully employed, as a "first guess" in a computer program interpolation loop.

Eurobonds

Some years ago, when Eurobonds were first evolved, a number of firms engaged in their marketing formed an association, the Association of International Bond Dealers, more generally known as the AIBD.

As the AIBD was formed after the advent of computers, there were no inhibitions derived from past conventions or "quill pen methods", and the association bravely laid down quite specific rules as how their Eurobonds were to be calculated. There was no reason why they should not do this, and indeed every reason why they should.

After some understandable delays in obtaining agreement from the original 300 member firms, covering some 30 markets (920 and 40 respectively in 1990), a set of AIBD Rules and Regulations were drawn up and these are updated every year. Consequently, a price and YTM of a Eurobond is quoted in precisely the same terms all over the world, in New York, London, Tokyo and Zurich; a highly desirable state of affairs which is generally agreed to be of great advantage in marketing and overall dealing.

Alas, this sensible example and the desire to form a common enterprise has failed to enthuse any other markets and, as we shall see, there still remains considerable divergence in trading and calculating bonds, other than Euros.

It is true that some markets have general guidelines, but they have no body like the AIBD to impose sanction against non compliance and all too often liberties are taken; indeed some computer programs, notably in some business type calculators, attempting to cover all aspects of bond yield calculations, fail to be precise in any!

Let us start with the Eurobond market, where there are specific rules to establish the basis of calculations and we can then move on to see where the other markets diverge.

The AIBD Rules
Eurobonds provide interest payments annually, and should national characteristics make semi-annual payments necessary some conversions and adjustments need to be made.

The calendar base is 30/360 and the days between settlement and maturity are divided always by 360, unless a semi-annual conversion is required and then the base becomes 180. The prices are always quoted clean of the accrued, the discounting always being compound, not simple, interest.

Members are expressly forbidden to calculate other than in accordance with the rules and should a firm need to calculate by any other method this must be so stated and the method outlined.

The accrued interest, unlike that for other traded bonds, *should* always be rounded to 2 decimal places; and this is the only rule, I know, in which any divergence is overlooked. The reason is simply that the methods employed by the AIBD for Eurobonds, as we shall see later, is precisely the same as that used by the Americans for their commercial "corporate" bonds, save that in the latter case there is no requirement to round.

Hence many calculate Eurobonds employing US-orientated computer programs, with the a/i being found and subsequently dealt in to full precision, It's wrong, but it's done!

Settlement is seven days after the trade, i.e., the purchase.

The AIBD rule 224(2) states that should maturity fall on the 31st of any month (or the 28th or 29th of February) the affected anniversary periodic payment dates will be treated as the 30th of the month.

Net calculations

Understandably, however, when it comes to calculations related to tax there can be no specific "rules", for any investor requiring net calculations will inevitably employ those methods most appropriate to his own national tax legislation. Nowadays there is no divergence, but some years ago, before the "big bang" reorganisation on the London market, while the US included the accrued within the net profile while London did not. In those days London charged "expenses" on Gilts so that when CGT was calculated everything legitimate was included, whereas New York treated the cost as "clean of all".

Small points, admittedly, but mentioned to show that, nowadays, even with the strictly controlled Eurobonds it is largely upto the individual investor to decide how he wishes to steer his net calculations to determine a net YTM.

The annual equivalent

Conventionally, Eurobonds pay interest once per year, nevertheless there are some bonds which carry their national characteristics and have coupons with a semi-annual profile.

Obviously, from an investor's perspective, receiving payments twice a year is slightly preferable to being paid only once. To compare like with like there needs to be a slight adjustment, in fact one could consider the "annual equivalent", or in modern terminology the "annualised rate", to be the same as the effective rate.

For example, if the YTM was found to be 10% as the result of a semi-annual calculation then this must be converted to its effective rate, namely:

$$100 \left(\left\{ 1 + \frac{10.00}{200} \right\}^2 - 1 \right) = 10.25\%$$

Once the conversion is made the listing will show a YTM of 10.25(S) the (S) denoting that the Eurobond in question is semi-annual paid.

Don't forget that if you see a YTM with an (S) and wish to calculate a price the YTM must first be reconverted to its nominal rate by:

$$200(\left\{ 1 + \frac{10.25}{100} \right\}^{1/2} - 1) = 10.00\%$$

Comment

In the previous chapter the actuarial formula was outlined, with the legend which is used throughout the following pages. The AIBD formula for calculating their bonds is presented, in their Rule Book, in a somewhat different format; but the reader can be assured that, in fact, the calculation is *exactly* the same as the "actuarial" methods given in this book.

Below are three examples, an annual calculation, a semi-annual calculation, and a bond with less than one period to run to redemption.

These examples could equally well be a US Corporate Bond, the only difference, as we already have mentioned, is that the US bond would not have its accrued interest reduced to 2 places of decimals. Three is no rule as to the YTM but the most customary method is to calculate to three places.

```
Assume a 8.75% Eurobond
Yield to Maturity 8.88%. Call 100
Purchase    September  8, 1989 (Friday)
Settlement September 15, 1989 (Friday)
Maturity   July      30, 2001 (Monday)
Days between  Actual    4336
              30/360    4275
```
thus
```
(n + k)  4275/360      = 11.875000
A/i days 1 - .875 x 360 =   .125 x 360 = 45
The i/p = 8.88/100      =   .08880
```

Find the clean price.

$$\frac{100 \times (1.0888^{-11} + 8.75(1 - 1.0888^{-11}/.0888) + 8.75}{1.0888^{.875}} = 100.122566$$

$$100.122566 - 8.75 \times (1 - .875) = 100.122566 - 1.093750 = 99.028816$$
$$- 1.09 = 99.032566$$
$$= \underline{99.033} \text{ CP}$$

It will be observed the difference the correct rounding makes to the quoted price; which becomes 99.033, instead of the incorrect price of 99.029.

The price being so close to 99 one could assume that the original price was probably 99 precisely; consequently the price plus accrued interest was 99 + 1.09 and that the YTM, found as 8.884576, was rounded to 8.88%.

It will thus be seen therefore that a little common sense adjustment sometimes provides a clearer picture of the yields and prices in question.

Assume now that the above bond was a semi-annual bond, with the YTM being listed as 8.88%(S).

Being semi-annual the (n + k) will be 4275/180 = 23.75 and after converting to the nominal rate:

$$200((1 + 8.88/100)^{.5} - 1) = 8.691159\% \text{ nominal}$$

the price will be:

$$\frac{100 \times (1.043456^{-23} + 4.375(1-1.043456^{-23}/.043456) + 4.375}{1.043456^{.75}} = 101.506869$$

$$101.506869 - 8.75 \times (1 - .875) = 101.506869 - 1.093750 = 100.413119$$
$$- 1.09 = 100.416869$$
$$= \underline{100.417} \text{ CP}$$

Alternatively, in the case of a Eurobond with a short life to redemption of 250 days, an annual payments coupon of 10%, a call of 100 and a clean price of 99.90, the working dirty price will be 99.90 plus RND((1 - 250/360) x 10) = 99.90 + 3.06 = 102.96.

Reminding ourselves of the compound interest short short formula:

$$100\left(\left\{\frac{RV + Coupon}{Price + a/i}\right\}^{1/k} - 1\right) = YTM\%$$

and the above DP produces a YTM of:

$$100\left(\left(\frac{100 + 10}{102.96}\right)^{1/.694445} - 1\right) = \underline{9.992425\% \ (CI)}$$

Average life - sinking funds - calculations

Some institutional borrowers sometimes partially redeem their issues at various stages during the life of the bond. In such cases, naturally, the YTM% is of limited value.

The calculations require the exact structure of each redemption amount and the date when it was effected. This means not only checking back to the details of the original loan but also any interim arrangements. For while the redemption dates and values, once notified, cannot be rescinded there is nothing to stop the companies increasing their redemption amounts if they so desire.

Such changes are published from time to time in the financial press. The resulting weighted mean value becomes the $(n + k)$ factor in the conventional actuarial formula/equation.

Assume a 20 million Eurodollar bond issued December 15, 1969 with maturity 20 years later. The redemption dates fall each December 15, and the amounts are: 1978 & 1979, $500,000; 1980 - 1986 (incl), $1,000,000; 1987 & 1988, $1,250,000 and in 1989 (some 20 years after issue) the residual will be repaid to holders.

The method is to work backwards from maturity, and so the first value to determine is the residual, namely:

```
20 - ((1.25M x 2yrs) + (1M x 7yrs) + (.5M x 2 yrs)) = $9.50M.
```

Year	# years RD to Issue		Repayment amount		Calculated value
1989	20	x	9,500,000 **	=	190,000,000
1988	19	x	1,250,000	=	23,750,000
1987	18	x	1,250,000	=	22,500,000
1986	17	x	1,000,000	=	17,000,000
1985	16	x	1,000,000	=	16,000,000
1984	15	x	1,000,000	=	15,000,000
1983	14	x	1,000,000	=	14,000,000
1982	13	x	1,000,000	=	13,000,000
1981	12	x	1,000,000	=	12,000,000
1980	11	x	1,000,000	=	11,000,000
1979	10	x	500,000	=	5,000,000
1978	9	x	500,000	=	4,500,000
			20,000,000		343,750,000

No capital repayments made before 1978   ** residual

What is required now is the weighted mean of the above and this is 343,750,000/20,000,000 = <u>17.1875 (n + k) average life</u>

If no weighted mean program is available, and many small calculators now have such facilities, a quick method of calculating the average life, the (n + k), "on the back of an envelope" is to employ arithmetical progression, namely:

$$\frac{\text{First term (F) + last term (L)}}{2} \times \text{ number of periods(n) = SUM}$$

$$\frac{F + L}{2} \times n = S \quad (\text{where } n = (L - F) + 1$$

Taking the example above:

$$20 \times 9.5 \qquad\qquad = 190.00$$

$$2 \times \frac{19 + 18}{2} \times 1.25 \quad = 46.25$$

$$(17 - 11 + 1) \times \frac{17 + 11}{2} \times 1.00 \quad = 98.00$$

$$2 \times \frac{10 + 9}{2} \times .5 \quad = \underline{9.50}$$

$$343.75$$

And 343.75/20 = <u>17.1875 (n + k) average life</u>

Assuming that the Eurobond issue had a coupon of 10% and a life of 20 years the conventional YTM, at issue, would be, naturally, 10% providing the issue price is not at a discount.

$$100(1.10^{-20}) + 10a_{\underline{20|}} = 100.00 \text{ CP}$$

But the yield based on the average life would be 9.782865%

$$\frac{100(1.097829^{-17}) + 10a_{\underline{17|}}}{1.097829^{.1875}} = 100.00 \text{ CP}$$

Settlement before repayments commence
If, in the above example, settlement was on, say, December 15, 1977 *before* the partial payments the revised average life is simply 17.1875 – (years 1977 – 1969) = 9.1875.

This can be verified by rearranging the above schedule:

Year	# years RD to Issue		Repayment amount		Calculated value
1989	12	x	9,500,000	=	114,000,000
1988	11	x	1,250,000	=	13,750,000
1987	10	x	1,250,000	=	12,500,000
1986	9	x	1,000,000	=	9,000,000
1985	8	x	1,000,000	=	8,000,000
1984	7	x	1,000,000	=	7,000,000
1983	6	x	1,000,000	=	6,000,000
1982	5	x	1,000,000	=	5,000,000
1981	4	x	1,000,000	=	4,000,000
1980	3	x	1,000,000	=	3,000,000
1979	2	x	500,000	=	2,000,000
1978	1	x	500,000	=	,500,000
			20,000,000		183,750,000

And 183,750,000/20,000,000 = 9.1876 (n + k) average life

Settlement after partial payments have commenced
If, however, settlement occurs after some repayments have already been made then a careful calculation is required taking into account the number of days between settlement and maturity.

Suppose the above Eurobond was traded at a Euro quoted price of 99 (CP) with settlement May 29, 1984. In this case the YTM will be 10.214% and the average life yield will be 10.253%.

The above yields are found from:

```
May 29, 1984 - December 15, 1989 = 1996 days (30/360) and consequently,
(n + k) = 1996/360              =   5.544444
a/i     = (1 - .544444) x 10    =   4.56 (rounded)
DP      = 99 + 4.56             = 103.56 DP
```

$$\frac{100(1.102144648^{-5}) + 10a_{\overline{5}|} + 10}{1.102144648^{.544444}} = 103.56$$

The average life at settlement will be:

Year	# years RD to Issue		Repayment amount		Calculated value
1989	5.544444	x	9.50	=	52.672222
1988	4.544444	x	1.25	=	5.680556
1987	3.544444	x	1.25	=	4.430555
1986	2.544444	x	1.00	=	2.544444
1985	1.544444	x	1.00	=	1.544444
			14.00		66.872222

And 66.872222/14 = <u>4.776587 (n + k) average life</u>

BUT .776587 x 360 = 1719.57 days – call it 1720 days – and therefore the (n + k) becomes 1720/360 = 4.777778

Working to a DP of 99 + ((1 - .777778) x 10) = 101.22 the average life yield becomes 10.252711611%

$$\frac{100(1.102527111^{-4}) + 10a_{\overline{4}|} + 10}{1.102527111^{.777778}} = 101.22$$

One last example,

40 million Swiss Fr issued	April 20, 1990
Redemption Fr 2 million commencing	April 20, 1998
Residual amount Fr 26 millions	April 20 2005

There are 15 years between 1990 and 2005 and 7 years of redemption payments, from year 1998 through to year 2004 (*incl*), consequently the average life can be found as:

$$15 \times 26 = 390.00$$

$$(14 - 8 + 1) \times \frac{8 + 14}{2} \times 2 = \underline{154.00}$$
$$544.00$$

And $544.00/40 = 13.60$ $(n + k)$ average life

US Bonds

While there are inflexible AIBD Rules for calculating Eurobonds, the US calculations of bond prices/yields have no set rules as such, but there are advisory calculations as set out in *Standard Securities Calculation Methods*, published by the Securities Industry Association. This contains numerous examples outlining various "required" methods of US conventions for calculating yields to maturity for different classes of money market instruments. These advisory methods are consistent with those previously outlined in 1962 by the Bankers' Association of America.

There are two classes of US stock, US Government Bonds, usually referred to as Treasury Bonds (T bonds), and Corporate Bonds, bonds issued by US companies. The calendar used in the latter case is the financial calendar (30/360) and the calculations are *precisely* the same as those just outlined above for *semi-annual* Eurobonds, save that (as already mentioned) while the calculation of Eurobonds requires the accrued interest to be rounded to 2 places of decimals, the a/i for US Corporate Bonds is "true", unrounded and while often *presented* to 2 places of decimals is always worked at full precision.

The rule, outlined above for Eurobonds, that should maturity fall on the 31st of any month (or the 28th or 29th of February) the relevant anniversary periodic payment dates will be treated as the 30th of the month, also obtains for US Corporate Bonds.

US corporate bonds

The example used above for Eurobonds will serve equally well as one example for US Corporate Bonds calculations; for the difference between rounding and not rounding the accrued was stressed. Below this example will be recalculated with a *net* profile which, again, will serve as a semi-annual net Eurobond calculation, save for the a/i rounding.

US T Bonds and the Quasi-Coupon period

This class of bond, with its semi-annual interest payments, employs the actual calendar, but the base used to determine the (n + k) is *not* 182.5.

For in the United States *any* stock, other than US Corporate Bonds as mentioned above, must be calculated employing the *quasi-coupon periods* method. US T bonds and all "foreign" stocks (other than Eurobonds) therefore fall into this category.

This method first determines the number of payment periods within the term of the bond, namely the number of half years between settlement and maturity, the "n factor". Then the number of days between the two payment periods in which the settlement date occurs. This second factor must be either 181, 182, 183 or 184. Whatever the figure, it becomes the "base", instead of the 182.5 factor used in the original example, in the previous chapter, demonstrating the general method of calculating yields to maturity.

This base is then divided into the odd days (the days between settlement to the next payment date) to find the k factor, and also into the a/i days (days between settlement back to the previous payment date) which is then multiplied by the half coupon to find the (unrounded) accrued interest. In practice, this system is somewhat less complicated than the above explanation. *In this type of calculation leap days are included in both the odd and a/i days.*

If the *maturity* date falls on the last day of the month the *coupon payments* will also be made on the last day of the month; for example if maturity falls on September 30 then the interest payments will be made on March 31 and September 30.

US bond conventions
Interest is semi-annual, save in a few exceptional circumstances (see Appendix A).

The mode is either actual or 30/360 depending on whether the class of stock is US Treasury or "foreign" bonds. (A mix is only applicable for certificates of deposit and other forms of "commercial paper").

For "actual" calculations the quasi-coupon period method will *always* be employed, and leap years will be included.

Discounting is by compound interest for a life greater than 5 years. When there is less than five years to run to maturity, either simple or compound discounting may be employed, save that with under *one* period to run to maturity (PER < 1) *simple interest* is obligatory.

Presentation for YTMs is usually to 3 places of decimals, gross yield usually to 2 places. The presentation of prices, which are always quite clean of (unrounded) accrued interest, is user optional and depends to a large extent on the price structure – 99 and 1/2 = 99.50, whereas 99 3/16th would be 99.1875.

For tax purposes, the a/i is always treated as a *net* value for both call and coupon adjustment.

Settlement is one day after purchase for Treasury bonds and for other bonds seven days after purchase (it used to be 5 days). In the States private arrangements for delayed settlement are not uncommon. Concessions (discounts on broker commissions) on bargains are permitted on the NYSE and are also sometimes included in either price or yield transactions. Such price/yield concessions in no way affect the basic calculations.

On yields the concessions take the form of a decimal value, such as .1 or .05, which is added to the YTM; the price, after recalculation, being automatically lower. Alternatively, .25 or 1,50, for example, can be deducted from the price, thus automatically raising the yields.

Sometimes these price concessions are quoted as, say, "ten" or "five and a half" if the price multiples are $1,000. In that case subtract the concession from the price – if in multiples of 100 divide by 10 before subtraction. For example, $985 – 5.5 = 979.50 or $98.50 – .55 = 97.50.

Some examples
Looking once again at the Euro example above, which can now be treated as a US 8.75% (semi-annual) Corporate Bond, the equation, with the same YTM of 8.88% will present as follows:

```
Assume a 8.75% US Corporate Bond
The call 100
Yield to Maturity 8.88% (semi-annual)
Purchase    September  8, 1989 (Friday)
Settlement September 15, 1989 (Friday)
Maturity    July      30, 2001 (Monday)
Days between  Actual      4336
              30/360      4275
(n + k)   4275/180       = 23.75
A/i days 1 - .875 x 360 =   .125 x 360 = 45
The i/p = 8.88/200       =   .0444
```

Find the clean price.

$$\frac{100 \times (1.0444^{-23} + 4.375(1 - 1.00444^{-23}/.0444) + 4.375}{1.0444^{.75}} = 100.133759$$

dirty price

$100.133759 - 8.75 \times (1 - .875) = 100.133759 - 1.093750 = \underline{99.040009}$

$100.133759 - 4.375x (1 - .75) = 100.133759 - 1.093750 = \underline{99.040009}$

clean price

A US corporate 5% bond matures February 6, 2003. It was purchased at a price of 99 with settlement November 15, 1983. If the bond was called at 101 on February 1990 what is (a) the yield to maturity, (b) the yield to call and (c) the *net* YTM, if the tax bracket was 40% and gains tax 25%?

The YTM will be computer-found as 5.081467%, the yield to call as 5.326893% and the net YTM as 3.059345%

The days between settlement and maturity (30/360) are 6921 and between settlement and the call date are 2241, consequently the two (n + k) values are 6921/180 = 38.45 and 2241/180 = 12.45 respectively. In both cases the (gross) a/i = (1 - .45) x 5/2 = 1.375, thus the (gross) DP is 100.375. For the net profile the price will be 99 + (1.375 x .6) = 99.825.

$$\frac{100 \times (1.025407^{-38} + 2.5(1 - 1.025407^{-38}/.025407) + 2.5}{1.025407^{.45}} = 100.375$$

(a)

and for the "call":

$$\frac{101 \times (1.026634^{-12} + 2.5(1 - 1.026634^{-12}/.026634) + 2.5}{1.026634^{.45}} = 100.375$$

(b)

The net RV for a 25% CGT = 100 - .25(100 - 99) = 99.75

$$\frac{99.75 \times (1.015297^{-38} + 1.5(1 - 1.015297^{-38}/.015297) + 1.5}{1.015297^{.45}} = 99.825$$

(c)

Some comparisons

Readers will recall the example used, in the previous chapter, to demonstrate the workings of a bond yield calculation. In that example the 5.5% bond was actual based, there being 665 days between settlement and maturity with a clean price of 96.1875. The YTM found was 7.777501%

If the same example applied to a US Corporate bond the days between, employing the financial calendar, would be 656 and the (n + k) would become 656/180 = 3.644444 and the 5.5/2 x (1 – .644444) = .977778 and the DP therefore becomes 97.165278. The YTM will be found as 7.777144%

$$\frac{100(1.038886^{-3} + 2.75(1 - 1.038886^{-3}/.038886) + 2.75}{1.038886^{.644444}} = 97.165278$$

If this bond had been a US Treasury Bond the quasi-coupon period method would have to be applied.

In this case there are 3 semi-annual periods and 117 odd-days. Assume that there are 182 days between the payment date prior to settlement and the next payment date.

Consequently the (n + k) becomes 3 + 117/182 = 3.642857 and, to meet a DP of 96.1875 + (2.75 x (1 – .6426875)) = 97.169643, the YTM is 7.778077%.

When employing the quasi-coupon period method the base days are always an integer, consequently the (1 - k) method, above, is perfectly legitimate.

$$\frac{100(1.038890^{-3} + 2.75(1 - 1.038890^{-3}/.038890) + 2.75}{1.038890^{.642857}} = 97.169643$$

One last example for US bonds; assume a "short dated" bond with only 98 days to run from settlement, February 7, 1988, to maturity, May 15, 1988, with base days of 182 days. Consequently there are 182 – 98 = 84 a/i days (1 leap day *included*).

As the convention is that a 4.75% US short (PER < 1) term note will be discounted by simple *interest methods*, if the DP is the clean price (99.875) plus the a/i of 84/182 x 4.75/2 the YTM will be:

$$200(\frac{100 + 4.75/2}{99.875 + 4.75/2 \times 84/182} - 1) \times \frac{1}{98/182} = 5.164\% \text{ YTM}$$

In parenthesis, if the above calculation was determined by a computer program not designed for quasi-coupon methods the base would be 182.5 and the leap day would be ignored, the YTM becoming:

$$200(\frac{100 + 4.75/2}{99.875 + 4.75/2 \times 84/182.5} - 1) \times \frac{1}{97/182.5} = 5.243\% \text{ YTM}$$

UK Bonds

General

Within the compass of market conventions, such as the consistent use of the actual calendar, payments being semi-annual and the price (nowadays) being quoted clean of the accrued, the London Market has no "rules", advisory or mandatory, as how to determine yields or prices. Any such calculations tend to be largely at the whim of the individual statistician or data processing manager – this has certain disadvantages for the inquisitive student!

The London market

This is no place to discuss the relative merits of the old jobber/broker system and the new "market makers", save to say that as this market does not employ bearer shares the ownership of a purchase is "registered", either with the Bank of England in respect of Government Stock or the Registrars of individual companies.

Purchases and sales are married up and any changes are duly reported to the respective registrars. In due course, on the due date, dividends or interest are posted to the holder.

As a result of this system it is inevitable that there will sometimes be a period when the purchaser of new shares is not registered in time to receive the dividend due – which is, or has been, posted to the old owner.

On such occasions the seller will forfeit his dividend, which will be collected by the broker and forwarded to the new owner.

To assist in these tiresome and complex arrangements, companies state that after a certain date shares, when bought or sold, are said to be "without the divided recently announced", namely that such shares are *ex-dividend*.

In respect of Government stock the Bank of England rules that all government securities are ex-dividend exactly 37 days prior to the next interest payment date – unless the declaration date falls on ta Saturday, Sunday or Bank Holiday. in which case D-day falls on the "next day for dealing" i.e., 35 or 36 days prior.

Market conventions
Or perhaps one should say lack of conventions.

The actual calendar is used, and leap days are ignored. The base is 182.5, some statisticians allow the half-day in the "odd-days" but never in the accrued interest days.

Payments are semi-annual, with prices being quoted clean of a/i.

"Shorts", those stocks with under five years to run to maturity, or short shorts, with under one payment period, can be calculated either by compound or simple interest. If redemption falls on a Sunday adjustments are permissible (see Chapter 12).

Occasionally, certain Government Securities are quoted with *two* redemption dates. The rule is that the *longest* date is taken as the maturity date providing the *clean* price of the stock is below the par value (100) – see Chapter 12.

Ex-dividend calculations

With ordinary shares ex-dividend purchases or sales make no difference to the (gross) yields, but with fixed interests stocks the yield to maturity is obviously affected by when the interest payment is, or is not due. The price of the stock is naturally affected if the purchase is cum or ex-div.

Consequently, there is a slightly different format to the formula for ex-dividend calculations.

Looking back at the formula, in the previous chapter, it will be seen that for an ex-dividend bond yield calculation the last D (semi-annual interest payments) in the numerator is deleted.

The ex-dividend accrued interest is *added* to the dirty price to provide a clean ex-dividend price. The a/i being found from multiplying the half coupon by the number of days from settlement to the next payment date (the "odd-days"), divided, as usual, by the base employed. In fact, this is the "k" factor and the correct number of odd-days must be found.

Take a UK debenture with a coupon of 6%, a call of 100, a life of 4019 days, and thus an "n" factor of $4019/182.5 = 22.021918$ If the quoted ex-div price is 54.50 what is the ex-div YTM%?

First the dirty price must be found by *subtracting* an accrued value of $4/182.5 \times 3 = .065753$ from the clean price.

By computer/calculator program the YTM will be found as 14.340214% nominal which divided by 200 = .071701:

$$\frac{100 \times 1.071701^{-14} + 3(1 - 1.071701^{-14})/.071701)}{1.071701^{\wedge}.021918} = 54.434247 \text{ DP}$$

and 54.434247 *plus* .065753 = 54.50 clean price.

Zero coupon bonds

Before leaving the various markets, there is one class of bond which has, in the last few years, become popular for tax reasons.

In short, these bonds have no coupon, no interest payable during the life of the bond, the attraction being the expectation of capital gains. A bond, for example. issued at 50 will, by the application of compound interest – annual or semi-annual – creep up to the maturity value of 100 over the years, thus providing a capital gain.

It should not be thought that because there is no coupon, and therefore no annual income, the benefit is solely a matter of capital gains – which may or may not be taxed at maturity.

For the taxation of zero or strip bonds is peculiar to the revenue requirements of individual countries. In Canada, for example, there is no capital gains tax but tax is levied on the assessed interest *every three years* which is added to the other annual income of the bond holder.

Taking an example of a 10% semi-annual zero-coupon bond, based 30/360, purchased May 19, 1986 with maturity June 30, 2000, find the price, at Issue, if the maturity value is 100. The 30/360 "days between" is 5081 days.

$$\$100 \div 1.05^{(5081/180)} = 25.227440 = \$25.23 \text{ quoted.}$$

A Canadian Treasury strip bond, another word for a zero coupon bond, with an interest rate of 11½% and a redemption value of Cdn\$ 2,040 on September 1, 2005. The price of the bond, at settlement, on September 9, 1987 is Cdn\$ 288. If the amount purchased is Cdn\$ 130,000 what is the realisation at maturity?

Canada uses the 365 calendar, thus there are 6562 days between settlement and redemption (excluding leap days).

$$\$200((2040/288)^{1/(6562/182.5)}) - 1) = 11.191533\%$$

$$\$130,000 \times (1 + 11.191533/200)^{35.956164} = \$920,833.33$$

In this case the three years' interest will be $130,000 x 11.5/100 x 3 = $44,850 which would be added to the other annual income of the bond holder.

CHAPTER 14

Anomaly and Annuity Bonds

General
Unhappily life is never simple and as soon as the statistician has mastered the conventional methods of calculating this or that, he or she will immediately find that there are various other ways of doing the same thing! Bond yield calculations are no exception.

For various market demands often require different methods of calculation to achieve the desired end, as instanced in the next example.

When the 1st coupon differs from the remaining interest payments
For reasons, which usually become obvious, the first payment after an Issue may sometimes differ from the remaining payments.

Take the example of a 13.25% UK Government stock issued at 100.00 on 17th July 1975 to be redeemed (at Par) on 22nd July 1997; the half annual payment dates would, conventionally, occur on the "anniversary" dates of 22nd Jan/July. But it would be absurd for the first interest payment to be made on 22nd July only five days after Issue; so sensibly the Bank of England stated that it would make a slightly increased payment on the first "actual" payment date, 22nd January 1976 – some 189 days after Issue. And this will be $13.25/2 \times 189/182.5 = 6.860959$, and, because of the lenders' benefit rule, it is rounded up to **6.87**.

Once settlement has passed the first actual payment date all future calculations become conventional, but between Issue and the first payment date, 22nd January 1976, the first interest payment must be 6.87 instead of 13.25/2.

In that case assuming settlement was on 1st October 1975, with a *clean* price of 96 precisely, what is the YTM%?

Remember that although there is a "k" factor *there is no accrued interest*, for no interest is due until the first (next) actual payment date. The required "life days" are 7959 and this divided by 182.5 = 43.610959 to provide the n + k factor. But consider; owing to the rearrangements above there is one *less* payment so the (n + k) will therefore be 42.610959, and assuming a YTM of 14.268% we can check the Issue price of 96 (here a DP).

$$\frac{(100 \times 1.071342) + 6.625(1 - 1.071342^{-42}/.071342) + 6.87}{1.071342^{.610959}} = 96.00$$

Alternatively, consider a 9.50% UK Government Issue 14th January 1976 at 93.25 is to be redeemed at 100 on 14 May 1980, the payment dates being 14th May/November. The Bank of England stated that the first interest payment, due on 14th May 1976, instead of 4.75, would be 9.50/2 x 120/182.5 = 3.123288, rounded to 3.13. There are 1580 days between Issue and Maturity giving an (n + k) of 8.657534. Find the YTM% at Issue. Assuming a YTM of 11.535% the following equation will meet the quoted Issue "dirty" price of 93.25.

$$\frac{(100 \times 1.057675^{43} + 4.75(1 - 1.057675^{43}/.057675) + \mathbf{3.13}}{1.057675^{.610959}} = 93.25$$

When maturity date differs from the last coupon date
It is rare for a public bond issue to have the final date of the interest payment and the date for repayment of the redemption value not matching. For a possibly awkward issue date is usually overcome by adjusting the date or value of the first payment.

But difficulties do sometimes occur, for example when loans, not on offer to the general public are private contractual arrangements between (say) Institutions and Local Government Authorities. For even nowadays Local Authorities are somewhat inflexible in their approach to their interest payment dates; the long established custom in many

Authorities being that interest payments will be made *only* twice a year, usually March 31 and September 30.

Such bonds are usually "bought for redemption" and are rarely traded. Nevertheless, it is still often necessary, perhaps for valuation purposes, to be able to determine the price at any point in time between the original issue date and the final redemption date. And so it is necessary to know how to calculate prices and yields when the last interest payment is before or after the final redemption repayment.

When maturity occurs AFTER last payment date (LPD)
Assume a 2.50% LGA bond issued July 27 1985 for three years, the final redemption date being July 27 1988. Redemption Value (or "call" if you prefer it) is 100 and the issue price is 83.47. This, as we shall see later, provides an YTM% at issue of 9.25% The dates for payment by this LGA are March 31 and September 30.

The first thing to remember is that the date of redemption is not important, what *is* important is the *last* payment date, from which interest is added or subtracted. The life of the above example, therefore, is not July 27 1985 through to July 27 1988 but is July 27 1985 to March 31 1988, namely 977 days (naturally ignoring any leap days). And the number of interest days from last payment date (3.311988) to final maturity (7.271988) is 118 days.

```
977/182.5  = 5.353425 (n + k)  and  118/182.5  = .646575 ( t )
2.50/2     = 1.25 = D
(D x t)    = 1.25 x .646575 = .808219 = .81
             (this value must be rounded as it is cash received)
1 + i/p    = 1 + 9.25/200    = 1.046250
```

$$\frac{((RV + (D \times t)) \times (1 + i/p)^{-(n+t)} + Da_{\overline{n}|} + D}{(1 + i/p)^k} = DP$$

$$\frac{(100 + .81) \times 1.046250^{-5.646575}) + 1.25(1 - 1.046250^{-5}/.046250) + 1.25}{1.046250^{.353425}}$$

$$= 83.47 \ DP$$

Accrued Interest

Since, for the purposes of valuation, the yield is assumed, the price found is usually the dirty price, the additional accrued interest being thought irrelevant. But if for other reasons a clean price is required, find the correct number of calendar days from settlement or valuation day back to the last payment date. In the above example 5 days and 5 x 2.5/2 ÷ 182.5 = 0.034247 and 83.47 − .034247 = 83.44 clean price. In these circumstances, of course, the $(1 - k)$ method must never be used.

Maturity BEFORE Last Payment Date (LPD)

This situation is rare, indeed I know no bond with such characteristics, nevertheless the formula is set out below.

9% Bond with a YTM of 15%, with a life (valuation date − LPD) of 725 days with 118 days interest not liable, the final payment being the redemption value plus coupon *less* the 118 days interest.

In this case the DP will be found as 84.62 resulting from the formula below:

$$
\frac{((RV - (D \times t)) \times (1 + i/p)^{+(n-t)} + Da\underline{\quad} + D}{(1 + i/p)^{k}} = DP
$$

The difference between the two formula is the [+] or [-] of the $(D \times t)$ factor.

Split Coupons – Convertibles

Many years ago, the board of a UK industrial company issued a prospectus for a debenture loan and, for reasons best known to themselves, decided that the coupons would be split so that for the first nine years they would be at 8% nominal, and for the remaining sixteen years at 12% nominal. The issue price was 95 but there was no mention of either the gross yield or the yield to maturity at issue.

As this structure was, at that time, a newcomer to the market such an omission caused no little concern, for no computer program was then available and no formula immediately apparent.

A few days later, talking to a friend about a totally different subject, I casually mentioned the issue to be told that it was not a favourite subject. Expressing the surprise, and stating that the YTM came to a shade under 10%, I was asked how on earth I knew.

For, I was told, several statistical departments had spend angry hours converting existing mainframe programs to find the YTM.

Somewhat embarrassed, as my friend was one of the leading statisticians in the City, I was able to show him in a few seconds on a cheap calculator, with DCF facilities, that the IRR was 4.993604% and the YTM 9.99%. So sometimes the less experienced are better able to see the wood for the trees...

For the answer was that while the required YTM was *at Issue* it meant that there were no odd-days to worry about and that there was no trouble about non-integer entries. The discounting is below:

```
Investment                                        = -95.00
Cash flows
                                 -1
   4  x   ä___  x  1.04993604                      =  46.78
          18|
                                 -19
   6  x   ä___  x  1.04993604                      =  38.95
          31|
                                 -50
   (6 + 100)    x  1.04993604                       =   9.27
                                            NPV  =    0.00
Consequently the IRR is 4.99360404608% and (x 2) the YTM%  =   9.987
```

In case the reader has forgotten the DCF group calculations (see Chapter 6) the annuities *due* factor is:

$$\ddot{a}_{\overline{n}|} = ((1 - (1 + i/p)^{-n}/(i/p) \times (1 + i/p)$$

and taking the second series above:

$$6 \times ((1 - 1.04994^{-31})/.0449) \times 1.04994 \times 1.04994^{-19} = 38.95$$

To find the Gross (flat) yield needs a little thought. Normally the flat yield is (coupon x 100/price) but in this case with two coupons it means that the final value used must be the result of a "weighted mean" calculation.

$$\frac{(cpn \times per) + (cpn \times per)}{per + per} = \frac{(8 \times 9) + (12 \times 16)}{9 + 16} = 10.56\% \text{ COUPON}$$

and 10.56 x 100/95 = **gross** (flat) yield = 11.12%

The Actuarial Formula for "Split Coupons"
While *at Issue* the YTM can be found by DCF methods, as seen above, but as soon as we have a settlement day, with the consequent odd-days, such calculations cannot be done on a conventional DCF program; and so, below, is set out the correct split coupon formula

$$\frac{RV(1 + i/p)^{-n} + Da\underline{\quad}_{n\,|} - (D - D')a\underline{\quad}_{n'\,|} + D'}{(1 + i/p)^k} = DP$$

Where D' = the first ½ coupon
D = the second ½ coupon
n' = 1st (coupon) period

Taking the above example, with the nominal YTM as 9.98720809216% at Issue:

$$\frac{100(1.049934^{-50}) + 6a\underline{\quad}_{50\,|} - (6 - 4)a\underline{\quad}_{18\,|} + 0.00}{1.049934^{0.00}} = 95.00$$

issue CP

(the 0.00 factors stand above because the bond was "at issue")

Assume now that the loan has been running and that it is traded and settled some 6662 days to redemption at a YTM of 10.50% nominal.

What is the quoted price?

The (n + k) = 6662/182.5 = 36.50410959

There are therefore 32 half years at $(12/2)\%$, consequently there must be $36 - 32$ half years at $(8/2)\%$ and assume that there are 91 a/i days.

$$\frac{100(1.0525^{-36}) + 6a_{\overline{36}|} - (6-4)a_{\overline{4}|} + 4.00}{1.0525^{0.50410959}} = 106.195757$$

$$106.196 - (91 \times 4/182.5) = 106.196 - 1.994521 \quad = 104.201 \text{ CP}$$

Convertibles

This split coupon formula can be employed for convertibles, for in effect such bonds have two coupons.

For example, a 9% bond, semi-annual interest paid, was Issued at 100 with 100 to be paid at Redemption, March 1980. It is converted into a 9% stock to be redeemed at 110 March 2000. Every unit of £100 held before conversion would be worth 10% more after conversion.

Consequently, the 9% coupon is now worth 9.90% and in the same way the 100 RV will be worth 110. If an investor purchased stock 1412 days *prior* to conversion at 94.75 (CP) What was his YTM% at purchase?

The N value must be $(20 \times 2) + (1412/182.5) = 47.736986$ and the n' factor becomes just the periods $(47 - 40) = 7$. The first coupon = 9%, the second coupon 9.9% and the accrued interest is 48 days x $9/365 = 1.183562$

$$\frac{110(1 + i/p)^{-47} + (4.95 \times (1 - (1 + i/p)^{-47}/(i/p))) - (4.95 - 4.5) \times (1 - (1 + i/p)^{-7}/(i/p)) + 4.50}{(1 + i/p)^{.736986}} = 95.93$$

and by computer/calculator program a YTM of 10.277% will be found for a (95.93 - 1.183562) clean price of 94.75

Currency considerations

When investing in bonds not of the country of the (domiciled) investor the concern is always what effect a currency revaluation will have on the investor's return. For if the revaluation is against the investor his income payments and his final redemption value will be adversely affected in terms of his own currency. And, of course, the converse is equally true.

The split coupon method of calculation can be usefully applied to the interest received before and after the revaluation. But whereas the coupon calculation is a quite straight adjustment of the percentage revaluation, more difficulty arises when determining the equation for the revaluation of the maturity value. It cannot be the original par value before revaluation or the original value adjusted by the percentage increment/decrement. For there are some periods relating to the RV "before and after" revaluation.

So the calculation once again must be a weighted mean. The example below will elaborate this important point.

Suppose that a 10% Eurobond was issued in XYZ currency with a call value of 100 at the end of 12 years (360 x 12 = 4320 days). After some 3 years (360 x 3 = 1080 days) the XYZ currency was valued upward by 5% against the US dollar.

A US investor, for one reason at least, found this revaluation not unwelcome; for he had purchased his bond at 89.56 some 700 days after issue and, as will be seen from the chart below, had held his stock some 380 days before revaluation. Thus his calculations were based on 380 days at 10% and 3240 days to redemption at 10.50%.

```
ID────────────────────────────────────────RD
     10%      re|val:        10.50%
   ID───────────────|────────────────────────RD
      |             |         3240 days
   10% |    10%    |         10.50%
   ID───────SD──────|────────────────────────RD
    700  |  320   |         3240 days
          SD───── 3620 days ───────────────RD
```

His YTM at purchase is 11.825% and he naturally wants to know what his YTM is from revaluation date to redemption, some 3620 days or 10 years and 20 odd-days onward. Consequently the (n + k) is 3620/360 = 10.055556.

The RV must be weighted:
```
(100 x 380/3620) + (105 x 3240/3620) = 104.4751318 call
```

The Eurobond original quotation was 89.56 (CP) and to convert this to a dirty price for YTM calculation:
```
89.56 + (10 x (1 - .055556)) =  89.56 + 9.4400  =  99.00 DP
```

$$\frac{104.4752(1 + i/p)^{-10} + 10.50a_{\overline{10|}} - .5a_{\overline{1|}} + 10}{(1 + i/p)^{.055556}} = 99.00 \text{ DP}$$

A computer program will find the YTM as 12.540% against the original YTM before revaluation of 11.825% – and please note that 11.825 x 1.105 does NOT equal 12.54!

Inflation

The split coupon discipline, having facilities for incorporating different coupon values during the life of a bond, permits various modelling exercises to be undertaken if required – currency revaluation being just one of them.

Some statisticians include inflation factors in such evaluations, but because these are inevitably loaded with assumptions, some scepticism as to their real usefulness persists. My own view is that the inflation indices of different countries are, usually, of more value in assessing the likelihood, or not, of re- or de-valuation in future years, rather than being material for imprecise and often complex calculation.

Nevertheless, if ever evaluations have to be made for investments in various countries with high annual inflation this factor obviously should not be totally ignored and any related calculation should include some suitable comment – even if only to the effect that such countries are best avoided for investment purposes!

Switching

It is no part of this book to give investment advice – just the calculations; but one final point, I think, needs to be made. Obvious it may be; but unhappily time and time again the rule is ignored.

When comparing the value of one bond against another the calculations *must* be similar. Comparing the yield listing of a Eurobond against a listing of a UK Debenture, each calculated by totally different means, is valueless.

The only sensible approach, if such comparisons are to be made, is to calculate *both* stocks by the *same* method, irrespective of which procedure is used. For I have seen cases where a switch between two stocks looked both attractive and obvious, until this practice was adopted when it became immediately apparent that the last thing that should be considered was the planned switch!

Immediate reinvestment

The whole concept of bond yield calculations, and indeed all amortised types of formula/equations, is based on the assumption that any interest is immediately reinvested at the IRR, the internal rate of return.

But, in practice, in the real world, is this always possible?

The whole matter of reinvestment at a more realistic "going rate" could perhaps warrant a detailed study. Earlier chapters on Discounted Cash Flow Calculations, Modified IRR and Financial Management Rate of Return refer.

Annuity Bonds

So far as I am aware, at the time of writing, there are not any of these rather rare types of bonds traded on the UK Market; but there have been in the past and there is no reason why there should not be other such Issues in the future.

Remembering the consternation mentioned above when there was no formula or program readily available for the split coupon problem, it would therefore seem sensible to cater for such eventualities.

Perhaps, the best way to understand annuity bond calculations is to take as an example of one such bond which came to maturity at the end of 1988.

On October 15, 1980 Zimbabwe made an issue of an annuity bond with a nominal annual interest rate of 10.25%, with payments of £50 each half year. The payments were in arrears, consequently the first interest payment was April 15, 1981. The final payment would be on October 15, 1988.

The above provides a present value (loan amount) of:

$$50a_{\overline{16|}} \text{ at } (10.25/2)\% = PV$$

$$50 \times ((1 - 1.05125^{-16})/.05125)) = £537.10 \text{ rounded.}$$

It will be appreciated that in this type of bond there is no redemption value or "call", for once the bond has matured all the repayments have been completed and there is "nothing more to come".

The Dirty Price/YTM

Prices are simple to calculate in that the equation is the same as any normal bond yield calculation, save that there is, unusually, no redemption value of 100 or "call" price. If, therefore, settlement occured on February 22, 1984 it will be found that there are 1694 days to maturity (October 15, 1988) ignoring any intervening leap days.

Dividing the life days by 182.5 we obtain an (n + k) of 9.282192 and, taking the yield to maturity as 13% nominal, the equation displays as:

$$\frac{pmts.a_{\overline{n|}} + pmts}{(1 + i/p)^k} = \frac{50a_{\overline{9|}} + 50}{1.065^{.282192}} = 376.06$$

$$\frac{(50 \times (1 - (1.065^{-9}))/.065) + 50}{1.065^{.282192}} = 376.06$$

The Clean Price

To find the clean price presents some difficulties. In the old days such bonds were always presented with dirty prices but since the UK Market reorganisation all such prices are now required to be quoted clean of accrued interest.

The conventional method of calculating the accrued does *not* obtain, the accrued is *not* a/i days ÷ 182.5 x 50 = 35.89

Before examining the correct method for this type of stock consider the schedule below.

The Issue date is October 15, 1980 and Present Value = £537.10

#	DATE	BAL	RATE/200		INTEREST	PMTS	End Month Balance
1	15 April 81	537.10	x .05125	=	27.53 + 527.10	− 50	= 514.63
2	15 Oct 81	514.63	x "	=	26.37 + 514.63	− 50	= 491.00
3	15 April 82	491.00	x "	=	25.16 + 491.00	− 50	= 466.16
4	15 Oct 82	466.16	x "	=	23.89 + 466.16	− 50	= 440.05
5	15 April 83	440.05	x "	=	22.55 + 440.05	− 50	= 412.60
6	15 Oct 83	412.60	x "	=	21.15 + 412.60	− 50	= 383.75
7	15 April 84	383.75	x "	=	19.67 + 383.75	− 50	= 353.42
8	15 Oct 84	353.42	x "	=	18.11 + 353.42	− 50	= 321.53
9	15 April 85	321.53	x "	=	16.40 + 321.53	− 50	= 288.01
10	15 Oct 85	288.01	x "	=	14.76 + 288.01	− 50	= 252.77
11	15 April 86	252.77	x "	=	12.95 + 252.77	− 50	= 215.72
12	15 Oct 86	215.72	x "	=	11.06 + 215.72	− 50	= 176.78
13	15 April 87	176.78	x "	=	9.06 + 176.78	− 50	= 135.84
14	15 Oct 87	135.84	x "	=	6.96 + 135.84	− 50	= 92.80
15	15 April 88	92.80	x "	=	4.76 + 92.80	− 50	= 47.56
16	15 Oct 88	47.56	x "	=	2.44 + 47.56	− 50	= 00.00

The Accrued Interest

The accrued interest in this type of loan is *not* the number of a/i days multiplied by the coupon divided by 365, for, since there is no final repayment of the loan at maturity, it will be appreciated that the interest is partly repaid as part of the "coupon".

Inherently, in each payment contains a slice of interest and before the statistician can determine the amount of interest due, the relevant "period" must be found.

With settlement on February 23, 1984 (an (n + k) factor of 9.282192) it will be seen from the above schedule that the next following interest payment date is April 15, 1984 and the value of the interest due is £19.67.

It will, therefore, be seen from the schedule that the precise interest period required, derived from the settlement date in question, is the 7th half year.

Without the benefit of the schedule the figure 7 can be found from the total number of periods less the "n" factor, namely here, (16 − 9) = 7.

With 130 accrued interest days we therefore have an accrued interest factor of 131/182.5 x 19.67 = 14.119288 and consequently a DP of £376.06 − 14.11 = £361.94 *Clean Price.*

Ex-dividend Calculations

There is no problem regarding ex-dividend calculations, for they are dealt with in the normal way by deleting in the formula the payment from the numerator and treating the accrued interest conventionally as the number of days between settlement and next payment multiplied by the interest amount due, divided by the base.

The Zimbabwe prospectus advised all annuitants that "balances would be struck" one month prior to the payment dates, *in other words the stock would go ex-div on the 15th of March and September. Settlement occurred on April 2, 1984 .*

Assuming, the same YTM of 13%, and an ex-dividend number of days of 1656 days to Maturity, the (n + k) factor would be 1656/182.5 = 9.073973 and the equation would become:

$$\frac{50 \times (1 - 1.065^{-9})/.065}{1.065^{\wedge}.073973} = £331.26 \text{ DP}$$
$$(ex\text{--}div)$$

The accrued interest calculation, to find the clean price, follows the same general principles for cum–div presentation; with the difference that the interest due on the 15th April 1984, is multiplied by the 13 a/i days, and *added* to the DP:

$$331.26 + (19.67 \times 13/182.5) = £332.66 \text{ Clean Price}$$
$$(rounded)$$

To Find the Interest Amount
Without the assistance of a schedule the correct interest amount, above £19.67, can be found my formula:

$$(Loan \times (1 + i/p)^{t-1)} - (pmts \times ((1 + i/p)^{t-1} - 1)/(i/p)) = bal$$
$$\times i/p = int$$

where "t" is the period required – in the above example # 7.

$$((537.10 \times 1.05125^{6}) - (50 \times (1.05125^{6} - 1)/.05125)) \times .05125$$
$$(724.92 - 341.17) \times .05125 = 19.67 \text{ interest.}$$

Annuity Capital and Payments
Above it has been assumed that the annuitant holds £100 annuity (£50 each half year) represented by the annuity capital amount of £537.10. Consequently an annuitant capital of (say) £98.01 will entitle the accepting holder to an annuity of £18.25 (£9.13 each half year).

$$£98.01 \times 100/537.10 = £18.25$$

and the holder of (say) an annuity of £55.78 (receiving £27.89 gross each half year) would have purchased a capital value of:

$$£55.78 \times 537.10/100 = £299.59$$

equally well found from 27.89a____ at 5.125% = 299.59
$$16 \mid$$

– *266* –

Net Calculations

Unhappily, neither the conventional method of "netting" the coupon, nor the MIRAS method of netting the issued interest rate, applies in this case and, tiresome as it may be, there is no short cut from employing a specific formula to cover net dealings. The formula, with a semi-annual profile, is below:

CUM div formula for net annuity bond trading

$$\frac{\text{Net Pmts } \ddot{a}\underset{n+1\,|}{\underline{\quad}}^{(at\ i/p\%)} + \text{B}\ddot{a}\underset{n+1\,|}{\underline{\quad}}^{(at\ j\%)}}{(1 + i/p)^k} = \text{Price (DP)}$$

Where:

i = the NET YTM (as a decimal)

p = the number of compounding periods in any one year

g = the nominal (issued) interest rate (10.25%)

t = the tax rate as a decimal (say 30% = .30)

$B = \text{gross pmts} \times (1 + g/p)^{-(n+1)} \times t$

and $(1 + j) = \dfrac{1 + i/p}{1 + g/p}$

Note $\ddot{a}$ = annuities DUE (pmts in advance): $\ddot{a}\underset{n|}{\underline{\quad}} = a\underset{n|}{\underline{\quad}} \times (1 + i/p)$

Retaining the 10.25% and the $(n + k)$ of 9.282192 above, assuming a tax rate of 30% and a dirty price of 376.06; taking the half annual net pmts as 50 x .7 = 35 and the NET redemption yield as 9.2593806%, find the net YTM:

The factor "J" becomes:

$$\frac{1 + i/p}{1 + g/p} - \frac{1.0462932806}{1.05125} = 1 + j = 0.995288$$

$$-1 \times 100 = -0.471163\% = \text{"j"\%}$$

Let "B" = $50 \times 1.05125^{-(n + 1)} \times .30 = 9.099786$

$$\frac{(\text{at } 9.2594/2\%) \quad 35\ddot{a}_{\overline{10}|} \quad + \quad 9.099786\ddot{a}_{\overline{10}|} \quad (\text{at } 10.25/2\%)}{1.046297^{.282192}} = 376.06$$

$$\frac{35(1 - 1.046297^{-10} \times 1.046297}{.046297} + \frac{9.099786(1 - .995288^{-10} \times .995288}{-004712}$$

$$1.012853$$

$$\frac{287.93 + 92.96}{1.012853} = \underline{£376.06 \text{ DP}}$$

and the *clean* price is the price less the NET accrued, namely:

$$376.06 - (19.67 \times .7 \times 131/182.5) = \underline{366.18 \text{ NET CP}}$$

Below is a schedule to demonstrate that the net redemption yield, provided above, derived from the regrettably rather complicated equation, is indeed the correct rate.   Taking settlement as 23 Feb 84 and the DP as £376.06:

Cum Div NET Schedule

Investment	= −376.06

$$\text{PMT} - (\text{INT} \times .3) \times (1 + i/p)^{-k}$$

50 − (19.67 × .3) × 1.046296903$^{-0.282191781}$	=	43.54037117
50 − (18.11 × .3) × 1.046296903$^{-1.282191781}$	=	42.05728483
50 − (16.48 × .3) × 1.046296903$^{-2.282191781}$	=	40.63823574
50 − (14.75 × .3) × 1.046296903$^{-3.282191781}$	=	39.27966240
50 − (12.95 × .3) × 1.046296903$^{-4.282191781}$	=	37.99470498
50 − (11.96 × .3) × 1.046296903$^{-5.282191781}$	=	36.75442949
50 − (9.06 × .3) × 1.046296903$^{-6.282191781}$	=	35.57962501
50 − (6.96 × .3) × 1.046296903$^{-7.282191781}$	=	34.45840171
50 − (4.76 × .3) × 1.046296903$^{-8.282191781}$	=	33.38736326
50 − (2.44 × .3) × 1.046296903$^{-9.282191781}$	=	32.36992113

NPV	=	0.00000030

Ex-div formula for net annuity bond trading
The only difference to the CUM div formula is that the annuities DUE reverts to annuities ORDinary, the term employed being "n" instead of "n + 1".

Taking the term as $1656/182.5 = 9.073973$, a DP of £331.26 and tax at 30% assume a NET Redemption Yield of 9.8308870% nominal.

$$\frac{(1 + i/p)}{(1 + g/p)} = \frac{1.049154435}{1.051250} = .998006597$$

$$\frac{\frac{35(1 - 1.049154^{-9})}{.049154} + \frac{9.099786(1 - .998007^{-9})}{-001993}}{1.049154435^{\wedge}.073972603} =$$

$$(249.71 + 82.72)/1.003555848 \quad = \quad \underline{£331.26 \ DP \ XD}$$

It will be seen that the B factor above is constant to both calculations, as indeed it should be.

Ex Div NET Schedule

Investment		= −331.26
PMTS (net)	x (1 + i/p)$^{-k}$	
50 − (18.11 x .3) x 1.049154435$^{-1.073972603}$ =		42.33130596
50 − (16.48 x .3) x 1.049154435$^{-2.073972603}$ =		40.79161555
50 − (14.75 x .3) x 1.049154435$^{-3.073972603}$ =		39.32051703
50 − (12.95 x .3) x 1.049154435$^{-4.073972603}$ =		37.93063112
50 − (11.96 x .3) x 1.049154435$^{-5.073972603}$ =		36.59250973
50 − (9.06 x .3) x 1.049154435$^{-6.073972603}$ =		35.32640119
50 − (6.96 x .3) x 1.049154435$^{-7.073972603}$ =		34.11997300
50 − (4.76 x .3) x 1.049154435$^{-8.073972603}$ =		32.96941115
50 − (2.44 x .3) x 1.049154435$^{-9.073972603}$ =		31.87764492
	NPV =	0.00000040

Please note that in both the above schedules the columns represented, for example, by $(50 - (18.11 \text{ x } .3) = 44.567$ are *rounded* to 2 places of decimals, namely 44.57, before being discounted.

One Final Problem

An interesting point arose in the closing days of the Issue in question. With settlement on August 8, 1988 and some 68 days to run to Maturity (October 15, 1988) the columns of one financial newspaper quoted a ex-dividend clean price of 47.

This was an obvious nonsense, for two reasons. In the first place this particular stock does not go ex-dividend until September 15,and so with 68 days to run it is still a cum div stock: and secondly, and probably more noteworthy, once an annuity bond has gone XD in its final period there is no market, no price and no yield!

For, if you think about it, as all the annuity bond debt is repaid by the semi annual repayments there is no maturity value and consequently once the final XD notice is filed there is obviously "nothing to come" and any further trade is unlikely.

Mathematically this lack of price or yield above is clearly shown by the conventional **ex–div** formula for bonds with less than one period to run is below:

$$\frac{\text{Redemption Value}}{(1 + i/p)^k} \quad \text{or} \quad \frac{\text{Redemption Value}}{1 + (i/p \ \times \ k)} = \text{XD Dirty Price}$$

And with no redemption value, the answer is a lemon!

A **clean** cum div price of 47, as quoted, would in this case provide a Yield of 16.25% as instanced by the following (simple interest) calculation:

Cum Div

$$\frac{RV + Cpn}{1 + (i/p \ \times \ k)} = \frac{0.00 + 50}{1 + (16.25/200 \ \times \ 0.371585)} = 48.534677$$

(dirty price)

$$48.526863 - 2.44 \times (1 - 0.371585) = 47.001344$$

(clean price)

Remembering that above that the "k" factor would be 68 days divided by 183 (the number of days within the coupon period term), namely $68/183 = 0.371585$ and that the last interest payment is £2.44 (see first schedule above).

With only a few weeks to run to maturity it is unlikely that there was much market trading for, with no redemption value, the only reason for a purchase at that stage would be to buy the "dividend" – hardly a worthwhile incentive!

So it is not unlikely that the price of 47 was just an educated guess, as being something near 50 and that a yield value was never considered. Nevertheless, 16.25% was not necessarily out of line with what was, at that time, an average yield to maturity of "Government Shorts" of around 10% For this stock in normal times was never a popular "buy" and the current redemption yield was always a few points above the "going rate".

CHAPTER 15

Bills, CDs, Floating Rate Notes and CDs, Commercial Paper

Discounting bills (simple interest discounting)

Readers will doubtless be well aware that the concept of discounting bills is based on the old adage that a "bird in the hand. . . ."

A manufacturer whose terms of sale are "payment within 90 days", selling equipment for £1,000 might well prefer to receive £1,000, less a small fee, *now* rather than having to wait for 3 months.

In other words, a bill of exchange is an order by one person requiring a second person to pay a third. It is used as a method of obtaining cash *now*, albeit a reduced amount, instead of waiting for the original bill to fall due.

There are many variations on this theme, ranging from the case of a small business seller, who wants a lesser cash flow now rather that waiting for his client to pay his bill in due course, to governments borrowing short term, by means of the well known Treasury or T bills.

A $1,000 bill due in 90 days time can be discounted in the market for (say) 15%. This will provide a discount value of:

```
$1000 - (1000 x 15/100 x 90/360)  =  $962.50 discount value
$1000 - 962.50                     =  $ 37.50 discount amount
```

If the bill is in sterling and the actual, rather than the financial calendar is used the value is:

```
£1000 - (1000 x 15/100 x 90/365)  =  £963.01 discount value
£1000 - 963.01                     =  £ 36.99 discount amount
```

Note
Above it will be seen that the dollar method was to take the *actual* number of days (90) but to discount by employing the 30/360 calendar. This mix, (actual–30/360), always obtains, unless otherwise stated, throughout *all* dollar discounting and dollar certificates of deposit calculations.

This method differs from the previous bond/price/yield calculations where the calendar is either actual or financial. Incidentally, from the experience of date examples in previous chapters the temptation might be to assume that the 30/360 days are always less that the actual days – but this is not so. For February 1, 1989 – March 9, 1989 is 36 (actual days) and 38 and by the 30/360 calendar 38 days!

The bankers yield
The *banker's return* provides a somewhat different perspective. In the above example a banker lays out £963.01 (rounded please) in order to obtain £1,000, after a delay of 90 days. His return, therefore, must be:

```
£((1,000/963.01) - 1) x 365/90 x 100 = 15.58% yield
```

Conversely, if the banker wanted a return of only 15% he could afford to discount at:

```
(15.58 x 365)/(365 + (15.58/100 x 90) = 15.003615
                                      = 15.00
(The decimal discrepancy is due to rounding the 15.58% rate)
```

Simple interest to yield basis
How much would the dollar discounted value be if, in the above example, the banker decided that he only required a 15% return?

$$\frac{1,000.00}{(1 + (15/100 \times 90/360)} = \$963.86 \text{ value}$$

```
1,000.00 - 963.86 = $36.14  amount
```

And for the sterling bill the values would be £964.33 and £35.67 respectively.

Discounting bills exceeding one year

Assume a bill has a face value of £1000 over a period of 500 days, with a lender's return required of 15%. The calculations to find the proceeds are as follows:

$$1{,}000.00 \div (1 + \frac{15 \times 365}{100 \times 365}) = 869.57$$

$$869.57 \div (1 + \frac{15 \times 135}{100 \times 365}) = 823.86$$

If dollar discounting is required change the base from 365 to 360.

Nowadays there are two sorts of dollars in the market, Eurodollars and conventional United States dollars (often referred to, on both sides of the Atlantic, as "yankee dollars"). Eurodollars are never discounted on a semi-annual bases, yankee dollars are – always.

If *semi*-annual discounting exceeding one year is required, the precise number of days in each half year must first be determined, thereafter it is a straightforward calculation taking the half annual interest rate as the "working rate per cent" (see the calculation, below, for a yankee dollar medium term bank certificate of deposit).

Certificates of deposit (CDs)

A CD is a receipt for a deposit made with an issuing bank. This receipt states the principal amount loaned, the nominal rate of interest, the issue date. and the date on which the loan is to be redeemed. Banks ensure that the maturity date never falls on a weekend of bank holiday.

A CD is in bearer form and is negotiable without endorsement; therefore it should be lodged, for safe custody, with an authorised depository.

CDs can be bought and sold on the "secondary" market , thus providing instant liquidity – one of the attractions of this form of money instrument. Consequently, there are no penalties for early realisation, no tax is withheld and all payments are gross. And, so far as the author is aware, no government levies any stamp (or equivalent) duty.

The max/min permissible borrowing varies with different markets and the life of the loan.

On the London market:
Short term CDs Life between 3 months and one year. Interest due is paid at the same time as the principal is repaid.

Medium term CDs Life is greater than one year but not more than five years. Interest is paid annually, or semi-annually, the final interest payment being made with the return of the principal amount.

Currencies CDs can be in any required currency and different banks and markets have their own conventions as to whether discounting will be annual or semi-annual.

Calendars The calculating base employed is either 365 or 360 (or 180) but the days between dates, between settlement and maturity, are *always* "actual". Leap days are *always* included.

Rounding Presentation is usually to 2 decimal places, for example £/p or $/c, but the intermediate calculations are normally at full precision of the computer or calculator employed. In fact, even if the intermediate discounted values are rounded the difference is not significant.

Short-term certificates of deposit

$$\text{Principal} \times \frac{1 + \dfrac{\text{Int rate\% x life days}}{100 \times 360}}{\dfrac{\text{Yield\% x remaining days}}{100 \times 360}} = \text{Price}$$

The above formula can usefully be transposed, and usually is, to:

$$\text{Principal} \times \frac{36{,}000 + (\text{interest rate\% x life in days})}{36{,}000 + (\text{yield rate\% x remaining days})} = \text{Price}$$

(for sterling calculations for 360 read 365)

Example: A Eurodollar CD of $50,000 (face value) issued with an interest rate of 16% (coupon) over a term of 90 days. The certificate is traded after holding for 60 days at a market rate (yield) of 15%. What is the price paid or the "proceeds"?

$$\$50,000 \times \frac{36,000 + (16 \times 90)}{36,000 + (15 \times (90-60))} = \$51,358.02$$

Note to computer programmers

Reverting to the main formula above, not the transposed equation, it should be noted that although *in practice* the actual days appear to be divided by 360, in fact the true perspective is a little different.

Taking the numerator, in reality the part of the equation which showed:

$$1 + \frac{16 \times 90}{100 \times 360} \quad \text{should be} \quad 1 + \frac{16 \times 365 \times 90}{100 \times 365 \times 360}$$

If this over simplification in the equation calculation is not fully appreciated, erroneous results may follow from incorrect programming. Whereas it may appear obvious above; with more complex semi-annual CDs where leap days are included, etc, clarity of thought on this point is essential.

Medium-term certificates of deposit

CD computer programs are relatively simple to construct, but are even easier if the programmer has a schedule to assist him.

For example, suppose a statistician wants to find the proceeds of a medium term dollar CD with a face value of $50,000 with a coupon of 17%, traded at 16½%, with settlement August 20, 1990 and maturity June 16, 1993, as $51,887.19.

He would need to take into account the fact that there would be an extra (leap) day in the second year (1992), which must be included in the schedule, and only 300 days in the last year.

The statistician would appreciate that:

$$\$50,000 \times 17/100 \times 365/360 = \$8,618.06$$

being interest for those years with the normal 365 days, whereas the interest in 1992 will be:

$$\$8,618.06 \times 366/365 = \$8,641.67$$

The schedule would present as follows:

$$\$(50,000.00 + 8,618.06) \div (1 + \frac{16.50 \times 365}{100 \quad \times 360}) = \$50,217.15$$

$$\$(50,217.15 + 8,641.67) \div (1 + \frac{16.50 \times 366}{100 \quad \times 360}) = \$50,403.61$$

$$\$(50,403.61 + 8,618.06) \div (1 + \frac{16.50 \times 300}{100 \quad \times 360}) = \$51,887.19$$
$$\text{proceeds}$$

Reflecting on the above data, and having digested the methods of calculating bond YTMs/prices earlier, why could this not be calculated as a bond to fix the price (proceeds)?

If we assumed the data to be on a percentage basis, employing the same characteristics, and calculating by simple interest discounting, would there be much difference – and if so why?

$$\frac{100(1.165)^{-2} + 17((1 \quad 1.165^{-2}/.165) + 17}{1 + (.165 \times 300/365)} = \begin{array}{l} 103.730079 \\ (\text{proceeds\%}) \end{array}$$

and $\qquad$ $103.730079/100 \times 50,000 = \text{proceeds} = 51,865.04$

The difference is, of course, that apart from the leap day calculated in the CD, but ignored in the bond, bonds are calculated with a base of either 365 or 360, whereas CDs have a mixed base. We were also calculating the bond on an annual basis which is hardly legitimate; nevertheless the comparison is not uninteresting.

A Yankee dollar CD with semi-annual payments

Exactly the same discipline is employed to calculate semi-annual CDs as is used for annual interest paid CDs, save that the nominal rate is halved and the correct number of days in each of the half years must be found first.

Example of a dollar semi-annual CD

Face Value	$500,000
Interest rate	7.75% nominal
Yield to maturity	7.625%
Settlement	July 2, 1983
Maturity	December 10, 1985

Date/Days/Interest schedule

DATES	DAYS	LOAN	RATES	½ Yr Int
10 Dec 85 – 10 Jun 85 = 183 (Maturity)		500,000 x	$\dfrac{7.75 \times 183}{200 \times 180}$	= $19,697.92
10 Jun 85 – 10 Dec 84 = 183		500,000 x	$\dfrac{7.75 \times 182}{200 \times 180}$	= $19,590.28
10 Dec 84 – 10 Jun 84 = 183				= $19,697.92
10 Jun 84 – 10 Dec 83 = 183 (incl. leap day)				= $19,697.92
10 Dec 83 – 2 Jul 83 = 161 (odd days to SD) (Settlement)				
2 Jul 83 – 10 Jul 83 = 22 + 161 = 183				= $19,697.92
	914 – 22 = 892			

Discount schedule

$$(500,000.00 + 19,697.92 \div (1 + \frac{7,625 \times 183}{200 \times 180}) = 500,305.86$$

$$(500,305.86 + 19,590.28 \div (1 + \frac{7,625 \times 182}{200 \times 180}) = 500,598.75$$

$$(500,598.75 + 19,697.92 \div (1 + \frac{7,625 \times 183}{200 \times 180}) = 500,882.26$$

$$(500,882.26 + 19,697.92 \div (1 + \frac{7,625 \times 183***}{200 \times 180}) = 501,155.20$$

$$(501,155.20 + 19,697.92 \div (1 + \frac{7,625 \times 161}{200 \times 180}) = 503,677.37$$
$$\text{(Proceeds)}$$

*** Leap day intervenes in this half year.

Floating rate certificates of deposit (FRCDs)

In 1977 there was a substantial dollar surplus in Japan and in consequence the Japanese Government instructed all the Japanese banks to suspend short-term dollar funding, only permitting medium-term dollar loans.

These instructions aroused little enthusiasm for, with a then weak dollar and a volatile prime rate, the Japanese investor was reluctant to commit funds medium-term, locked-in to coupons which would almost certainly, in the short term, become both unrealistic and uncommercial.

As a result the Japanese banks simply changed the rules and restructured their short-term borrowing from short-term CDs to medium-term CDs – but one with a striking difference.

The concept of the new CD involved a "floating rate" coupon which could be changed every six months. The rate is changed, if required, 2 days prior to the next interest rate payment date, anticipating the rate for the next six months. The rate is usually "fixed" as being "LIBOR plus a quarter" (London Inter-Bank Offered Rate + ¼ of 1%).

But if this rate was changed every six months, how would it be possible to find the cost? The short answer is, not without some difficulty.

The formula used by the banks in Japan is both long and cumbersome, in that a notional price is found from an assumed yield. This price is then converted to "an equilibrium price", which is merely a price suitably rounded, up or down, according to taste!

The formula employed below is the author's somewhat shorter method, which is designed to provide a notional price so close to that found by the banking method that, after adjustment, the equilibrium quoted price will be the same.

$$\left(100 \times \frac{36000 + (\text{coupon coupon days})}{36000 + (\text{yield} \times \text{odd days})} - \frac{\text{coupon} \times \text{a/i days}}{360}\right) = NP$$

The NP (notional price) is then adjusted to a sensible quotation price, which when divided by 100 and multiplied by the face value of the FRCD, equals the cost or proceeds.

Example:
A floating rate CD (FRCD) of $500,000 has an investment rate of 17%. Settlement is on March 6, 1981, with maturity on May 5, 1983. To calculate a price for this type of certificate, the yield is always assumed and, here, it is assumed to be 10%.

There are 60 odd days between settlement and the next payment date, with 121 accrued interest days between settlement and the previous payment date.

$$(100 \times \frac{36000 + (17 \times 181)}{36000 + (10 \times 60)}) - \frac{17 \times 121}{360} = 101.053871 \text{ notional price}$$

This notional price now has to be converted to an equilibrium price, which will be either to 101 or, possibly, 101.0625, i.e. 101 & 1/16th. The face value being $500,000 the quoted cost would be: $500,000 x 101.00/100 = $505,000.00

Sometimes there is a concession, to selected clients or for a substantial loan, and to scale down the price a "points spread" is applied. A "40 point spread" is .4% of the cost, here $500,000 x .004 = $2000 – a modest saving on half a million dollars!

Forward rate agreements
Forward rates are reasonably simple to calculate. The interest from each nominal interest rate, based on the number of days per period, is rolled up with the interest for the subsequent periods, and the total simple interest so engendered is treated as the *annualised* rate. Annualised, because in many cases the interest and periods will not be consistent with a full year.

The underlying reason for a program such as this is that although the annualised rate is often known, together with some of the period rates, it is the missing rates that are required. Assume the following FRA's: 8.875% for 92 days, 9.20% for 92 days, 9.07% for 91 days 9.32% for 90 days. What is the annualised rate%?

First, a formula is used to find the annualised rate:

$\Big[$ (1 + rateA/100 x daysA/365) x

(1 + rateB/100 x daysB/365) x

(1 + rateC/100 x daysC/365) x

(1 + rateD/100 x daysD/365) $\Big]$ − 1, x 100

= <u>annualised%</u>

$\Big[$ (1 + 8.875/100 x 92/365) x

(1 + 9.20/100 x 92/365) x

(1 + 9.07/100 x 91/365) x

(1 + 9.32/100 x 90/365) $\Big]$ − 1, x 100 =

((1.022370 x 1.023189 x 1.022613 x 1.022981) − 1) x 100 = <u>9.431580%</u>

To find the "missing rate" merely requires the transposition of the formula as above but as there are a substantial number of variables a small computer/calculator program, on the lines of a small spread sheet, is the ideal method of finding the answers required.

It is worth adding a rider if making a calculator program: divide the annualised rate by the total number of the days given – and multiply by 365 – necessary in case the days do not add up 365.

With the above data if the annualised rate was 10% exactly the last rate would be 11.47% (instead of 9.32%).

If there were just two periods, 8.00% for 91 days and 8.57 for 92 days what is the annualised rate?

(((1 + (8.00/100 x 91/365)) x ((1 + (8.57/100 x 92/365)) − 1)

x 36500/(91 + 92) = <u>8.37%</u>

Forward/Forward rates
Another short but useful, and slightly esoteric, calculation may be of interest; being employed by those who operate in both the Futures and Cash Markets.

In its simplest form, a borrower finds that he can obtain a 3 months loan at a rate of 13.8125%. But, although only wanting a loan for 3 months, he finds that he can borrow cheaper, at 13,75%, providing he accepts a longer term of 6 months.

Borrowing longer, in this case, means that he can re-lend the unwanted 3 months loan, at 13.75% – or, obviously, higher if he can arrange it.

Even if he fails to re-lend the unwanted 3 months loan at a higher rate, he can congratulate himself that, by the above machinations, his required 3 months loan has, actually, been borrowed at 13.24%!

The methods of calculation can be either conventional:

$$(\frac{1 + (13.75/100 \quad \times \ 180/365)}{1 + (13.8125/100 \ \times \ 90/365)} - 1 \ ) \times \frac{365 \times 100}{(180 - 90)} = 13.236682$$

Or,

$$\frac{(days \ 1 \quad \times \quad rate \ 1) - (days \ 2 \times rate \ 2)}{(1 + (rate \ 2/100 \times days \ 2/365)) \times (days \ 1 - days \ 2)} = Fwd \ rate\%$$

$$\frac{(\quad 180 \quad \times \quad 13.75 \ ) - (\quad 90 \quad \times 13.8125)}{(1 + (13.8125/100 \quad \times \quad 90/365 \ )) \times (\ 180 \quad - \quad 90 \ )} = Fwd \ rate\%$$

$$\frac{2,475 - 1,243}{1.034058 \times 90} = \underline{13.236682}$$
$$13\frac{1}{4}\%$$

Hedged floating rate notes
A Eurodollar FRN is a negotiable interest-bearing security with a coupon which is usually "fixed" at periodic intervals.

The calculation most usually required is to find the return available when an investor buys a Eurodollar or a US-dollar FRN and hedges into his own, or a required, currency.

Assume that a Deutschmark investor purchases a $1.0 million FRN and the coupon is "fixed" at 11% (1/4 of 1% over 6 months LIBOR) on October 6, 1988. The coupon period runs from October 6, 1987 to April 6, 1989, a period of 182 days. The spot $/DM exchange rate is 2.50% and the (6 months) forward $/DM exchange rate is 2.45% The price is 99.80

The investor hedges the same amount of dollars, which he buys at the spot rate, over the next (refix) date, which in this example is 182 days, as well as the dollar interest payment.

The calculations
The calculations are a good deal less complicated than they might at first appear.

```
FRN x price/100                              =  cost in $
    x spot rate                              =  cost in DM
FRN x (price/100 + cpn x days/36000          =  proceeds in $
    x forward rate)                          =  proceeds in DM

((DM proceeds/DM cost - 1) x 36000/days      =  Yield% (annualised)

1,000,000 x (99.8/100 + (11 x 182/36000)
                          x 2.45  =  2,581,347.22

1,000,000 x 99.80/100 x 2.50      =  2,495,000 cost DMs

((2,581,347.22/2,495,000) - 1) x 36000/182 = 6.845559% yield
```

Notes with interest at maturity
Yet another type of interest bearing obligation is that of maturity discounting with rolled-up interest, namely a note with no coupon but with interest paid when the loan matures.

Assume a note was issued (ID) on October 1, 1992, to (RD) mature on November 1, 1993. Settlement (SD) was on March 17, 1993. The interest rate on the note was 9.50%; if the yield required is 9.00% what is the price?

The days between issue and settlement are 77 days, between issue and maturity 181 days, and between settlement and maturity 104 days. The calculations to find the price are:

$$\frac{\left(1 + \dfrac{ID - RD \text{ days}}{360} - \dfrac{rate}{100}\right) - \left(\dfrac{price}{100} + \dfrac{ID - SD \text{ days}}{360}\right) \times \dfrac{rate}{100}}{\dfrac{price}{100} + \left(\dfrac{ID - SD \text{ days}}{360} \times \dfrac{rate}{100}\right)}$$

and

$$above \times \frac{360}{SD - RD \text{ days}} \times 100 = YTM\%$$

$$100 \times \left(\frac{1 + \left(\dfrac{ID - RD \text{ days} \times rate}{360} \times \dfrac{rate}{100}\right)}{1 + \left(\dfrac{SD - RD \text{ days} \times YTM}{360 \times 100}\right)} - \frac{ID - SD \text{ days} \times rate}{360 \times 100}\right)$$

$$= \underline{Price}$$

$$((1 + (390 \times 9.50/36000)/(1 + 224 \times 9/36000) - (166 \times 9.5/36000))$$
$$\times 100 = \underline{100.062511}$$

Assuming that the true quoted price was 100 1/16th (100.0625) find the true YTM%

$$\frac{((1 + 390 \times 9.5/36000) - (100.0625/100 + (166 \times 9.5/36000)))}{100.0625/100 + (166 \times 9.5/36000)}$$

$$\times 36000/224 = \underline{8.999692 \text{ YTM\%}}$$

Pistols at dawn – A CD postscript

From the previous pages in Part II, readers will, I think, realise that, unlike some commercial paper, certificates of deposit offer a straightforward and uncomplicated way of lending to a bank, attractively providing instant liquidity if sold on the secondary market.

I have never encountered any abnormalities or anything unusual in this particular market, save once – some years ago.

The directors of a local bank in Illinois, for reasons best known to themselves, dreamed up a new type of certificate of deposit, and suddenly made a $1,500 issue. The conditions appeared, to the eyes of more conservative bankers, somewhat unusual to say the least; in that, *in lieu* of interest payments, there would be an "instant gift" of two pistols – in a walnut case.

The pistols (and the walnut case), at the time of the issue, were advertised as being worth $725 a price which, the bank was at pains to point out, had doubled over the previous 6 years. Consequently, the bank averred, the gift was equivalent to a yield of 15.50%.

Now unless my mathematics are at fault it would appear that for the advertised rate to be valid not only would a number of willing buyers need to be found at the end of 6 years to purchase the pistols but they would also have to be prepared to pay nearly *three times* the issue-valuation! For to yield 15.50% over 6 years, with annual interest payments, the said pistols (together with the walnut case) would surely need to be worth between nearly 3 times the advertised $725 at issue:

$$(1,500 \times 1.1550^6) = 3,561.09$$

and after the return of the capital amount:

$$3,561.09 - 1.500 = \$2,061.09$$
$$2.061.09/725 = 2.84 \text{ times}$$

Of course, with semi-annual payments the cost would be even greater to equate with the required 15.50% yield.

At the time, this was thought to be an interesting variation on some of the minor league US banks' inducements-to-account-opening, always rather a sore subject with the more conservative banks.

The mind then began to boggle at the possible "gifts" for more substantial CDs, a summer cruise perhaps – or a missile?

Classes of US Interest-Bearing Obligations

Money Instrument	Base	Interest paid
Certificates of deposit (3)	Actual/360	Semi-annually
Certificates of deposit	Actual/360	At maturity
Certificates of deposit (3)	Actual/360	Discounting
Corporate bonds	30/360	Semi-annually
Floating rate certificates of deposit	Actual/360	Semi-annually
Municipal bonds	30/360	Annually
Municipal bonds	30/360	Semi-annually
US Treasury bonds**	Actual/365	Semi-annually
US Treasury notes**	Actual/365	Semi-annually
Assessment supported bonds	30/360	Semi-annually
Assessment supported notes	30/360	At maturity
Assessment supported warrents	30/360	At maturity
Bankers acceptances	Actual/360	Discounting
Banks for Co-operative debentures	30/360	At maturity
Certificates of indebtedness	Actual/360	At maturity
Commercial paper (2)	Actual/360	At maturity
Commercial paper	Actual/360	Discounting
Commodity Credit Corporation	30/360	Semi-annually
Export-Import Bank Particular Certs	30/360	Semi-annually
Farmers' Home Admin. insured notes	Actual/360	Annually
Fed. Home Loan Bank notes/bonds	30/360	Semi-annually
Fed. Housing Admin. (FHA) debentures	Actual/360	Semi-annually
Fed. Intermediate Credit Bank deb:(2)	30/360	Semi-annually
Fed. Intermediate Credit Bank debentures	30/360	At maturity
Federal Land Bank bonds	30/360	Semi-annually
FNMA debentures	30/360	Semi-annually
FNMA short-term notes	Actual/360	Discounting

** Employ quasi-coupon period method of calculation

Money Instrument	Base	Interest paid
Foreign bonds (NOT Eurobonds)	Actual/365	Semi-annually
GNMA bonds & Participating certs	30/360	Semi-annually
Inter-American Devel't bonds	30/360	Semi-annually
IBRD bonds	30/360	Semi-annually
Merchant Marine bonds	30/360	Semi-annually
New Communities Act debentures	30/360	Semi-annually
Repurchase agreements	Actual/360	At maturity
Revenue supported bonds	30/360	Semi-annually
Revenue supported notes	30/360	At maturity
Revenue supported warrants	30/360	At maturity
Special supported bonds	30/360	Semi-annually
Special supported notes	30/360	At maturity
Special supported warrants	30/360	At maturity
Tax supported bonds	30/360	Semi-annually
Tax supported notes	30/360	At maturity
Tax supported warrents	30/360	At maturity
Tennessee Valley Authority bonds	30/360	Semi-annually
Tennessee Valley Authority notes	Actual/360	Discounting
U.S. Postal Services bonds	30/360	Semi-annually
U.S. Treasury bills	Actual/360	Discounting
U.S. Treasury Tax-Anticipated bills	Actual/360	Discounting

SOLVE FOR "i"

General
The readers have been told in many of the previous pages that this or that rate of interest must be found with the aid of a computer or programmed calculator. The reason being that it was not possible to obtain the required answer by simply transposing the formula or "function" under reference.

This appendix is addressed to those fortunate possessors of computers or calculators capable of finding the "i" values who know next nothing about the processes involved,

It will explain in full how the process of "interpolation" and "iteration" works, in its simplest terms, and later how this interpolation is converted by a computer program into a "looping" process.

And, finally, for those who are contemplating constructing their own computer program to "solve for i", a method will be outlined and an algorithm provided.

The concept – the iterative process and tolerance factors
From the earlier chapters we know that a repayment loan of £1,000 over a term of 25 years will require annual payments of £118.74 *if the interest rate is 11% nominal.*

This was simply calculated by:

$$\text{loan} \div ((1 - (1 + i)^{-n})/i\ )\ =\ \text{pmts}$$
$$1{,}000 \div ((1 - 1.11^{-25})/.11)\ =$$
$$1{,}000 \div 8.42174466467\ =\ 118.740242054$$

Consequently, we know if that the "factor", the 8.42174466467 above, is multiplied by 118.740242054 the product will be *exactly* £1,000.

Note. Throughout this appendix, in whatever form the values are shown, whether 2 or 6 decimal places, they are all "worked" to 13 significant figures rounded to 12 places; consequently if following the arguments on your own computer/calculator (with perhaps slightly different "full precision") the decimal fractions may be very slightly different.

The factor

It will be clear that if the payments are to be *exactly* £118.74 the factor will no longer be 8.42174466467 but must be:

$$1,000 \div 118.74 = 8.4217613258$$

And this is where we came in, so to speak, for if you dissect the factor you will not be able to isolate the "i" value by a transposition of the formula. And this is the root of all the problems that arise when we seek another way of solving for the "i" value.

The "guess and guess again syndrome"

Ships at sea when "shooting at sight" will "bracket" the target, first firing over it, then under it, and after working out the "difference", continuing to reduce the differences until the target is successfully destroyed.

The statistician attempting to discover the interest rate of the above example would proceed along exactly the same lines as the gun-layer, treating the differences as *absolute*, in that the negative is disregarded.

The trouble is where does he start? If he knew the rate was around 11%, as he does in this example, he could bracket by taking 10% and then 12% – and gradually narrowing the field. But obviously the closer to the true answer the better, for this will enable him to save time – even with a computer program.

But in every type of calculation most statisticians and programmers have their own pet way of getting a rough estimate, a "back of an envelope" kind of answer.

Readers may perhaps recall that a calculation of this type was mentioned in relation to using the Japanese method of finding a bond yield to maturity; it is not completely accurate but near the truth and is a method often used to "start" a computer loop – more anon.

In this type of repayment loan calculation a neat but rough guide is to take the integer of the payments divided by the loan and multiplied by 100, or if monthly, by 1200.

$$118.74/1000 \times 100 = 11.874000 = \text{(say) } 11\%$$

In fact this is so close to the truth that it will provide a loan amount of 8.421475 x 118.74 = 999.997961. We will return to this value shortly, but for the moment I want to demonstrate the interpolation method somewhat more clearly. So by taking 10% and 12% we will get a more useful spread.

Assuming that the statistician tests for the loan amount:

$$118.74 \times (1 - 1.10^{-25})/.10 = 1,077.80 \text{ (truncated)}$$
$$118.74 \times (1 - 1.12^{-25})/.10 = 931.29 \text{ (truncated)}$$

There are various ways of "fining down" these value to increase or decrease the "i" rate; the one given below is merely one of many:

$$10\% + ((1,077.80 - 931.29) \div 100) =$$
$$10\% + \qquad 146.51000 \qquad\qquad = 11.465100$$

If this rate is used it will be found that the loan amount is *less* than the 999.997 (above), so it is clear that the rate required is less than 11.47, but greater than 10%. Perhaps the division by 100 was bit optimistic; substituting 1000 would only lift the 10% to 10.147%, but dividing by 200 we get a new rate of 10.732550 and this provides a new loan amount of £1,019.85.

Now go back to interpolating, but this time divide by 1,000; for one wants to increase the rate slowly to see what is happening.

$$10.732550 + ((1,077.80 - 1,019.85) \div 1,000 =$$
$$10.732550 + \qquad 59.95 \qquad\qquad = 10.790500$$

One continues this slow and time-consuming method until the correct rate is reached, namely 10.9999720802%

But wait! Surely one does not have to go to find 10 places of decimals? Indeed not. One decides the level of rate accuracy required, say 6 places of decimals, and "tests" against .000001 or 10^{-6} – the "tolerance" or T factor.

In that case, when the rate last employed provides a loan amount of 999.999, as the difference is only 1,000 – 999.999 = 0.001. If this is not considered accurate enough one would then have to continue, until the loan amount provided by the last rate is 999.999999 and in that case the tolerance of .000001 is fully met; 1,000 – 999.999999 = .000001 and the rate to provide that value is found as 10.99997209939

But cutting this down to 6 places 10.999972 lifts the loan amount to 1,000.00000586 which when rounded to the normal 2 places of decimals provides the correct £1,000 loan.

The "function" f(x)
The mathematical nomenclature for the formula/method for which the interpolation is undertaken is the "function" and can apply to many different requirements. Our requirement above for the repayment loan would be:

$$(\text{LOAN} \times ((1 - (1 + i/p)^{-np})/(i/p)) - 1,000 = 0 = f(x)$$

One iterative method
Obviously, the manual, and the fortunately out-dated, method outlined above is not used in computer programs.

Admittedly, in the early days, using the computing language BASIC, a modified form of the above method was used; but nowadays one of the most popular disciplines is the Newton-Raphson method of interpolation. This has the sophisticated device of incorporating the tolerance factor as an integral part of the formula and not, as in some other methods, merely for comparing the "differences". The result is that the response time is very rapid and the T factor can be substantially less.

Generalisations, especially in mathematics, are usually dangerous but it could be said that, by this method, a T factor of, say, only 0.001 will provide a rate accurate to at least 6 places of decimals.

The Method
Let FNC = the function
    D = the difference (absolute)
  PD = the previous difference
   T = the tolerance factor
   F = (Rate % + T)

Note. The rate% is the IRR, the nominal rate *not* the "i" or "i/p" within the calculation.

The loop
An algorithm, at the end of this appendix, may be found useful.

1. Calculate a first guess.
2. Employing this guess rate calculate the function to provide the first difference (D).
3 *Phase A:*
  Consider that now D has become the PD.
  Adjust the previous rate to F (old rate + T).
  With the new rate calculate the next D.
4 *Phase B:*
  Adjust this rate by:

$$(\text{RATE} - F) - \frac{F}{(D/PD) - 1} = \text{"next" RATE}$$

5. Now TEST:

$$\text{IF}\quad \text{ABS} - \frac{}{(D/PD) - 1} < T \text{ then the "nest rate" above} = \text{IRR}$$

But if the above test finds the value is greater than the T factor recalculate the FNC by the new (next) rate above.

Then go to PHASE A above. This is the "loop", and the whole process starts again with the new, adjusted, rate.

It may be unlikely, but it is possible, that in between the tests the current D = 0; if so, the current i/p *is* the IRR and can be produced as such.

Example
Take the above example, the £1,000 loan over 25 years but this time find the interest rate if the annual payments are exactly £118.00.

Although a computer program will, must, always start off with a calculation to determine a "first guess" it is hardly necessary here, for we are already fully aware that at 11%, precisely, the payments are £118.74.

Consequently, to save time, we could guess a sensible "near miss", one which must be slightly less than the known 11%. Therefore, taking 10.90% and a tolerance of .001 we can start the loop:

$$118 \times ((1 - 1.109^{-25})/.109 = 1001.067072$$
```
assumed value - given value = difference (D)
1001.067072  -  1,000.00   = 1.067072
```

Now we must assume that D (1.067072) becomes the previous difference, the PD, and with a T factor of .001 we now enter:

PHASE A:
```
10.90 + (10.90 + .001) = 10.9109 new ("next") rate
```

Recalculating, as above, with this rate will find a loan value of £1,000.2666813 and so the *next* difference = 0.26668130 (D).

PHASE B:

$$(10.9109 - (10.9 \times .001)) - \frac{10.90 \times .001}{(0.266813/1.067072) - 1}$$

```
10.9                    - (0.014534151) = 10.91453415
        (This rate is the "next rate" or a possible IRR)
```
TEST   Is the ABS 0.014534151 less than the   factor of .001?

As the test is negative, go back to *Phase A,* and employing the new rate of 10.91453415 and recalculate as before (that is, begin another loop).

Continuing to calculate the FNC, it will be found that the next difference is 0.000242000 – BUT do not immediately jump to the conclusion that the IRR is the current rate, just because the difference is less than the T factor of .001.   For, remember, you are still in *Phase A* and that you MUST complete this phase correctly before any "test" is made.

The last difference 0.00024200 now becomes the previous difference (PD) and the current 10.91453415 becomes 10.91453415 x 1.001 = 10.92544868 (next rate). Employing this new rate the new loan value becomes 999.2003692 which, when 1,000 is subtracted, finds a difference of – 0.77996308 (D).

We are now in *Phase B* again:

$$10.91453415 - \frac{10.9145345 \times .001}{(-0.7996308/.0002420) - 1} = \text{next rate}$$

$$10.91453415 - (-0.00003302) \qquad\qquad = 10.91453745$$

TEST Is the ABS (–.00003302 < .001? YES

IRR = <u>10.91453745</u>

Again, it must be stressed that the "test" must be made in the correct order, namely *after* the "next rate" calculation has been completed.

The tolerance factor limit
In the FNC calculations the rate will almost certainly require to be converted to an i/p, It is therefore essential not to have the T factor less than 10^{-6} or .000001.

For in the above example, the first guess rate was 10.90% which when converted to an (1 + i/p) would become:

$$1 + 10.90/100 = 1.1090$$

The second rate would 10.90 x .001 = .01090 = F and when added to the rate (10.90) becomes:

$$10.90 + .01090 = 10.9109$$

which when converted to an $(1 + i/p)$ becomes 1.01091090.

So far no problem. But consider, if the T value was chosen as 10^{-9} when working to, say, 10 decimal places the first and second value would be the *same*.

```
First  (1 + i)                              = 1.109000000

                     10.90 x (1 + 10^-9)
Second (1 + i) = 1 + ------------------- = 1.109000000
                            100
```

And without a *second* rate to provide the first difference the calculation becomes invalid. In any event, there is no need ever to employ a T factor less than 10^{-6}, for this is quite sufficient when using the Newton-Raphson method.

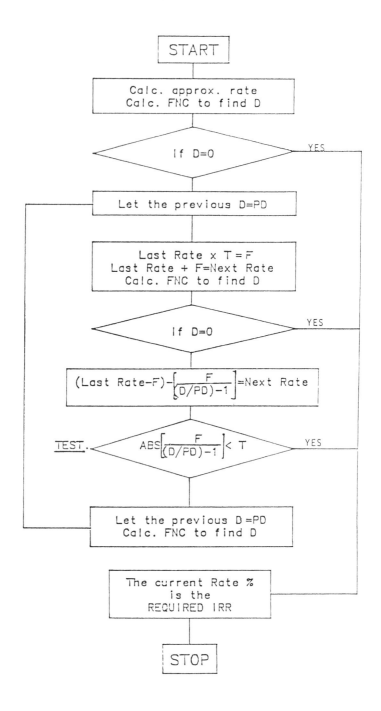

How to Construct a Computer Calendar Program and the methodology for finding payment dates before/after settlement

General

Nowadays nearly all spread sheet programs and most of the sophisticated business calculators have programs which will find the number of days between two dates or find a new date, given one date and +/- a number of days. These are essential requirements, used daily, in nearly all forms of rate interest calculations and in practical market bargains, as opposed to theoretical examples. A fact which, doubtless, the reader has noticed throughout the preceding pages.

And because date programs are now common place it seemed pointless to reprint the date formulae, from the relevant *Business Interest Calculations* appendices; but just as both my editor and myself so decided I received a telephone call from a programmer friend who had contracted to write a one-off program – which included dates. He was already using some of my date appendices and required some further advice. On the strength of that query it was decided to retain a suitably amended reprint.

The Julian calendar and the "Julian dating system"

The Julian *calendar*, named after Julius Ceasar, measuring time in years and months (treating each fourth year as a leap year), was authorised for use in 42 BC. This calendar should not be confused with the astronomers's use of the Julian *dating* system, derived from a work published in 1582 by a Joseph (Julius) Scaliger (after whom it was called), measuring time from midday 4713 BC. Such esoteric items however, have little or no place in normal present-day calculations, related to dates and days between dates. For during the 16th century it was realised that the correct number of year/days was not, as had been thought, 365.25 days but was, in fact, around 365.2425 days.

The Gregorian calendar (our everyday actual" calendar)
As a result Pope Gregory XIII decided on a new style (NS) calendar designed to correct past errors and, in order to effect such adjustments, decided, *inter alia*, to treat all century years as *non*-leap years – *unless* such years were precisely divisible by 400. Thus on October 4, 1582 the "Gregorian" calendar came into being, causing the removal, or the loss, of some 10 days for those using the old style (OS) calendar.

The British Empire, and consequently the then American Colonies, adopted the Gregorian calendar on September 14, 1752. So for UK/US date calculations, between the years 1582–1752, there is a difference of 11 days between the two old and new calendars.

For example, George Washington was born on February 11, 1732 (OS) and any celebrations, to that end, nowadays should therefore be held on February 22. In practice, the United States' annual holiday, commemorating this event, takes place always on the third Monday in February.

From the above it will be realised that not all countries conformed immediately; Turkey, for one, was a little dilatory, waiting until 1927 to effect the change – and I read only recently that a small island in the Shetlands, called Foula, with a population of around only 50 souls, still employs the old calendar!

The date factor (DF)
To find the number of days between two dates, or a new date from a date +/– a number of days, requires a "date factor". This factor is then subtracted from another date factor to find the days between. Or a date factor with a number of days added, or subtracted, provides a new date factor which must then be *unscrambled* to find a new date.

There are various methods available; the ones outlined below are, in my view, the simplest to program. But remember, whichever method is employed the formulae must never be mixed.

Formula: Date(1) – Date(2) = Days between (actual)

```
Where:   INT = integer     FRAC = decimal fraction
         DF  = Date Factor,  Y = Year,   m = month

      Year' = Year–1    if m  = 1 or 2 (Jan–Feb)
            = Year      if m>2 = 2     (Mar–Dec)
        m' = month +13 if m  = 1 or 2
           = month + 1 if m>2
```

$$INT(365.25Y')+INT(30.6M')+D = DF$$

To find the days between Christmas Day 1976 and New Year's day 2000:

```
         INT(1976 x 365.25 + INT(30.6 x (12 – 1)) + 25 =  DF (Xmas)
              721734      + INT(397.80123      + 25 =
INT((2000–1) x 365.25) + INT(30.6 x (1+13)   + 1 =  DF (NEW Yr)
             730563      +      428          + 1 =  730563
             730563 – 722156      = 8407 days between
```

Leap Days

If the requirement is to find the "days between" LESS any leap days intervening (as employed in bond yield calculations) in the above formula for 365.25 read 365.

```
             (1976 x 365) + 397 + 25 = 721662
             (1999 x 365) + 428 +  1 = 730064
and          730064 – 721662     = 8402 days less leap days
        (1980,1984,1988,1992,1996 are the relevant leap years)
```

To find the days of the week

Let 1 = Monday through to 6 + Saturday: Sunday = 0 or 7

$$(7 \times (FRAC \frac{DF - 2}{7})) = \text{Day of the week}$$

$$(7 \times (FRAC \frac{722156 - 2}{7})) = 7 \times .857100$$

```
(always round up to integer)   = 5.99970  = 6 = Saturday
and 7 x FRAC((9730563 – 2)/7)  = 5.99970  = 6 = Saturday
```

Formula: Date +/- Days = Date

Now to "unscramble" a "new date DF".

```
Where:
      month = m'- 13   if   m' = 14 or 15
            = m'- 1    if   m' < 14
      year  = Y'       if   m > 2
            = Y'+ 1    if   m = 1 or 2
```

$$\text{Year} = \text{INT} \frac{DF - 122.4}{365.25}$$

$$\text{Month} = \text{INT} \frac{DF - \text{INT}(365.25 \times Y)}{30.6}$$

$$\text{Day} = (DF - \text{INT}(356.25 \times Y)) - \text{INT}(30.6 \times m)$$

Obviously, the best example to unscramble is one whose answer is already known, namely the above December 25, 1976 + 8047 days: the Xmas Day DF is 722156 and with 8407 added becomes 730563 from which a new date is found below.

NOTE. Any "adjustments" necessary must be wait until the end of the calculations when all the data is available, for the *unadjusted* values obtain during the whole calculation.

$$\text{INT}(730563 - 122.4)/365.25 \quad = \quad 1999 = 1999 + 1 = 2000 \text{ year}$$

$$\text{INT}\frac{(730563 - \text{INT}(1999 \times 365.25)}{30.6} \quad = \quad 14 = 14 - 13 = 1 \text{ month}$$

$$(770563 - \text{INT}(365.25 \times 1999)) \quad - \quad \text{INT}(30.6 \times 14) = 1 \text{ day}$$

$$\text{and} \quad \text{INT}(722156 - 122.4)/365.25 \quad = 1976 \text{ year}$$

$$\text{INT}\frac{(722156 - \text{INT}(1976 \times 365.25)}{30.6} \quad = \quad 13 = 13 - 1 = 12 \text{ month}$$

$$(722156 - \text{INT}(365.25 \times 1976)) \quad - \quad \text{INT}(30.6 \times 13) = 25 \text{ day}$$

The following calculations maybe of interest:

```
         (Jan)  (Feb)
365 -  31  -  28 = 306.00 and divided by 10 months = 30.6
                                        30.6 x 4 = 122.4
```

The Century zones

Nowadays most date programs, whether computer or calculator, cover the years between 1600 to many centuries in the future. But when the original appendix was drafted date programs only ran from 1901 to 2099. No one could cross the century zone because programs were written to test for leap years or not by dividing by 4, and the programmer presumed that the year 2000 was a leap year, as indeed it is (2000/400 has no fraction), but no one bothered to 400 test 2100 which appeared to be a leap year; but in fact it is NOT a leap year for 2100/400 has a fraction.

Therefore to cross a century zone correctly, to get the correct days of the week, essential in some cases, a neat little addition to the above calculation is necessary.

```
INT(.75INT(Year/100) − 7 = century zone factor
(where year = (year − 1) if date is Jan or Feb)
```

Subtract the CZ factor from the DF to become the DF(cz) factor and when used the dates and the days of the weeks will be correct.

To find the day of the week, using the DF(cz) do NOT subtract 2 as outlined previously, for example:

```
      722156 − INT.75(INT(1976/100) − 7 = DF(cz)
      722156 − 9                        = 722147
and   FRAC(722147/7) x 7                = 6 = Saturday
```

Many years ago, before sophisticated date programs became available, because it was known that I had such facilities, I was approached by a leading finance house in the City of London to discover if a certain day, well into the 22nd century, was a banking day or not. In fact it was, but I am still wondering what possible long-term loan stock they were contemplating!

A Digression

In the early '70s, *The Times* newspaper made a small offer to its readers of half a dozen tea mugs on which there were reproductions of some famous past front pages, births and death and coronations of the Royal Family etc. One of which was dated Tuesday 1 January 1806.

Checking the day of the week, for my own amusement, on one of my century zone related date programs, imagine my horror when I found that I made it a Wednesday. I feared that my particular method of crossing the century zones, as outlined above, was a washout and it was a case of back to the drawing board.

But checking and rechecking I became convinced that either I was crazy – or *The Times* was! So I telephoned *The Times* Library to be told that the day in question was, indeed, Wednesday!

The department responsible for selling the mugs were equally horrified when I pointed out the error and, in due course, we discovered that the mugs were not "printed on" as we all supposed, but had in fact been painted freehand by the suppliers, who presumably thought that finding the correct day of the week as far back as 1800 was of no moment!

The Days Table
At the end of the book will be seen a days table. In the old days such a table under glass on the desk was a tremendous help to statisticians who needed to find, as indeed we do to this day, the number of days between dates.

While date programs have taken over such pedestrian methods those away from their computers or bereft of their business calculator may still even now find it useful. In fact the last time I saw these pages used was on an air passage to Canada by a passenger who presumably (in those days) was not permitted to use a calculator in flight.

From the calculations above we know that there are some 8407 days between the years 1976 and the year 2000; we also know that there are 5 leap days intervening consequently: $(365 \times (2000 - 1976 - 1)) + 5$ which gives us 8400 and although, in this case, the days between Christmas and the New Year are easy to determine mentally, namely 7.

But more difficult days will be simplified by the tables. The number of days, for instance, between the 8th March and the 13th September by the tables will be 256 – 67 = 189

To find the number of leap years between, or rather leap *days* between two dates, divide each of the years by 4 and subtract the two integers, remembering to subtract 1 from those dates which occur prior to March 1.

$$\frac{INT(1940-1)}{4} - \frac{INT(2000-1)}{4} = -15 \text{ leap days}$$

$$\frac{INT(\ 1940\ )}{4} - \frac{INT(\ 1999\ )}{4} = -14 \quad " \quad "$$

A Month/Days chart

January	(31)	31	July	(31)	212
February	(28)	59	August	(31)	243
March	(31)	90	September	(30)	273
April	(30)	120	October	(31)	304
May	(31)	151	November	(30)	334
June	(30)	181	December	(31)	365

(for a leap year add one day from march onward)

Finally, if you are making a date program remember that it will need some sub routine for checking not only a bad input but also an invalid date, such as 31 November or, equally important, an input of 29 February for a non-leap year.

Finally, a plea, let the sub routine for a invalid entry throw up on display the *reason* – and not just a rather unhelpful "error"!

The financial (30/360) calendar
The basic method of calculating a date factor is much the same as the above but a 30 day month produces its own complications.

Formula: Date – Date = Days between (30/360)

Where: dd' = date 1   dd" = date 2 and <> = not equal to

```
For DF1     if dd'  =  31   then z   =  30
            if dd"  <> 31   then z   =  dd'

For DF2     if dd"  =  31   and dd' =  30 or 31   then  z  =  30
            if dd"  =  31   and dd' <  30          then  z  =  dd"
            if dd"  <  31                          then  z  =  dd"
```

then   **360(yyyy) + 30(mm)+ z = DF**

Taking the example above, Christmas Day 1976 and New Year's Day 2000, find the days between by the 30/360 method:

```
(1976 x 360) + (12 x 30) + 25 = 711745   DF1
(2000 x 360) + ( 1 x 30) +  1 = 720031   DF2
720031 − 711745 = 8286 days between (30/360
```

Find the days between August 31, 1980 and June 30, 1985:

```
(1980 x 360) + ( 8 x 30) + 30 = 713070   DF1
(1985 x 360) + ( 6 x 30) + 30 = 714810   DF2
714810 − 713070 = 1740 days between (30/360)
```

Days of the week for 30/360 days

To find the correct day of the week the calculation *must* be on a "actual" basis, for calculating by using the 30/360 DF will give erroneous results. This is not merely academic, for in many cases short term 90 day loans are 30/360 based and it is often necessary to check whether redemption day is on a banking day or not – and this of course must be an "actual" day.

To find the days of the week (30/360)

In the case of 30/360 calculations, to find the new date, it will never be possible to determine whether the last date of the month is 30 or 31 (if the month concerned is a 31 days month) otherwise the "unscrambling" is simply one of "adjusting" as the calculation unfolds.

Formula: Date +/– Days = Date (30/360)

```
(a)   INT(DF/100)      = Year  PROVISIONAL
(b)   FRAC(year)  x 12 = Month PROVISIONAL
(c)   FRAC(month) x 30 = Day (must always be rounded up to integer)
```

```
NOTE.
If month < 1. then (provisional year  – 1) = Year and 12      = Month
If day   = 0. then (provisional month – 1) = Month and 31/30 = Day
```

Calculate the new 30/360 date from a given date of June 30, 1980 plus 1965 (30/360) days:

```
The DF for June 30 1980 plus 1965 (30.360) days is:
       (1980 x 360) + (6 x 30) + 30 + 1965 = 714975
```

```
and to unscramble:
       INT(714975/360) = 1986.041667 = 1986 Year ** = 1985
       .041667 x 12    =  ** .500000 =   12 Month    = Dec
       .500000 x 30       15.000001 =   15 Day     = 15
(see note above for **)
```

First find the DF (30/360) for May 31, 1984 and thereafter unscramble:

```
       (1984 x 360) + (5 x 30) + 30  = 714000 (see formula)
       INT(714420/360) = 1984.50000 = 1984 Year    = 1984
       .500000 x 12    =     6.00000 =    6 Month** = May
       .000000 x 30    =  ** .00     =    0 Day  ** = 30 or 31 day
(see note above for **)
```

How to find the payment dates before/after settlement

In the evaluation of the prices and yields to maturity of Bonds, where the fixed interest is paid twice annually, it is usually necessary, at some stage in the calculation, to discover the interest (coupon) payments dates both before and after Settlement Day (SETT). Assuming, of course, that the dates for the semi-annual payments are the anniversaries of the Redemption or Maturity Date (MAT).

If settlement is on April 1, 1991 and maturity falls on June 15, 2000, it hardly stretches our mental capabilities to work out that the interest payment date *prior* to settlement, the accrued payment date (A/DTE) is on December 15, 1990 and that the next payment date after settlement, namely the odd days date (O/DTE), is June 15, 1991.

A computer, unhappily, only has the mental capacity of its programmer so if a program is to be constructed to replicate the above thought process some *mathematical* means must be found to convert it to computer-code. Below is one method.

For simplicity in the calculations the US date format (mm.ddyyyy) is employed.

To find the date PRIOR to settlement (A/DTE)

1. If the mmdd of the SETT is > that the mmdd of the MAT :

```
(mmdd of MAT + .yyyy of SETT)/100  = A/DTE
but add 6 if (mmdd of SETT - mmdd of MAT) > 600
```

2. If the mmdd of the SETT is < then the mmdd of the MAT:

```
(mmdd of MAT + .yyyy of SETT)/100 - 6 = A/dte
but if (mmdd of MAT - mmdd of SETT) > 600 re-add the previously
           subtracted 6 and subtract one year.
```

```
If the months are < 1 add 12 and subtract 1 year; alternatively
if the months are ever > 12 subtract 12 and add 1 year.
```

To find the date AFTER settlement (O/DTE)

```
Take the a/i date just found and add 6 months to find the O/DTE:
             A/DTE + 6 = O/DTE
If the O/DTE is greater than 12, subtract 6 and add one year.
```

If, for example, SETT is April 26, 1980 (4.261980) and MAT is June 15, 1995 (6.151995) as mmdd of SETT (426) is < than mmdd of MAT (615) use the second method:

$$((615 + .1980)/100) - 6 = 0.151980$$

Test:

```
(615 - 425) = 189 (<600) A/DTE stands, but as year is 0 add 12
and subtract 10⁻⁶  (or add 11.999999)
```

$$= \underline{A/DTE = 12.151979}$$

Consequently the O/DTE becomes:

12.151979+12 = 18.151979 and–12+10^{-6} = <u>O/DTE = 6.151979</u>

To find the number of semi-annual periods (#PER)
Apart from the above, it is often necessary to find the total number of half years involved, the number of coupon days, (days between A/DTE and O/DTE), the a/i days (days between A/DTE and SETT), and the odd days date (days between SETT and O/DTE). The "days between" can be found by conventional methods, as outlined earlier, but the total number of semi-annual payments can be found as follows:

(mm.ddyyyy of MAT – mm.ddyyyy of O/DTE x 2 x 10^6)   = # PER

but if the above provides ad integer replace by;

(mm.ddyyyy of MAT – mm.ddyyyy of A/DTE x 2 x 10^6) – 1 = # PER

and, in the above example the correct number of semi-annual payments between SETT and MAT:

<u>6.151995</u> – <u>6.151980</u> = .000015 and x 2 x 10^6 = 30 (#PER)

A further example, if SETT is February 1, 1984 (2.011084) and MAT on January 1, 1988 (1.011988) as mmdd SETT (201) is > mmdd of MAT (101) use formula 1.

(101 + .1984)/100 = <u>A/DTE = 1.011984</u>

Test:

(201 – 101) = 100 (< 600) so A/DTE stands

with   1.011984 + 6 = O/DTE = 7.011984

1.011984 – 7.011984 = 5.999996 and having an integer adjust:
1.011984 – 1.011984 = .000004 and x (2 x 10^6) – 1 = 7 (#PER)

Note Care must obviously be taken to adjust any non-valid date, but a A/DTE of 6.31983 adjusted to 6.301983 will still find a O/DTE of 12.311983 (not 12.301983) – unless, of course, any of the rules for end-of-month anniversary payments apply.

APPENDIX D

The programs on the Deltasoft Finance disk, mentioned in the Introduction, cater for nearly all the financial calculations in Part I of this book (save those chapters relating to Building Society Calculations which are available as a separate product).

The related @*FINANCE Manual* is mainly concerned with advising Users how to get the best out of their disks, and provides just sufficient examples and explanations to this end, being neither a manual of financial instruction nor a treatise on market practices in general.

Consequently, this book, from which most of Deltasoft's examples were taken, may be useful to those who wish to follow on their PCs the explanations and instructions herein, or to discover exactly how and why certain examples, provided on the disks, were actually calculated.

Disks are suitable for use with IBM PCs and compatibles and for details for purchase, availablity, and any other technical questions, please apply directly to the developers (below) – and not to me or my publishers!

DELTASOFT Ltd
3a Museum Street
Ipswich
Suffolk
IP1 1HQ
Telephone (0473) 233234
Facsimile (0473) 226787

LIST of ABBREVIATIONS

The first time any abbreviation appears full explanation is provided; nevertheless the list below may be found useful for quick reference.

Part I

i	As the decimal of an interest rate
	(for 10%, "i" = 10/100 = 0.01)
n	Number of years in the term of a loan
p	Number of compounding periods in any one year
$(1 + i/p)$	If the rate was 10% with monthly compounding:
	$(1 + i/p) = 1 + (10/1200) = 1.008333$
$(1 + i/p)^{-np}$	May be shown as $(1 + i/p)\wedge{-np}$ or $(1 + i/p)**{-np}$
#	Number or number of
NOM	Nominal interest rate%
EFF	Effective rate%
APR(UK)	Effective rate *truncated* to 1 place of decimals
APR(US)	The *nominal* rate%
TAP	Total Amount Payable
a/i	Accrued interest
INT	Integer
FRAC	Fraction e.g., 10.12 INT = 10 and FRAC = .12
PV	Present value
FV	Future value
Pmt(s)	Payments
BAL	Balloon payment
LOS	Loan outstanding
RES	Residual
SI	Simple interest (also sometimes SINT)
CI	Compound interest
e	Exponential factor (2.718281828)
LOG	Logarithm (ln – logs natural unless otherwise stated)
ABS	Absolute (disregards negative. If ABS = (– 10) = 10)
CPP	Constant payment to principal
CF	Cash flow
DCF	Discounted cash flow
DEDCF	Decimal entry discounted cash flow
NPV	Net present value
IRR	Internal rate of return
MIRR	Modified internal rate of return

FMRR	Financial management rate of return
CCA	Consumer Credit Act
OFT	Office of Fair Trading
DTI	Dept of Trade and Industry (changes name regularly !)
BSA	Building Societies Association
BS	Building societies
LGA	Local government authorities
MIRAS	Mortgage interest relief at source
Actuarial	Annuities ORDinary $a_{\overline{n}|}$ DUE $\ddot{a}_{\overline{n}|}$
signs	Savings ORDinary $s_{\overline{n}|}$ DUE $S_{\overline{n}|}$
	(sinking funds) (savings)

Part II

ID	Issue date
SD	Settlement date (day)
SETT	Settlement date (day)
RD	Redemption date (day)
MAT	Maturity date (day)
CP	Clean price (price clean of a/i)
DP	Dirty price (price includes a/i)
RV	Redemption value
RV^n	Notional Redemption value
NP	Notional price
C	Coupon% (nominal interest paid)
D	Half annual coupon (C/2)
YTM	Yield to maturity
YTM(S)	Eurobond adjustment for half annual interest payments
YMC	Yield to call
RY	Redemption yield (related to YTM)
XD	Ex-dividend
CGT	Capital gains tax
FPP	Forward projected price
PER	Period (usually per < or > years)
(n + k)	Periods and odd day fractions
(m + k)	A variation on (n + k)
AIBD	Association of International Bond Dealers

LABs	Local authority bonds
CD	Bank certificates of deposit
FRNs	Floating rate notes
FRCDs	Floating rate certificates of deposit
LIBOR	London inter bank offered rate
PC	Personal computer
DF	Date factor (Appendix C)
CZF	Crossing century zone factor (Appendix C)

INDEX

NUMBER OF DAYS TABLE FOR THE TWO YEARS A TO B

For anyone dealing continuously with accrued interest (a/i),
"clean" and "dealing prices", Gross Yields, Redemption Yields,
"k factor" etc, a "Day Table" is a great convenience.

YEAR A

Days	1	2	3	4	5	6	7	8	9	10	11	12	13	14	15	16	17	18	19	20	21	22	23	24	25	26	27	28	29	30	31
Jan	1	2	3	4	5	6	7	8	9	10	11	12	13	14	15	16	17	18	19	20	21	22	23	24	25	26	27	28	29	30	31
Feb	32	33	34	35	36	37	38	39	40	41	42	43	44	45	46	47	48	49	50	51	52	53	54	55	56	57	58	59			
Mar	60	61	62	63	64	65	66	67	68	69	70	71	72	73	74	75	76	77	78	79	80	81	82	83	84	85	86	87	88	89	90
Apr	91	92	93	94	95	96	97	98	99	100	101	102	103	104	105	106	107	108	109	110	111	112	113	114	115	116	117	118	119	120	
May	121	122	123	124	125	126	127	128	129	130	131	132	133	134	135	136	137	138	139	140	141	142	143	144	145	146	147	148	149	150	151
Jun	152	153	154	155	156	157	158	159	160	161	162	163	164	165	166	167	168	169	170	171	172	173	174	175	176	177	178	179	180	181	
Jul	182	183	184	185	186	187	188	189	190	191	192	193	194	195	196	197	198	199	200	201	202	203	204	205	206	207	208	209	210	211	212
Aug	213	214	215	216	217	218	219	220	221	222	223	224	225	226	227	228	229	230	231	232	233	234	235	236	237	238	239	240	241	242	243
Sep	244	245	246	247	248	249	250	251	252	253	254	255	256	257	258	259	260	261	262	263	264	265	266	267	268	269	270	271	272	273	
Oct	274	275	276	277	278	279	280	281	282	283	284	285	286	287	288	289	290	291	292	293	294	295	296	297	298	299	300	301	302	303	304
Nov	305	306	307	308	309	310	311	312	313	314	315	316	317	318	319	320	321	322	323	324	325	326	327	328	329	330	331	332	333	334	
Dec	335	336	337	338	339	340	341	342	343	344	345	346	347	348	349	350	351	352	353	354	355	356	357	358	359	360	361	362	363	364	365

(add one day, where applicable, for leap year)

YEAR B

Days	1	2	3	4	5	6	7	8	9	10	11	12	13	14	15	16	17	18	19	20	21	22	23	24	25	26	27	28	29	30	31
Jan	366	367	368	369	370	371	372	373	374	375	376	377	378	379	380	381	382	383	384	385	386	387	388	389	390	391	392	393	394	395	396
Feb	397	398	399	400	401	402	403	404	405	406	407	408	409	410	411	412	413	414	415	416	417	418	419	420	421	422	423	424			
Mar	425	426	427	428	429	430	431	432	433	434	435	436	437	438	439	440	441	442	443	444	445	446	447	448	449	450	451	452	453	454	455
Apr	456	457	458	459	460	461	462	463	464	465	466	467	468	469	470	471	472	473	474	475	476	477	478	479	480	481	482	483	484	485	
May	486	487	488	489	490	491	492	493	494	495	496	497	498	499	500	501	502	503	504	505	506	507	508	509	510	511	512	513	514	515	516
Jun	517	518	519	520	521	522	523	524	525	526	527	528	529	530	531	532	533	534	535	536	537	538	539	540	541	542	543	544	545	546	
Jul	547	548	549	550	551	552	553	554	555	556	557	558	559	560	561	562	563	564	565	566	567	568	569	570	571	572	573	574	575	576	577
Aug	578	579	580	581	582	583	584	585	586	587	588	589	590	591	592	593	594	595	596	597	598	599	600	601	602	603	604	605	606	607	608
Sep	609	610	611	612	613	614	615	616	617	618	619	620	621	622	623	624	625	626	627	628	629	630	631	632	633	634	635	636	637	638	
Oct	639	640	641	642	643	644	645	646	647	648	649	650	651	652	653	654	655	656	657	658	659	660	661	662	663	664	665	666	667	668	669
Nov	670	671	672	673	674	675	676	677	678	679	680	681	682	683	684	685	686	687	688	689	690	691	692	693	694	695	696	697	698	699	
Dec	700	701	702	703	704	705	706	707	708	709	710	711	712	713	714	715	716	717	718	719	720	721	722	723	724	725	726	727	728	729	730

Examples: Find the number of days between November 15 and October 21

$$319 - 294 = 25 \text{ days}$$

Find the number of days between November 15 and April 5 next,
assuming that the coming year is a leap year

$$460 + 1 - 319 = 142$$